DANIEL

TREATISE ON
IRREVERSIBLE AND STATISTICAL
THERMOPHYSICS

AN INTRODUCTION TO
NONCLASSICAL THERMODYNAMICS

Wolfgang Yourgrau

Alwyn van der Merwe
UNIVERSITY OF DENVER

Gough Raw
SAINT LOUIS UNIVERSITY

DOVER PUBLICATIONS, INC.
NEW YORK

This Dover edition is dedicated to the memory of
Professor Wolfgang Yourgrau.

Published in Canada by General Publishing Company, Ltd., 30
Lesmill Road, Don Mills, Toronto, Ontario.
Published in the United Kingdom by Constable and Company,
Ltd., 10 Orange Street, London WC2H 7EG.

This Dover edition, first published in 1982, is an unabridged and
extensively corrected republication of the work originally published
by The Macmillan Company, N.Y., 1966.

Manufactured in the United States of America
Dover Publications, Inc.
180 Varick Street
New York, N.Y. 10014

Library of Congress Cataloging in Publication Data

Yourgrau, Wolfgang.
     Treatise on irreversible and statistical thermo-
physics.

     Reprint. Originally published: New York: Macmillan,
1966.
     Includes bibliographies and index.
     1. Irreversible processes. 2 Statistical thermo-
dynamics. I. Van der Merwe, Alwyn. II. Raw, Gough.
III. Title.
[QC318.I7Y68 1982]   530.1′2   81-19450
ISBN 0-486-64313-1 (pbk.)   AACR2

Dedicated

to the memory of

Erwin Schrödinger

PREFACE

The revolutionary triumphs of quantum theory and relativity theory, as well as the startling results of elementary particle physics, have dramatically changed our picture of physical reality. It cannot be gainsaid that these areas of physics treat the "grand and sublime" and therefore enjoy a privileged position within the natural sciences. Needless to say, there is nothing deplorable in this state of affairs.

However, our interest in *thermophysics* can never remain marginal. First of all, a thorough study of physico-chemical systems must take into account their temperature and entropy, in addition to their nonthermal parameters. Secondly, thermophysics poses one of the most exciting questions in theoretical physics: how can one reconcile the irreversibility of natural processes with the reversible mechanics governing the elementary constituents of thermal systems?

The term *thermophysics* was proposed by Guggenheim, and strongly advocated by R. J. Seeger, as being the most appropriate to describe the science that examines the connection of temperature and entropy with the nonthermal properties of matter and radiation. Some authors have extended the conventional meaning of *thermodynamics* to connote the very same science. Although in the subtitle of this book we make a concession to this rather ambiguous practice, in our text we follow the stricter tradition. Hence, *thermodynamics* without qualification, denotes solely the phenomenological part of thermophysics. It should be noted that this term refers generally to dynamic situations. We have adopted this interpretation, at least in Chapter 1. In other words, we do not arbitrarily limit ourselves to a discussion of systems in thermomechanical and chemical equilibrium and to hypothetical processes involving such states—as is frequently done in literature. We believe, along with some other authors, that such a restricted form of thermodynamics could better be designated as *thermostatics*.

Thermophysics is naturally subdivided into two parts: *phenomenological* thermophysics and *statistical* thermophysics. The former discipline deals directly with the macroscopic or bulk properties of any thermophysical system, while the latter is concerned with these in terms of the statistical-mechanical laws that determine the behavior of the microscopic or atomic constituents of the system.

We might finally explain how we interpret the qualification *classical*. When applied to thermophysics, the term excludes the whole of statistical mechanics, while in the phenomenological domain it includes only thermostatics. The axiomatic foundation of classical theory thus rests upon the zeroth, first, second, and third laws of thermodynamics and encompasses mainly equilibrium situations and reversible processes.

We wish to acknowledge our indebtedness to Professors W. M. Elsasser (Princeton), S. Mandelstam (Berkeley), L. Onsager (Yale), and M. J. Stephen (Yale) for their critical reading of different parts of the manuscript. Invaluable suggestions were also offered by Professors J. Bardeen (Illinois) and P. G. Bergmann (Syracuse), Dr. D. Gray, and Professors M. J. Klein (Case Institute of Technology) and A. Landé (Ohio State). We have further benefited from the very helpful advice of Professor L. Rosenfeld (Nordita) and are extremely grateful to Professor W. Heisenberg (Max-Planck-Institut für Physik) for his incisive evaluation of the completed manuscript.

At the end of each chapter we have listed the most essential papers and books consulted. Our appreciation for the indispensable aid derived from these sources should not go unmentioned.

W. Yourgrau
A. van der Merwe
G. Raw

CONTENTS

3. ASSEMBLIES OF NONINTERACTING STRUCTURELESS PARTICLES

GLOSSARY OF SYMBOLS AND PHYSICAL CONSTANTS

GLOSSARY OF SYMBOLS

A	area
A	chemical affinity
A_{ks}^{jr}	probability of transition from state ϕ_{jr} to state ϕ_{ks}
B_{ij}^{kl}	coefficient in the collision number hypothesis
C_p	heat capacity at constant pressure
C_V	heat capacity at constant volume
D	degree of gas degeneration
$D(y)$	Debye function with argument y
D	operator defined in Eq. (55), Chapter 4
E	energy of macroscopic system
E	Young's modulus
$\bar{E}$	average energy of isothermal system
E^*	energy of supersystem
E_j	energy eigenvalue of macroscopic system
E_k	kinetic energy
E_j^0	eigenvalue of H^0
F	Helmholtz free energy
$\mathfrak{F}$	Faraday constant
$\bar{F}$	phase, or ensemble, average of function $F(q,p)$
$\bar{F}$	time average of function $F(q,p)$
$\langle F \rangle$	phase average of function $F(q,p)$
F_i	Onsager force
$F_s(\alpha)$	function defined in Eq. (115), Chapter 3
$F_D(y)$	function $(y^3/3)D(y)$
G	Gibbs free energy
H	enthalpy
H	Hamiltonian function
H	Hamiltonian operator
H_B	Boltzmann's H-function
H^0	unperturbed Hamiltonian

xi

H'	perturbation on H^0
H^*	quantum-mechanical H-function
H_0^*	equilibrium value of H^*
I	electrical current
I	moment of inertia of rotator
I_0	value of moment of inertia I for $r = r_0$
J	magnitude of $\mathbf{J}_e$
J	magnitude of $\mathbf{J}$
J	quantum number determining magnitude of $\mathbf{J}$
J_i	generalized flux of process i
J_z	z-component of $\mathbf{J}$
J	flux
K	elasticity constant
K	strength of vortex in liquid helium
L	length
L	magnitude of $\mathbf{L}$
L	quantum number determining magnitude of $\mathbf{L}$
L_z	z-component of $\mathbf{L}$
L_{ij}	phenomenological coefficient
M	mass of diatomic molecule
M_i	molar mass of component i
N	number of particles
$\overline{N}$	average number of particles in open isothermal system
N_0	Avogadro's number
N_j	number of image points in cell j of position-velocity space
N^*	number of systems in Gibbs ensemble
N_r^*	number of systems (in Gibbs ensemble) occupying quantum state ϕ_r
N_{jr}^*	number of systems (in Gibbs ensemble) occupying quantum state ϕ_{jr}
P^*	probability of given distribution $N_1^*, N_2^*, \ldots$
P_r	probability of finding system (of Gibbs ensemble) in quantum state ϕ_r
P_{jr}	probability of finding system (of Gibbs ensemble) in quantum state ϕ_{jr}
Q	heat absorbed by system
R	electrical resistance
R	gas constant
R	radiancy of surface
R_b	radiancy of blackbody
R_c	radiancy of cavity
R_λ	radiancy per unit interval of λ
R_ν	radiancy per unit interval of ν

S	entropy
S^0	equilibrium value of statistical entropy
S^*	entropy of supersystem
S	magnitude of $\mathbf{S}$
S	spin quantum number
T	absolute temperature
T	kinetic energy
T_0	Bose-Einstein condensation temperature
T_λ	lambda-point temperature
U	internal energy
U_0	zero-point energy
V	potential energy
V	volume
V^*	volume of supersystem
W	work done by system
W	thermodynamic probability
W^*	number of supersystem-states for given distribution $N_1^*, N_2^*, \ldots$
$W_{sr}^{(k)}$	probability of transition from quantum state ϕ_{kr} to quantum state ϕ_{ks}
X_i	generalized thermodynamic force of process i
Z	partition function of macroscopic system
Z_1	partition function of single particle
Z_{class}	classical limit of Z
$\mathcal{Z}$	grand partition function
$\mathbf{B}$	magnetic flux density
$\mathcal{B}$	magnetic flux density
$\mathbf{J}$	total angular momentum
$\mathbf{J}_e$	charge flux density
$\mathbf{J}_i$	mass flux density of component i
$\mathbf{J}_m$	mass flux density
$\mathbf{J}_q$	heat flux density
$\mathbf{J}_s$	entropy flux density
$\mathbf{J}_u$	energy flux density
$\mathbf{L}$	orbital angular momentum
$\mathbf{S}$	spin angular momentum
a_i	Onsager coordinate
c	speed of light
c	speed of particle
c	speed of sound

c_l	speed of longitudinal sound wave
c_t	speed of transverse sound wave
dp	product of dp_i's
dq	product of dq_i's
e	base of natural logarithms
e	charge
e	elementary charge
e	specific charge
f	distribution function
$f^0(\mathbf{v})$	Maxwell velocity distribution function
f	number of degrees of freedom
g	Landé g-factor
g_0	degree of degeneracy of energy eigenvalue ε_0
g_k	degree of degeneracy of energy eigenvalue E_k
g^A	degree of degeneracy of energy eigenvalue ε^A
$g(\varepsilon)$	number of quantum states per unit interval of ε
$g(p)$	number of quantum states per unit interval of linear momentum p
$g(\nu)$	number of quantum states per unit interval of ν
h	Planck's constant
$\hbar$	constant $h/2\pi$
h	specific enthalpy
j	general quantum number
j	quantum number determining magnitude of $\mathbf{J}$ for particle
k	Boltzmann's constant
k	general quantum number
k_{AB}	velocity constant of reaction $B \to A$
l	quantum number determining magnitude of $\mathbf{L}$ for particle
m	mass of particle
m_j	quantum number determining J_z for particle
m_l	quantum number determining L_z for particle
m_s	quantum number determining S_z for particle
n	general quantum number
n	number of molecules
n	number of particles per unit volume
n_A	number of moles of isomer A
n_i	number of moles of component i
n_j	occupation number of one-particle energy eigenstate j
n_x, n_y, n_z	integral quantum numbers
n^*	number of particles in supersystem
$\bar{n}_j$	average value of occupation number n_j
$\hat{n}_j$	most probable value of occupation number n_j
$\bar{n}(\varepsilon)$	average number of particles in quantum state with energy ε
p	set of generalized momenta

p	total pressure
p_i	generalized momentum
p_i	partial pressure of component i
$p(n_j)$	probability of given occupation number n_j
q	set of generalized coordinates
q_i	generalized coordinate
q^*	heat of transfer
r	general quantum number
r_0	distance between nuclei at equilibrium
s	distance
s	general quantum number
s	molar entropy
s	quantum number determining magnitude of S for particle
s_i	specific entropy of component i
u	displacement in elastic wave
u	energy density of radiation field
u_i	specific internal energy of component i
u_λ	radiation energy density per unit interval of λ
u_ν	radiation energy density per unit interval of ν
u^*	energy of transfer
v	chemical reaction rate per unit volume
v_i	partial molar volume of component i
v_i	specific volume of component i
w_i	mass fraction of component i
z_i	electrovalency of component i

$\mathbf{a}, \mathbf{b}, \mathbf{c}$	primitive translation vectors of lattice
$\mathbf{n}$	unit normal vector
$\mathbf{p}$	linear momentum
$\mathbf{r}$	position vector
$\mathbf{v}$	velocity

$\Gamma(n)$	gamma function
Δ	minimum roton energy
Θ	characteristic temperature
Θ_D	Debye temperature
Θ_E	Einstein temperature
Θ_r	characteristic temperature for rotation
Θ_v	characteristic temperature for vibration
Λ	thermal wavelength $h/(2\pi mkT)^{1/2}$
$\Phi(E)$	number of quantum states with energy $\leqslant E$

$\Omega(E)$	number of quantum states with energy lying in interval ΔE
Ω^*	number of supersystem-states for given E^* and N^*

α	parameter $-\beta\mu$
α	fraction of incident radiant energy absorbed by surface
β	reciprocal of kT
γ	ratio C_p/C_V
γ-space	phase space of gas
ε	one-particle energy
ε_0	Fermi energy
ε_0	lowest value of ε
ε_j	energy associated with cell j of position-velocity space
ε_j	one-particle energy eigenvalue
ε^A	part of ε relating to set of degrees of freedom A
ζ_A	partition function for set of degrees of freedom A
$\zeta_{A\,\text{class}}$	classical limit of ζ_A
$\zeta(s)$	Riemann zeta function with argument s
θ	angle between radius vector and z-axis
κ	isothermal compressibility
κ	ratio defined in Eq. (60), Chapter 4
λ	de Broglie wavelength
λ	wavelength
λ_A	absolute activity of component A
λ_m	value of λ at maximum of $R_{b\lambda}$
μ	chemical potential per particle
μ	effective mass of roton
μ	reduced mass
μ_A	chemical potential per mole of isomer A
μ_B	Bohr magneton
μ_i	chemical potential per mole of component i
μ_i	chemical potential per unit mass of component i
$\bar{\mu}$	average component of μ in direction of $\mathcal{B}$
μ-space	phase space of molecule
ν	frequency
ν_D	Debye cutoff frequency
ν_E	Einstein frequency
ν_i	stoichiometric coefficient of component i
ν_r	eigenfrequency of solid
$\hat{\nu}$	maximum frequency in Born-von Kármán theory
ξ	extent of reaction per unit volume
ξ_i	Cartesian component of atomic displacement in solid
$\bar{\xi}$	extent of reaction

ρ	fraction of incident radiant energy reflected by surface
ρ	mass density
ρ	number of particles per unit volume
ρ_v	density of photons per unit interval of ν
$\rho(E)$	number of quantum states per unit interval of energy E
$\rho(q,p,t)$	density-in-phase
σ	entropy source density
σ	Poisson's ratio
σ	Stefan-Boltzmann constant
σ	Thomson heat
σ_D	Debye cutoff wave number
σ_x	root mean square deviation of variable x
$\hat{\sigma}$	maximum wave number in Born-von Kármán theory
τ	fraction of incident radiant energy transmitted by surface
ϕ	azimuthal angle
ϕ	electrical potential
ϕ	lattice potential energy of solid
ϕ	thermionic work function $x - \mu$
ϕ_i	energy eigenfunction
ϕ_{jr}	energy eigenfunction
ϕ_j^0	eigenfunction belonging to E_j^0
ϕ_{ij}	second-order derivative of potential energy ϕ with respect to ξ_i and ξ_j
χ	height of potential-energy step for electron at metallic surface
$\psi(q,t)$	quantum-mechanical wave function
ω_j	volume of cell j in position-velocity space
ω_p	plasma (angular) frequency
ω_r	angular eigenfrequency of solid
$\boldsymbol{\mu}$	magnetic moment
$\boldsymbol{\sigma}$	wave number vector
$\boldsymbol{\omega}$	angular velocity

IMPORTANT PHYSICAL CONSTANTS

(According to the National Bureau of Standards Technical News Bulletin, October 1963.)

Speed of light in vacuum

$$c = (2.997925 \pm 0.000003) \times 10^{10} \text{ cm sec}^{-1}$$

Elementary charge

$$e = (4.80298 \pm 0.00020) \times 10^{-10} \text{ esu}$$

Avogadro's constant

$$N_0 = (6.02252 \pm 0.00028) \times 10^{23} \text{ mol}^{-1}$$

Electron rest mass

$$m_e = (9.1091 \pm 0.0004) \times 10^{-28} \text{ gm}$$

Proton rest mass

$$m_p = (1.67252 \pm 0.00008) \times 10^{-24} \text{ gm}$$

Faraday constant

$$\mathfrak{F} = (9.64870 \pm 0.00016) \times 10^3 \text{ emu mol}^{-1}$$

Planck's constant

$$h = (6.6256 \pm 0.0005) \times 10^{-27} \text{ erg sec}$$

Bohr magneton

$$\mu_B = (9.2732 \pm 0.0006) \times 10^{-21} \text{ erg gauss}^{-1}$$

Gas constant

$$R = (8.3143 \pm 0.0012) \times 10^7 \text{ erg mol}^{-1} \text{ deg}^{-1}$$

Boltzmann's constant

$$k = (1.38054 \pm 0.00018) \times 10^{-16} \text{ erg deg}^{-1}$$

Stefan-Boltzmann constant

$$\sigma = (5.6697 \pm 0.0029) \times 10^{-5} \text{ erg cm}^{-2} \text{ sec}^{-1} \text{ deg}^{-4}$$

TREATISE ON
IRREVERSIBLE AND STATISTICAL
THERMOPHYSICS

Boltzmann Constant

$k = 1.38054 \times 10^{-16}$ erg/deg

THERMODYNAMICS OF IRREVERSIBLE PROCESSES

IN phenomenological thermophysics we seek to describe physicochemical systems in terms of a few simple measurements capable of being performed by means of macroscopic, or large-scale, instruments. Such a procedure will obviously be the more fruitful the more it approximates a so-called *adequate* description. A description shall be deemed adequate if it is such that whenever its numerical data reoccur, the whole measurable subsequent course of the system is reproduced (provided the environment of the system is the same as before). It becomes plain that insistence upon adequacy will cause some processes for ever to defy thermophysical treatment. Such a process is, for instance, an atomic disintegration, an event so intrinsically microscopic that a detailed study employing thermophysical instruments is permanently ruled out. Indeed, it is a maxim of quantum mechanics that the occurrence of an atomic decay is governed by chance, and that a causal explanation is therefore meaningless. Less fundamental but no less capricious (from a thermophysical point of view) is the formation of a nucleus which initiates the sudden crystallization of a supercooled liquid or of a supersaturated solution. Most commonly, however, our inability to find an adequate description is due to the complexity of the process under consideration. We may cite the turbulent motion of a fluid as a case in point.

The processes quoted above as not being amenable to adequate treatment are all irreversible; obviously, all reversible processes do admit adequate description. Yet it would be a serious error to assume that irreversible phenomena without exception are outside the range of adequate presentation. In fact, a number of irreversible changes easily come to mind, which are so lacking in complexity that an adequacy of description can be realized. Here are some illustrations: the conduction of heat along a metal bar whose ends are kept at fixed but different temperatures; the development of Joule heat when an electric current flows through a metallic conductor; diffusion of a solid or fluid across a concentration gradient; laminar flow of a viscous fluid; and so on. All these simple processes can be characterized with the aid of a few parameters such that, once their values are specified, all measurable aspects become predictable. Thus the heat passing from one end of a homogeneous, laterally insulated metal bar at temperature T_1 to its other end at the temperature T_2, will always be proportional to $(1/L)(T_1 - T_2)$, L being the length of the bar. Again, an electric current I flowing through an ohmic resistance R will without fail develop $I^2 R$ units of heat per unit time.

After these preliminary remarks, it is clear that in traditional thermodynamics one only scouts around the periphery of the total area that should be open to thermophysical attack. To elaborate this assertion, we distinguish between the *detailed* and the *overall* treatments of physical processes. A detailed discussion deals with quantitative statements about every step of a process, whereas in an overall approach one is content to restrict all quantitative assertions to the process as a whole. The essential limitation of classical thermodynamics may now be expressed by saying that it attains detailed descriptions only for a very special kind of changes—namely, reversible processes. Such a process—defined as a concatenation of equilibrium states—is, of course, an idealization to which a real process can at best only approximate in the limit when it is artificially conducted with infinite slowness. This reservation notwithstanding, reversible transformations have been shown to furnish a method for deriving immensely important relationships among thermophysical parameters for different equilibrium situations. Moreover, the concept of a reversible process permits overall treatment of many irreversible changes if one mentally substitutes a reversible process for a given irreversible transformation. It enables us, for example, to compute the increments of characteristic functions accompanying rapid expansions, chemical reactions, and other irreversible phenomena—no matter how violent or complex they are.

However, it should be frankly conceded that traditional theory fails to make quantitative statements concerning the behavior of a system *during* the course of an irreversible process—in other words, about the *dynamics* of thermophysical systems. This theory, which comprises the energy conservation law, the entropy principle, Nernst's heat theorem, and the unfolding of their consequences, is customarily designated as "thermodynamics" or "classical thermodynamics." But in view of the emphasis upon equilibrium, or static, states, it is surely more appropriate to talk in this context of *thermostatics* and reserve the name *thermodynamics* for the discipline to be developed in the present chapter—that is, for the detailed examination of dynamic, or off-equilibrium, situations. For the sake of clarity, we shall mainly adhere to this terminology.

An analogy with the science of mechanics will be helpful in an appreciation of what thermostatics has achieved and what remains to be attempted under the heading of thermodynamics. In mechanics the static equilibrium configurations of a conservative mechanical system are those for which the potential energy assumes stationary values. This means that any variation of the potential energy corresponding to virtual displacements of the parts of the system vanishes, or in symbols: $\delta E_p = 0$. If furthermore the equilibrium is to be stable, the associated configuration should minimize the potential energy, or $\delta^2 E_p > 0$. Should E_p be known as a function of a set of independent mechanical coordinates, the last two equations would enable one to calculate the equilibrium values of the coordinates and of any function of them. The two given differential statements may be compared with the conditions $\delta S = 0$ and $\delta^2 S < 0$, which constitute one of many ways to signify thermostatic equilibrium. The thermostatic relations, like their mechanical analogues, may theoretically be solved, once S is known, to furnish results valid for equilibrium states and the overall changes among them. In classical mechanics, the transition from statics to dynamics is effectuated by an appeal to Newton's equation of motion, $\mathbf{F} = m\mathbf{a}$; and it emerges that statics is not a separate topic but simply the treatment to which dynamics reduces in the limit when the forces balance one another and all velocities vanish. It is our intention to broaden in the same spirit the scope of thermophysics by adding to its classical laws some new postulates, and by requiring that the theory so constructed should recover the results of thermostatics in the limit of reversible transformations.

Attempts to enlarge classical thermophysics in order to include irreversible changes have been made ever since the second law was enunciated in the middle of the previous century. The early incursions into thermodynamics were, however, confined to the treatment of some very special irreversible occurrences, such as thermoelectric effects. No theory capable of embracing even a restricted class of irreversible phenomena existed at that stage; hence each problem was treated separately on the basis of certain ad hoc assumptions, which, although they led on occasion to the experimentally verified results, were admittedly unjustified.

Thermodynamics was rescued from this despairing state of affairs and resuscitated thanks to the publication of a theory by Onsager in the year 1931, which for the first time submitted a unified approach to irreversible processes. The formalism to be expounded in the following sections centers around a theorem proved by Onsager, but it also relies greatly on some additional, subsidiary postulates. These postulates will be introduced first. It is not claimed that they apply to all irreversible changes, but solely to those consisting of a succession of states that are always close to equilibrium; as to the general type of process, the postulates should be regarded as providing the basis for only a first approximation to a rigorous description. For this reason, the theoretical edifice we wish to erect on these postulates might preferably be called *first-order* thermodynamics. By parity of reasoning, thermostatics may be referred to as *zero-order* thermodynamics. The notion of a first approximation will be sharpened further on, when quantitative measures for the deviation of a given state from an equilibrium state are formulated.

1–1. Some Concepts of First-Order Thermodynamics

Suppose one is confronted with a thermophysical system in which a natural process takes place, and determines empirically all its measurable properties. In general, it will be found that the extensive properties vary with time, and the intensive properties vary both with time and from point to point in the space occupied by the system. The reader will recall that in thermostatic equilibrium the macroscopic properties of a single-phase system are functions of parameters which are defined in the first place only for equilibrium states and depend neither on position nor on time. Naturally, we are reluctant to discard notions that have served us so well; the question therefore arises whether it is feasible to generalize these variables so that they acquire operational meaning for the dynamic state and reduce to the familiar notions in the limiting equilibrium situation.

Such a generalization has tacitly been made for more than two centuries regarding the temperature concept. People are wont to talk about the temperature of the atmosphere, of an oven, a heat-conducting body, reacting chemical substances, and a host of other nonequilibrium systems. As a matter of fact, the habit of basing the idea of temperature on the state of equilibrium was conceived fairly late, only after thermodynamics had reached an advanced stage of sophistication. Fahrenheit, a pioneer in the standardization of temperature scales (1720), was unlikely to employ the concept of equilibrium when explaining what he meant by temperature; and Fourier wrote his classic, *La Théorie analytique de la chaleur* (1822), without fathoming the true physical meaning of the temperature parameter that appeared in his formulas. To all these researchers temperature was essentially a pointer-reading on a suitable instrument called a thermometer. An idea construed in such a naïve fashion was, however, not destined to figure prominently in the second and third laws, which are applicable to physical systems regardless of their physicochemical nature.

The fundamental importance of temperature in thermostatics stems from the fact that when a system is in equilibrium, all possible thermometers, after suitable calibration and correction, register the same temperature, viz., the absolute or Kelvin temperature. Experiment shows that this uniformity is lost for a system not in equilibrium; thermometers of different construction will on the whole indicate different temperatures. Thus if one wishes to ascertain the temperature of the air, a thermometer with a clear bulb placed in the shade will register a lower reading than the same thermometer with a blackened bulb exposed to sunlight. The difference in thermal behavior is, of course, due to the fact that in the presence of a black surface the exchange of energy between the thermometric fluid and its surroundings takes place by the mechanism of radiation as well as that of molecular collisions. This explanation provides the clue why thermometers should frequently disagree: different types of thermometers are sensitive to diverse forms of energy, and will therefore respond differently when brought into contact with the system under examination, unless equilibrium has been established among the various kinds of energy.

Instruments may conceivably be devised that will measure in nonequilibrium situations the temperature associated with each molecular process or form of energy. But no direct practical method seems capable of determining a *general* temperature which—since it must not make any reference to particular microscopic processes—can be expected to enter into a comprehensive macroscopic theory of irreversible phenomena.

Under these circumstances we can do no better than base the temperature concept on the following indirect procedure, which might not be a practical one but at least has the merit of permitting implementation in principle. To find the temperature at a point in a system undergoing a change, let us suddenly isolate a small element of space surrounding the point and allow the matter in it to reach equilibrium; the temperature then measured in the usual manner defines the *temperature at the point*. This property will naturally admit measurement only provided the element contains many thousands of molecules and is therefore large from a microscopic standpoint. From a macroscopic point of view, on the other hand, we shall require the element to be small, so that if the whole system is divided into such elements and the temperature of each element is assigned to its center, a variation of temperature over space is obtained that is both smooth and independent of the way in which the system is subdivided.

The objection raised against the traditional definitions of temperature for nonequilibrium systems applies also to the current definitions of non-equilibrium pressure in terms of instrument readings. A satisfactory general definition of pressure, like that of temperature, can be found in principle only if one isolates elements of the system under consideration. The concepts of volume and chemical concentration (or mole number) are analyzable without difficulty for any system. Similarly, the internal energy, or rather its increment defined as the amount of work done on a system under adiabatic conditions, retains its thermostatic meaning.

The notion of entropy belongs to a somewhat different category. Unlike temperature, pressure, and internal energy, thermostatic entropy is not directly measurable, nor does it have an obvious molecular significance. The entropy of an arbitrary equilibrium state has been equated to the integral of dQ/T over a reversible path leading from the zero-entropy state to the state before us. The experimental determination of entropy does, however, not proceed along the lines suggested by this definition; that is, in practice one does not impart elements of heat dQ to a system in small reversible steps and then add dQ/T for all the steps to obtain the entropy of the system. Instead, one carries out some direct measurements of the temperature, pressure, and other simple parameters, and subsequently evaluates the entropy with the aid of a formula expressing entropy as a function of these parameters. The formula is found, as is well known, when the integral of dQ/T is calculated theoretically, and it provides us in effect with a second, alternative definition of thermostatic entropy. This definition, because it refers to equilibrium only indirectly, we shall adopt as a basis for the extension of the idea of entropy to nonequilibrium systems, in the form of a postulate that will now be formulated.

Let any given thermophysical system be divided mentally into microscopically large but macroscopically small elements or regions (also called *cells* or *subsystems*) as explained earlier. Every cell shall have a fixed volume V, and we assume that it is meaningful to specify at any chosen moment that the subsystem has an internal energy U and contains m_i mass units of the molecular species i. At equilibrium, temperature T, pressure p, *partial specific Gibbs function* $\mu_i = (\partial G/\partial m_i)_{T,p}$, and entropy S of a subsystem are well-defined parameters; and because V is constant, these parameters are determined solely by U and the m_i for the subsystem. (Note that here μ_i stands for the partial Gibbs function, or *chemical potential*, per unit mass, whereas ordinarily this symbol denotes the chemical potential per mole.)

If equilibrium does not prevail, it becomes necessary to redefine the concepts of temperature, pressure, partial specific Gibbs function, and entropy. We suppose that T, p, μ_i, and S for a cell in a nonequilibrium state depend on U and the m_i in exactly the same manner as in an equilibrium situation. In other words, one operates as if equilibrium obtains in each cell separately; this is known as the *assumption of local equilibrium*.

From an experimental point of view, the temperature, pressure, etc., defined on the basis of this assumption, are the temperature, pressure, etc., which would be measured at a point of the system if the subsystem containing this point were suddenly isolated and allowed to reach equilibrium. Analytically, the assumption of local equilibrium implies that *Gibbs' fundamental relation*, which combines the first and second laws, remains valid in first-order thermodynamics. To stress the fact that Gibbs' relation is supposed to hold at each point of the system—not for the system as a whole—we write the relation in a form that refers to intensive, or *local*, variables only. For this purpose let s, u, v, and w_i stand for the *specific* values of the entropy, energy, volume, and mass of the substance i; that is, if m is the total mass of the subsystem containing the point considered, then $s = S/m$, $u = U/m$, $v = V/m$, and $w_i = m_i/m$ (the *mass fraction* of substance i). In terms of these quantities, Gibbs' relation for unit mass at a point of the system becomes *

$$Tds = du + pdv - \sum_i \mu_i \, dw_i \,. \tag{1}$$

The differentials ds, du, dv, dw_i, it should be remarked, are the first-order approximations to the increases of the above quantities at a given point with the lapse of time, or at a given time when one passes from one point to another, or even when both time and position change. The entropy of the system is found on adding the entropies of the individual cells calculated with the help of Eq. (1).

In thermodynamics, even more than in thermostatics, entropy is a pivotal concept. It is therefore essential that we dwell upon the reasons for adopting the above definition of entropy, and examine the scope of the underlying idea of local equilibrium.

As far as thermostatics is concerned, an infinite number of equally acceptable thermodynamic definitions of entropy present themselves. For the second law requires merely that the entropy of an adiabatically isolated system should not decrease when a transition occurs between equilibrium states, and this demand will be fulfilled by any definition that at equilibrium entails the

---

*In Eq. (1) we identify the work attending an infinitesimal reversible change with the volume work pdv. This step involves the assumption, adequate for our immediate purposes, that the subsystem under consideration is an isotropic region, free of surface phenomena, for which both the electric and magnetic polarizations, $\mathscr{P}$ and $\mathscr{M}$, vanish.

agreement between the sum of the entropies of the cells and the thermostatic entropy. The acceptable definitions will, in general, render the entropy at a point dependent on the values of the intensive variables not only *at* that point but also in its neighborhood—i.e., on the gradients of the local parameters— in such a way that one recovers the thermostatic entropy when the gradients tend to zero. From among all the alternatives, definition (1) selects the simplest entropy *s*, which distinguishes itself by the fact that it depends explicitly only on the variables *u*, *v*, w_i themselves, not on their gradients.

Whether this particular choice of entropy is the correct one is conditional on the demands one wishes to impose on the entropy, in addition to those forementioned. Now it is clear that a thermodynamic entropy will hardly suffice unless it does not only display positive jumps between one equilibrium state and the next, but also increases continuously *during* any adiabatic irreversible process. We posit that this aim has been achieved by our simple definition (1)—that is, without explicit inclusion of gradients in the differential expression for this specific entropy.

If one adheres to a discussion on the phenomenological level, the proof of this assumption can be furnished by experiment alone. To be precise, one should adopt the uniform increase of the entropy introduced by Eq. (1) as a hypothesis, compute all its practical consequences, and then verify them empirically. Such a procedure seems to be a test that is conclusive, and moreover concords with the descriptive nature of phenomenological thermo-physics. Accordingly, our attitude may be stated thus: the hypothesis, that the entropy function reposing on the assumption of local equilibrium is a uniformly increasing function of the time, is vindicated in retrospect by the verification of its predictions. This is true at least for *first-order* thermodynamics—in other words, when the gradients of the local parameters are small compared with unity.

At this point it will deepen our understanding and lend support to our mode of reasoning if we digress a little to consider the interpretation placed by the statistical-mechanical theory of molecules upon the concepts of temperature, pressure, internal energy, and entropy.

The reader will remember that kinetic theory, dealing with matter from a molecular standpoint, defines: (a) the internal energy of a fluid as the sum of the kinetic and potential energies of its molecules, (b) the temperature as $2/3k$ times the average translational kinetic energy per molecule, and (c) the pressure on the wall as the time-average of the linear momentum surrendered by the incident molecules to unit area of the wall per unit time.

These interpretations did not seem forced and were easily decided on. The situation is markedly different for entropy, for which no molecular analogue

---

If one or more of these conditions are not fulfilled, the work dW performed by a homogeneous region, of volume V and surface area A, is not simply pdV but rather

$$dW = -V\boldsymbol{\tau}:d\mathbf{e} - \sigma dA - \mathbf{E}\cdot d(V\mathcal{P}) - \mu_0\mathbf{H}\cdot d(V\mathcal{M})$$

suggests itself immediately. All the same, Boltzmann (c. 1877) proposed a statistical-mechanical definition for the entropy of a thermodynamic state, namely,

$$\boxed{S = k \log W + \text{const.}} \qquad (2)$$

in terms of the probability W for the occurrence of the state. Statistical mechanics assigns an exact meaning to the probability of a state and supplies a general expression for log W that employs the idea of the *distribution function* of a system. This function measures the probability for the coordinates and velocities of the molecules of the system to have specified values at a given time. The statistical entropy (2) possesses the quality that it never decreases in time for an adiabatically isolated system.

It is now apposite to inquire whether or not the statistical definition predicts the validity of Gibbs' relation (1). Prigogine (1949) examined this question for a certain category of phenomena, starting with the theory of dilute gases as developed by Chapman and Enskog (1916, 1917). For dilute gases it is sufficient to consider the distribution function f of a single molecule rather than that of the whole system; thus, $f = f(x,y,z,u,v,w,t)$, where x, y, z are the cartesian coordinates of the molecule, u, v, w its velocity components, and t the time. In this notation, $f\,dxdydzdudvdw$ will give the probable number of molecules whose coordinates (at time t) lie within the ranges dx, dy, dz about the point (x,y,z) in coordinate-space, and whose velocity components are restricted to the ranges du, dv, dw about the point (u,v,w) in velocity-space. At equilibrium the function f is independent of space and time, while the dependence on velocity is expressed by the Maxwell distribution function (1860), i.e., by

$$f_0 = n \left(\frac{m}{2\pi kT}\right)^{3/2} \exp{-\frac{m}{2kT}(u^2 + v^2 + w^2)}.$$

In nonequilibrium situations, however, the function f will in general depend on both space and time. If we focus our attention on a particular point in space—and measure the components u, v, w relative to the local center of mass moving with a velocity $\bar{u}$, $\bar{v}$, $\bar{w}$—it turns out that the function f is Maxwellian only as a first approximation. To get better approximations, one uses a series expansion due to Enskog (1922), viz.,

$$f = f_0 + f_1 + f_2 + \cdots; \qquad (3)$$

in general, where τ and $\mathbf{e}$ (in the double inner product) denote the stress and strain tensors of the medium and σ its surface tension, while $\mathbf{E}$ and $\mathbf{H}$ are the electric and magnetic field strength vectors and μ_0 the permeability of vacuum.

the terms f_1, f_2, etc., depend on the derivatives of the functions n, T, $\bar{u}$, $\bar{v}$, $\bar{w}$ with respect to space and time, and represent corrections of increasing order in the deviations of the system from equilibrium. Prigogine now established that the results of thermodynamics for dilute gases founded on Gibbs' equation are the same as those arising from statistical theory, provided that the series on the right-hand side of Eq. (3) converges so fast that $f = f_0 + f_1$ is a good enough approximation to the distribution function. Inclusion of the term f_2 gives specific entropy values depending explicitly on the gradients of functions such as n and T.

We thus appear to have found a qualitative criterion for the validity of the thermodynamics based on Eq. (1). Within its scope fall those occurrences that can be adequately described by means of the distribution function $f = f_0 + f_1$, such as phenomena involving the transport of momentum, energy, or mass, and chemical reactions slow enough not to disturb appreciably the Maxwellian distribution function of each of the reacting components. Outside its ambit remain phenomena requiring for their description the term f_2 or terms of still higher order.

1–2. Entropy Balance and Entropy Production

Now that we have assigned a meaning to the entropy of a system under dynamic as well as static conditions, we shall investigate how to deal with this property quantitatively.

It is evident that the statement $dS \geqslant dQ/T$, because it is not an equality, cannot be invoked to calculate the entropy increase occasioned by an irreversible process. Besides, it is valid only for a closed system, whereas we want to examine open systems too. The key to a successful manipulation of the entropy property is the artifice of visualizing entropy as a substance capable of flowing like water from one part of space to another. In the cases of electric charge and energy, this practice is accepted as satisfactory, or at least tolerably so, since charge and energy, like water, are conserved. For entropy (as for heat) this is no longer true! Indeed, while the first law tells us that the energy of an isolated system is constant in time, the second law maintains that its entropy increases as long as changes occur inside it. To remedy this discrepancy and at the same time retain the picture of entropy as something that flows, we think of entropy as a fluid that can be destroyed and created, or *produced*. With this understanding it is natural to define the following quantities.

The *entropy production* is the amount of entropy created per unit time; for an isolated system, and only then, this is dS/dt. The *entropy source density* σ is the *entropy production per unit volume*. The *entropy current density*, or *entropy flux density*, $\mathbf{J}_s$, is a vector that coincides with the direction of entropy flow and has a magnitude equal to the entropy crossing unit area perpendicular to the direction of flow per unit of time. Both σ and $\mathbf{J}_s$ will, in general, be functions of position and time.

The specific entropy s, the entropy production per unit volume σ, and the entropy flux vector $\mathbf{J}_s$ are not independent of one another; they are connected by a rather important equation which we shall presently derive.

The entropy that crosses an arbitrary infinitesimal surface element dA per unit time, or the *entropy flux* across dA, is the scalar product $\mathbf{n} \cdot \mathbf{J}_s \, dA$, $\mathbf{n}$ being a unit vector perpendicular to the element dA. Therefore, the outward flux from a space of volume V becomes $\int \mathbf{n} \cdot \mathbf{J}_s \, dA$, where the integral is extended over the surface A enclosing the volume V, while the unit vector $\mathbf{n}$ points outward from the enclosed space and is normal to dA. We apply this result to an infinitesimal rectangular parallelepiped whose center is at the fixed but arbitrary point (x,y,z) in space, and which has edges of lengths dx, dy, dz parallel to the axes of x,y,z, so that its volume is $dV = dxdydz$. Consider now the contribution of the two faces parallel to the yz-plane to the outward flux from the parallelepiped. Because these faces have the same area $dydz$, and their x-coordinates are $x - \frac{1}{2}dx$ and $x + \frac{1}{2}dx$, respectively, they contribute the amount

$$-\left(J_{sx} - \frac{1}{2}\frac{\partial J_{sx}}{\partial x}\, dx\right) dydz + \left(J_{sx} + \frac{1}{2}\frac{\partial J_{sx}}{\partial x}\, dx\right) dydz$$
$$= \frac{\partial J_{sx}}{\partial x}\, dxdydz = \frac{\partial J_{sx}}{\partial x}\, dV$$

to the outward flux. Similarly, the two faces parallel to the zx-plane is responsible for the amount $(\partial J_{sy}/\partial y)\, dV$, and the two faces parallel to the xy-plane for the amount $(\partial J_{sz}/\partial z)\, dV$. Addition of the separate contributions finally yields for the outward flux from the parallelepiped the value $(\mathrm{div}\, \mathbf{J}_s)\, dV$, if one employs the abbreviation

$$\mathrm{div}\, \mathbf{J}_s = \frac{\partial J_{sx}}{\partial x} + \frac{\partial J_{sy}}{\partial y} + \frac{\partial J_{sz}}{\partial z}. \tag{4}$$

According to the foregoing argument, the *divergence* of $\mathbf{J}_s$, defined in Eq. (4), simply represents the net entropy leaving unit volume per unit time—in other words, the excess of the entropy that leaves over the entropy that enters.

We deviate here temporarily to find the outward flux from a finite space of volume V. To this end, one mentally divides this space into infinitesimal parallelepipeds, each of volume dV. For every one of them we may write: net outward flux $= (\text{div } \mathbf{J}_s)\, dV$. If this equation is summed over all the parallelepipeds, whose sizes are then allowed to tend to zero, one obtains on the right-hand side the space integral over V of div $\mathbf{J}_s$; on the left, the fluxes across the surfaces separating contiguous parallelepipeds cancel, so that the integral of $\mathbf{n} \cdot \mathbf{J}_s$ only over the *outer* surface A remains. In short, we get

$$\int_A \mathbf{n} \cdot \mathbf{J}_s \, dA = \int_V \text{div } \mathbf{J}_s \, dV. \tag{5}$$

This result will be referred to as the *divergence theorem* or *Gauss' theorem*. Its importance stems from the fact that it permits one to transform a surface integral into a volume integral, and conversely. It should be mentioned that the proof here given of Eq. (5) is patently not rigorous inasmuch as an arbitrary volume cannot be constructed from an infinite number of rectangular parallelepipeds.

Let us now revert to our main line of argument. In keeping with the model of entropy as a (nonconserved) fluid, one may write:

$$\begin{bmatrix} \text{Rate of increase of} \\ \text{entropy inside } dV \end{bmatrix} + \begin{bmatrix} \text{outward flux of} \\ \text{entropy from } dV \end{bmatrix} = \begin{bmatrix} \text{entropy production} \\ \text{inside } dV \end{bmatrix},$$

i.e.,

$$\frac{\partial \rho s}{\partial t} \, dV + (\text{div } \mathbf{J}_s)\, dV = \sigma \, dV,$$

ρ being the mass per unit volume, or the density, of the matter contained in dV. Cancellation of dV finally leads to the anticipated connection between s, σ, and $\mathbf{J}_s$:

$$\boxed{\frac{\partial \rho s}{\partial t} + \text{div } \mathbf{J}_s = \sigma} \tag{6}$$

This essential equation is called the *balance equation for entropy* or *the entropy density* ρs, if one so prefers.

An equation of the form (6) evidently holds not only for the entropy, but for any property that can be pictured as a fluid. The analogue of Eq. (6) becomes especially simple when the property under consideration is conserved, because the source density of such a property is zero. For instance, the conservation of mass is expressed by the equation

$$\frac{\partial \rho}{\partial t} + \text{div } \mathbf{J}_m = 0, \tag{7}$$

where $\mathbf{J}_m$ is the *mass flux density*. Likewise, the conservation of energy may be written as

$$\frac{\partial \rho u}{\partial t} + \text{div } \mathbf{J}_u = 0, \tag{8}$$

$\mathbf{J}_u$ being the *energy flux density*.

A comparison between the last three equations will facilitate an understanding of the conceptual difficulties that confront us with regard to the entropy flux vector $\mathbf{J}_s$. The vector $\mathbf{J}_m$ is definable independently of its balance equation as the time rate at which matter penetrates unit area. The vector $\mathbf{J}_u$, on the other hand, is *defined* by its balance equation and can be visualized only as an imagined fluid. Nevertheless, one is usually oblivious of a conceptual problem in this context, because $\mathbf{J}_u$ is defined uniquely (apart from a divergenceless term) by Eq. (8), and one is left with the reassuring picture of energy as a waterlike fluid. When one attempts, however, to answer what is meant by the entropy flux vector $\mathbf{J}_s$, one's ideas become less tangible—i.e., more abstract. Not only can visualization now be realized solely at the expense of thinking in terms of an anomalous fluid capable of being destroyed and created, but worse still, the balance equation (6), regarded as a definition for $\mathbf{J}_s$, contains another undefined quantity, viz., the entropy production σ. Fortunately though, it is possible to derive an equation whose form is identical with that of Eq. (6), so that, by comparison between the two equations, a sensible choice can be made for $\mathbf{J}_s$ and σ as functions of flux vectors and other thermodynamic parameters.

We proceed to deduce this equation for a motionless fluid of uniform density ρ in which a diffusion of matter and transfer of energy occur. The derivation is effected when one combines the Gibbs relation (1) with the energy balance equation (8) and with the relation expressing the conservation of mass for the chemical component i in the absence of chemical reaction, to wit,

$$\frac{\partial \rho w_i}{\partial t} + \text{div } \mathbf{J}_i = 0, \tag{9}$$

where $\mathbf{J}_i$ is the *mass flux density* for the component i (in gm cm^{-2} sec^{-1}). For this purpose, we take the time derivative of Eq. (1), delete the term in $\partial v/\partial t$, and multiply what remains by ρ/T, to obtain

$$\rho \frac{\partial s}{\partial t} = \frac{\rho}{T} \frac{\partial u}{\partial t} - \sum \frac{\mu_i}{T} \rho \frac{\partial w_i}{\partial t}. \tag{10}$$

On substitution of $\partial u/\partial t$ and $\partial w_i/\partial t$ from Eqs. (8) and (9), the result is

$$\rho \frac{\partial s}{\partial t} = -\frac{1}{T} \text{div } \mathbf{J}_u + \sum \frac{\mu_i}{T} \text{div } \mathbf{J}_i. \tag{11}$$

Now, if $\mathbf{A}$ is a vector and B a scalar, both arbitrary functions of position, then

$$\operatorname{div}(\mathbf{A}B) = B \operatorname{div} \mathbf{A} + \mathbf{A} \cdot \operatorname{grad} B,$$

so that Eq. (11) may be transformed into

$$\rho \frac{\partial s}{\partial t} + \operatorname{div} \frac{1}{T}\left(\mathbf{J}_u - \sum \mu_i \mathbf{J}_i\right) = \mathbf{J}_u \cdot \operatorname{grad} \frac{1}{T} - \sum \mathbf{J}_i \cdot \operatorname{grad} \frac{\mu_i}{T}. \quad (12)$$

We notice that this equation becomes identical with Eq. (6) provided the entropy flux density and the entropy production per unit volume are defined as follows:

$$\mathbf{J}_s = \frac{1}{T}\left(\mathbf{J}_u - \sum \mu_i \mathbf{J}_i\right), \quad (13)$$

$$\sigma = \mathbf{J}_u \cdot \operatorname{grad} \frac{1}{T} - \sum \mathbf{J}_i \cdot \operatorname{grad} \frac{\mu_i}{T}. \quad (14)$$

The foregoing discussion may easily be generalized to furnish the entropy production for a system in which the flows of energy and matter are accompanied by a flow of electricity and the occurrence of a chemical reaction. Let e_i be the specific charge of the component i, ξ the extent per unit volume and A the affinity (both defined in Problem 8) of the chemical reaction, and ϕ the electric potential. Then Gibbs' fundamental relation (1) for constant volume can be written as*

$$T ds = d\bar{u} - \sum \bar{\mu}_i dw_i = d\bar{u} - \phi de - \sum \mu_i d_e w_i + \frac{1}{\rho} A d\xi, \quad (15)$$

where the tilde emphasizes the dependence of $\bar{u}$ and $\bar{\mu}_i = \mu_i + \phi e_i$ (the so-called *electrochemical potential*) on the electric parameters, $e = \sum w_i e_i$ denotes the total specific charge, and $d_e w_i$ stands for the part of dw_i that is due to ions entering and leaving the elementary region under consideration. Equation (15) should be combined with the balance equations (8) and (9) and the relation expressing the conservation of charge, viz.,

$$\frac{\partial \rho e}{\partial t} + \operatorname{div} \mathbf{J}_e = 0, \quad (16)$$

$\mathbf{J}_e$ being the *charge flux density* (in coulombs $cm^{-2}\ sec^{-1}$). Instead of to Eq. (12), one is then led more generally to

$$\rho \frac{\partial s}{\partial t} + \operatorname{div} \frac{1}{T}\left(\mathbf{J}_u - \sum \mu_i \mathbf{J}_i - \mathbf{J}_e \phi\right)$$
$$= \mathbf{J}_u \cdot \operatorname{grad} \frac{1}{T} - \sum \mathbf{J}_i \cdot \operatorname{grad} \frac{\mu_i}{T} - \mathbf{J}_e \cdot \operatorname{grad} \frac{\phi}{T} + \frac{1}{T} v A; \quad (17)$$

here v is *not* the specific volume but the *chemical reaction rate per unit volume*, i.e., $v = d\xi/dt$. The corresponding values of the entropy flux density and the

---

*Since $d\bar{u} = du + \phi de = du + \phi \sum e_i dw_i$, one gets $\bar{\mu}_i = \mu_i + \phi e_i$, with $\mu_i \equiv (\partial \bar{u}/\partial w_i)_{s,v,w_{j\neq i}}$ and $\mu_i \equiv (\partial u/\partial w_i)_{s,v,w_{j\neq i}}$, where it is assumed that u depends on T, p, and the composition of the subsystem but not on its charge. Thus, $\sum \bar{\mu}_i dw_i = \sum \mu_i dw_i$

entropy production are seen, on comparing Eq. (6) with Eq. (17), to be

$$\mathbf{J}_s = \frac{1}{T}\left(\mathbf{J}_u - \sum \mu_i \mathbf{J}_i - \mathbf{J}_e \phi\right), \tag{18}$$

$$\sigma = \mathbf{J}_u \cdot \operatorname{grad} \frac{1}{T} - \sum \mathbf{J}_i \cdot \operatorname{grad} \frac{\mu_i}{T} - \mathbf{J}_e \cdot \operatorname{grad} \frac{\phi}{T} + \frac{1}{T} vA. \tag{19}$$

If one inspects Eq. (19), one notices that there appears one term for each process (energy transfer, diffusion, electric flow, and chemical reaction) and that this term vanishes when the corresponding process ceases. In other words, in the computation of the entropy production due to the simultaneous presence of several processes we simply add the productions which would accompany the processes if they took place separately.

It is of particular interest to our further understanding of entropy flow and production to examine the implications of the balance equation (17) for a system as a whole. Let the system be closed and have an entropy S, a volume V, and a surface area A. On integration over the volume V, Eq. (6) reads

$$\frac{d}{dt}\int_V \rho s \, dV + \int_V \operatorname{div} \mathbf{J}_s \, dV = \int_V \sigma \, dV. \tag{20}$$

The first term on the left-hand side of Eq. (20) is simply dS/dt, while the term on the right-hand side is the entropy produced in the volume V per unit time. The second term on the left-hand side may be transformed with the aid of the divergence theorem (5) into the surface integral $\int_A \mathbf{n} \cdot \mathbf{J}_s \, dA$. In this integral one now has to substitute for $\mathbf{J}_s$ the value of the expression (18) on the surface A. For the closed system here considered, the fluxes $\mathbf{J}_i$ and $\mathbf{J}_e$ are all zero *on* the surface (although not necessarily *inside* the system), while the energy flux $\mathbf{J}_u$ can be identified as a pure *heat flux density* $\mathbf{J}_q$; therefore, Eq. (20) becomes

$$\frac{dS}{dt} + \int_A \frac{1}{T}\mathbf{n} \cdot \mathbf{J}_q \, dA = \int_V \sigma \, dV. \tag{21}$$

Equation (21) is easily recognized as a formulation of the second law for a closed system, especially when it is simplified, by the assumption that T is constant over A, to

$$\frac{dS}{dt} - \frac{1}{T}\frac{dQ}{dt} = \int_V \sigma \, dV, \tag{22}$$

dQ/dt being the time rate of addition of heat to the system. The version (22) of the second law differs from the familiar one, viz., $dS \geqslant dQ/T$, in that the time parameter appears therein; but more important still is the fact that we have here for the first time a statement for irreversible changes in terms of an equation rather than an intractable inequality.

+ ϕde, and the last two terms of Eq. (15) then result from the decomposition $dw_i = d_e w_i + d_r w_i$, where $d_r w_i = \rho^{-1}\nu_i M_i d\xi$ (see Problem 8) is the contribution to dw_i arising from the chemical reaction.

It is customary to introduce the inexact differentials

$$d_e S = \frac{dQ}{T} \tag{23}$$

and

$$d_i S = dt \int_V \sigma \, dV, \tag{24}$$

so that Eq. (22), after multiplication by dt, can be written as

$$\boxed{dS = d_e S + d_i S} . \tag{25}$$

Equation (25) may be verbalized as follows (Prigogine, 1947): the entropy increase dS of a system is composed of two, and only two, terms—namely, the term $d_e S$, which derives from the transfer of heat from external sources across the boundary of the system, and the term $d_i S$, which is due to changes inside the system. *

According to the second law, the increase $d_i S$ can never be negative, i.e.,

$$d_i S \geqslant 0. \tag{26}$$

The splitting of the increment dS into the parts $d_e S$ and $d_i S$ has here been justified for a system that is closed. But it is evident that one can, starting from Eq. (20) and substituting the full expression (18) for $\mathbf{J}_s$, finally write down Eq. (25) for an open system as well. In that case, however, while $d_i S$ is still defined by Eq. (24), the definition (23) for $d_e S$ must now be replaced by

$$d_e S = -dt \int_A \frac{1}{T} \mathbf{n} \cdot \left(\mathbf{J}_u - \sum \mu_i \mathbf{J}_i - \mathbf{J}_e \phi \right) dA. \tag{27}$$

Thus, although Eq. (25) is retained in form, it must now be interpreted differently: the entropy increase dS of an open system is composed of a part $d_e S$, which is the contribution to dS owing to the exchange of heat, matter, and charge between the system and its environment, and a part $d_i S$, which issues from processes occurring inside the system.

To complete the parallel between an open and a closed system, we postulate that Eq. (26) is valid for open as well as for closed systems. The assumption (26) is stated for the quantity S, which pertains to the system as a whole. One may rewrite Eq. (26) using the property σ defined for each point of the system. For, if $d_i S$ is to be nonnegative for an arbitrary volume, however small, the definition (24) requires that

$$\boxed{\sigma \geqslant 0} . \tag{28}$$

The assertion that the entropy produced in any process is zero or positive—expressed in its *global* form by Eq. (26) and in its *local* form by Eq. (28)—

---

*Note that, according to this interpretation of Eq. (25), work exchanged between the system and its surroundings contributes to $d_i S$, not to $d_e S$.

constitutes one of the basic postulates of irreversible thermodynamics.

It is relevant here to show that theorem (28) leads to some verifiable results. The ensuing discussion will also demonstrate a connection between thermodynamics and a few well-known experimental laws, that was not fully recognized prior to the advent of irreversible thermodynamics in its modern structure.

The derivation of the empirical consequences of Eq. (28) begins with the observation that in the expression (19) for σ, each term is either a scalar product of a flux vector and a gradient, or contains an ordinary product of the reaction rate v and the affinity A. Hence when chemical reactions are absent and only one kind of flux exists, σ reduces to a single term and the condition (28) demands that the angle between the flux vector and its conjugate gradient be less than or equal to 90°. For example, if only a flow of heat occurs, then $\sigma = \mathbf{J}_q \cdot \mathrm{grad}\,(1/T)$, and the angle included between the vector $\mathbf{J}_q$ and the vector grad $(1/T)$ (or the direction in which temperature decreases most rapidly) must be less than or equal to 90°. This angle is known to be zero for isotropic substances, but in general it will be different from zero. Alternatively, if a chemical reaction alone occurs, the immediate conclusion is that the reaction rate v has the same sign as the affinity A.

A second set of testable consequences of Eq. (28) may be deduced from Eq. (19) when it is combined with the experiential circumstance that, subject to a few restrictions soon to be enumerated, each flux vector or reaction rate appearing in Eq. (19) is proportional to its conjugate gradient or affinity. To be more precise, we appeal to the following oft-quoted empirical laws:

$$\mathbf{J}_q = -\lambda\,\mathrm{grad}\,T, \quad \text{(Fourier)} \tag{29}$$

$$\mathbf{J}_i = -D\,\mathrm{grad}\,\mu_i, \quad \text{(Hartley-Fick)} \tag{30}$$

$$\mathbf{J}_e = -\gamma\,\mathrm{grad}\,\phi, \quad \text{(Ohm)} \tag{31}$$

$$v = CA. \tag{32}$$

λ (thermal conductivity), D (diffusion coefficient), γ (electric conductivity), and C are constants—that is, not explicitly depending on space or time. Fourier's law (29) is valid for isotropic substances, while Ohm's law is applicable to metallic conductors. The validity of the laws (29) to (31) is further limited by the stipulation that a single flow should occur and that the gradients are small compared with unity. The affinity A in Eq. (32) is likewise required to be much less than unity, so that the postulated proportionality between v and A holds only for a reaction close to equilibrium.

Consider now, for instance, a system in which a heat flow takes place, i.e., $\sigma = \mathbf{J}_q \cdot \mathrm{grad}\,(1/T)$. Substituting for $\mathbf{J}_q$ its value from Eq. (29), one obtains, since grad $(1/T) = -(1/T^2)$ grad T,

$$\sigma = \frac{\lambda \, (\text{grad } T)^2}{T^2}. \tag{33}$$

Because the function of T in (33) is always positive, it follows from $\sigma > 0$ that its coefficient λ must be positive; this implies that in an isotropic medium, heat can only flow from high to low temperature regions. In a similar fashion, one may establish that the coefficients D, γ, and C are positive numbers.

1–3. Forces, Fluxes, and Phenomenological Equations

As in any other physical theory, the ultimate goal of a theory of thermodynamics is to provide predictions amenable to experimental verification. A very modest beginning in this direction has been made in the last few paragraphs. From our discussion there, one may draw the lesson that it is profitable to combine Eq. (19) for the entropy production with expressions for the flux vectors. We should emphasize that this step represents a marriage between a purely thermodynamic result and a set of equations not derivable from thermodynamic principles. Admittedly the adoption of the recommended procedure has so far led only to relatively trivial results. This is attributable to the fact that we have ignored the possibility of one process affecting or interfering with another when they happen simultaneously. Should more than one process occur at the same time, the one-flux laws of Fourier, Ohm, and others actually become inadequate and must be replaced by postulates of broader scope. To discover them will be our immediate aim.

First we introduce a few terms and notations intended to improve the orderliness and economy of our subsequent presentation. Equations (29) to (32) have the general form $J = LX$, where X is of the nature of a gradient or affinity and J of a flux or reaction rate; L is a coefficient not depending on either X or J. Each of the equations (29) to (32) asserts that a gradient or affinity X induces a flux or reaction rate J. This cause-effect relation between X and J, which is reminiscent of the connection between force and acceleration in Newtonian mechanics, renders it plausible to call X a *thermodynamic force*. By the same manner of reasoning, the equations $J = LX$ may be referred to as *thermodynamic equations of motion*; but it is more customary to designate them as the *phenomenological equations* of thermodynamics, in allusion to their mere experimental origin. Correspondingly, the constants L are known as *phenomenological coefficients*. The quantities J will in future simply be referred to as *fluxes*, unless a more specific description becomes necessary. Further, both X and J will be slightly redefined to stand for scalar quantities (e.g., vector components) rather than vectors.

Proceeding with the outlined problem—that is, the generalization of the single-flux equations of motion—we choose as a point of departure the following typical experimental observation. In a certain class of events described as *thermoelectric phenomena*, generation of heat is exhibited as a result of an electric potential difference, while, conversely, an electric potential difference may appear when only a temperature gradient is present. From this we conclude: in the presence of an electric potential gradient, the flow of heat is dependent upon the gradient of the electric potential as well as that of temperature. Analogously, the flow of electricity is a function not only of the electric potential gradient but also of the temperature gradient. Assuming, for simplicity, that the system is isotropic and that the flows of heat and electricity are one-dimensional (in the x-direction, say), we may summarize our conclusion thus: each of the fluxes J_u and J_e is a function of both forces dT/dx and $d\phi/dx$ or, if one prefers, of the forces

$$X_u = \frac{d}{dx}\frac{1}{T} \tag{34}$$

and

$$X_e = -\frac{d}{dx}\frac{\phi}{T}; \tag{35}$$

that is, $J_u = J_u(X_u, X_e)$ and $J_e = J_e(X_u, X_e)$.

The functions J_u and J_e may now be expanded in a Taylor series about the point ($X_u = 0$, $X_e = 0$). In this expansion, one can dispense with the zero-order terms $J_u(0,0)$ and $J_e(0,0)$, because the flows of energy and electricity vanish when the gradients X_u and X_e become zero; one is left with

$$J_u(X_u, X_e) = X_u\left(\frac{\partial J_u}{\partial X_u}\right)_{X_u=0, X_e=0} + X_e\left(\frac{\partial J_u}{\partial X_e}\right)_{X_u=0, X_e=0} + o(X_u, X_e),$$
$$\tag{36}$$

and a similar equation for J_e. Equation (36) is further simplified by the assumption—already familiar from our discussion of single fluxes—that X_u and X_e are so small compared with unity, that the terms $o(X_u, X_e)$, of order two and higher, may be neglected relative to terms of order one. J_u is then approximated with sufficient accuracy by terms of the first order in the forces:

$$J_u = L_{uu}X_u + L_{ue}X_e, \tag{37}$$

where the coefficients L_{uu} and L_{ue} are abbreviations for

$$L_{uu} = \left(\frac{\partial J_u}{\partial X_u}\right)_{X_u=0, X_e=0} \tag{38}$$

and

$$L_{ue} = \left(\frac{\partial J_u}{\partial X_e}\right)_{X_u=0, X_e=0} \tag{39}$$

An analogous equation can be established for the flow of electricity, viz.,

$$J_e = L_{eu}X_u + L_{ee}X_e, \tag{40}$$

with the coefficients

$$L_{eu} = \left(\frac{\partial J_e}{\partial X_u}\right)_{X_u = 0, X_e = 0} \tag{41}$$

and

$$L_{ee} = \left(\frac{\partial J_e}{\partial X_e}\right)_{X_u = 0, X_e = 0}. \tag{42}$$

Each phenomenological coefficient provides a numerical measure of the extent to which the force prefixed by it in Eq. (37) or (40) contributes to the flux under consideration. The first subscript attached to L characterizes the nature of the flux, while the second signifies the nature of the contributing force. If the subscripts are the same, the flux and force are similar, and a nonzero coefficient gives rise to a so-called *direct effect*; if they are not the same, the flux and force are dissimilar, and a nonzero coefficient produces a so-called *cross-effect*. The coefficients L_{ue} and L_{eu} gauge the interaction, or *coupling*, existing between energy and charge flows, and are responsible for the appearance of cross-effects commonly referred to as thermoelectric phenomena.

The coefficient L_{ee} is proportional to the electric conductivity γ. For, if one examines an isothermal state, defined by grad $T = 0$, or $X_u = 0$, Eq. (40) reduces to

$$J_e = L_{ee}X_e = -L_{ee}\frac{1}{T}\frac{d\phi}{dx}, \tag{43}$$

which, on comparison with Ohm's law $J_e = -\gamma(d\phi/dx)$, gives

$$\gamma = \frac{L_{ee}}{T}. \tag{44}$$

The dependence of the heat conductivity λ on the phenomenological coefficients is found when it is assumed that the electric current is zero, i.e., $J_e = 0$. Equation (40) may then be solved for $X_e = -(L_{eu}/L_{ee})X_u$, and on substituting this result in Eq. (37), one has

$$J_u = \left(L_{uu} - \frac{L_{ue}L_{eu}}{L_{ee}}\right)X_u = -(L_{uu}L_{ee} - L_{ue}L_{eu})\frac{1}{L_{ee}T^2}\frac{dT}{dx}, \tag{45}$$

or Fourier's law for a substance of thermal conductivity

$$\lambda = \frac{L_{uu}L_{ee} - L_{ue}L_{eu}}{L_{ee}T^2}. \tag{46}$$

The coupling between simultaneously occurring processes is not peculiar to the flows of heat and electricity, nor need the coupling be confined to two processes. Reasoning predicts and experiment confirms that interference exists, for example, between the flows of chemical components, energy, and electricity. Physically, it is not difficult to understand why the flows of mass, energy, and electricity should be interrelated. After all, electric charge is an attribute of material particles possessing both mass and energy, so that a flow of any one of the mentioned properties must in general be accompanied by a flow of the remaining two.

On the whole, one should be prepared to encounter mutual interference of any two concurrent processes in the same system. However, an important class of interactions can be excluded prior to experiment—to wit, those that would bring about cross-effects between processes of scalar and vectorial character. This rule is a consequence of a general symmetry principle, due to P. Curie (1908), asserting that macroscopic causes cannot have more elements of symmetry than the effects they produce. To illustrate how the rule follows from the principle in a particular case, we consider the simultaneous occurrence of a flow of heat and a chemical reaction. If the quantity A/T is accepted as the force conjugate to the reaction rate v, the equations of motion read

$$J_u = L_{uu} \frac{d}{dx} \frac{1}{T} + L_{uc} \frac{A}{T} \tag{47}$$

and

$$v = L_{cu} \frac{d}{dx} \frac{1}{T} + L_{cc} \frac{A}{T}, \tag{48}$$

where the subscript c refers to the chemical reaction. In the isothermal state (grad $T = 0$), Eq. (47), for instance, reduces to $J_u = L_{uc}(A/T)$. Unless $L_{uc} = 0$, this would mean that a scalar cause A/T produces a vectorial effect J_u, which is forbidden by the symmetry principle. Therefore, $L_{uc} = 0$, or the coupling between the heat flow and the chemical reaction is zero. Similarly, the coupling between any vectorial and any scalar process vanishes.

In spite of the fact that some coefficients L are zero by virtue of the symmetry principle, we shall retain them in the subsequent mathematical formalism for the sake of uniformity. With this understanding, we may postulate in analogy to Eqs. (37) and (40), that when n processes occur simultaneously, the associated fluxes J_i are linearly dependent on the conjugate forces X_i, i.e.,

$$\boxed{J_i = \sum_{j=1}^{n} L_{ij} X_j}, \qquad (i = 1, 2, \ldots, n) \tag{49}$$

where

$$L_{ij} = \left(\frac{\partial J_i}{\partial X_j}\right)_{X_k} \qquad (k \neq j) \tag{50}$$

are partial derivatives at the point $X_1 = X_2 = \cdots = X_n = 0$. Equations (49) are the *generalized phenomenological relations* we set out to deduce at the beginning of this section. The assumption that these equations are valid represents a basic postulate of our theory. The terms appearing on the right-hand side of Eq. (49) are, of course, only the first-order contributions in a Taylor expansion of J_i as a function of the forces X_j. Thus, Eq. (49) should be applied solely to changes involving forces so small compared with unity, or states so close to equilibrium, that terms of order two and higher may be neglected relative to those of the first order. This restriction furnishes a quantitative criterion for the irreversible phenomena to be studied with the aid of the linear equations (49). The neglect of second- and higher-order terms in the equations of motion explains, incidentally, why it would be proper to give the unpretentious name "first-order thermodynamics" to the present inquiry.

We next ask what the entropy production will be for a process involving n fluxes. As in the case of the equations of motion, the solution of this problem for n fluxes is suggested by an examination of the simpler two-flux situation. Consider again the simultaneous flow of heat and electricity. On inspection of the entropy production in this case, viz.,

$$\sigma = \mathbf{J}_u \cdot \operatorname{grad} \frac{1}{T} - \mathbf{J}_e \cdot \operatorname{grad} \frac{\phi}{T},$$

one notices that each flux is multiplied by the force conjugate to it according to Eqs. (34) and (35), that is,

$$\sigma = J_{ux}X_{ux} + J_{uy}X_{uy} + J_{uz}X_{uz} + J_{ex}X_{ex} + J_{ey}X_{ey} + J_{ez}X_{ez}, \tag{51}$$

where X_{ux} is the x-component of the vector grad $(1/T)$, X_{ex} the x-component of the vector $-\operatorname{grad}(\phi/T)$, and so on. Relations similar in appearance to Eq. (51) can be established for other two-flux examples. It is suggested, therefore, that in the general case, where n forces X_i give rise to n fluxes J_i, the entropy production is

$$\boxed{\sigma = \sum_i J_i X_i}, \tag{52}$$

a bilinear form in the fluxes and the forces.

Finally, substitution of Eqs. (49) into Eq. (52) yields the entropy production as a quadratic form in the forces alone:

$$\sigma = \sum_i \sum_j L_{ij} X_i X_j \, .$$ (53)

1-4. The Onsager Reciprocity Theorem

Hitherto our discussion has been founded on three basic postulates: (1) the entropy balance, and therefore the entropy production, can be computed from Gibbs' relation; (2) the entropy production, a sum of products of forces and fluxes, is nonnegative; and (3) each flux entering into the expression for the entropy production is a linear combination of the forces. Although these postulates cannot be derived rigorously from the first and second laws, they represent none the less plausible extensions of thermostatic ideas. For this reason, they are not essentially new principles comparable in status with the first and second laws. This fact is reflected in the relative barrenness of our exposition up to this point. True, we have been able to view some thermostatic concepts in a broader context and have derived a few results of rather academic interest, but we have failed so far to make any major predictions that can be put to experimental test.

The additional postulate that breaks the impasse and enables us for the first time to deduce verifiable consequences was formulated and proved by Onsager in 1931. He stated, in a theorem named after him, that the coefficients L_{ij} of the phenomenological equations are symmetrical, i.e.,

$$\boxed{L_{ij} = L_{ji}} \, . \qquad (i,j = 1, 2, \ldots, n)$$ (54)

These are usually referred to as *Onsager's reciprocity relations*. If, in agreement with Eq. (50), one casts Eqs. (54) in the alternative form

$$\left(\frac{\partial J_i}{\partial X_j} \right)_{X_{k \neq j}} = \left(\frac{\partial J_j}{\partial X_i} \right)_{X_{k \neq i}} ,$$ (55)

the physical significance of the Onsager relations is shown to be this: The increase in the flux J_i caused by unit increase in the force X_j (while the remaining forces are held fixed) is equal to the increase in the flux J_j due to unit increase in the force X_i. The reader will observe, no doubt, the resemblance between the reciprocity relations (55) and the relations of Maxwell known from thermostatics.

Long before 1931, the symmetry (54) was suggested by experiments on the conduction of heat in anisotropic crystals, after it was noticed that a flow of heat along one axis of an anisotropic crystal is accompanied by temperature gradients along the other axes. This observation seemed to indicate that a flow of heat along the x-axis must be related not only to the gradient of T along that axis, but also to the gradients along the y- and z-axis. It was therefore proposed more than a century ago that for anisotropic crystals the law of Fourier should be generalized to

$$J_{ux} = L_{11} \frac{\partial T}{\partial x} + L_{12} \frac{\partial T}{\partial y} + L_{13} \frac{\partial T}{\partial z},$$

$$J_{uy} = L_{21} \frac{\partial T}{\partial x} + L_{22} \frac{\partial T}{\partial y} + L_{23} \frac{\partial T}{\partial z}, \tag{56}$$

$$J_{uz} = L_{31} \frac{\partial T}{\partial x} + L_{32} \frac{\partial T}{\partial y} + L_{33} \frac{\partial T}{\partial z}.$$

Experiments to determine the coefficients L_{ij} then led to the curious results $L_{ij} = L_{ji}$ ($i,j = 1, 2, 3$). For highly symmetric crystals, these equations could easily be understood theoretically on the grounds of crystal symmetry alone. But careful investigations by Soret (1893–94) and Voigt (1903) confirmed that, even for the more asymmetric crystals, where mere symmetry considerations cease to afford an explanation, the relations $L_{ij} = L_{ji}$ remain nevertheless valid.

The theory of Onsager now gives us a statistical-mechanical demonstration of the reciprocity relations (54), not only for heat conduction in crystals, but— in principle at least—for all the phenomena in which cross-effects occur.

Onsager was led to the proof of his theorem by the following observation: when two or more independent reactions take place in a system, chemists are accustomed to regard each reaction as *balanced separately* at equilibrium. What makes this restriction most interesting is the circumstance that it is not demanded by thermostatics. After all, thermostatic theory asserts only that the concentration of each chemical component remains constant in time when equilibrium is attained. The so-called *detailed balancing* of chemical reactions thus constitutes an additional hypothesis not derivable from the principles of thermostatics. The implications of this supposition can be illustrated best with reference to a chemical process known as *triangular* reaction. Such a reaction involves a substance capable of existing in a homogeneous phase in three different forms A, B, C. Each form can undergo, directly or indirectly, a transition into either one of the other two according to the scheme

$$A \rightleftharpoons B \atop \diagdown \diagup \atop C \tag{57}$$

A concrete example of such a triangular reaction is the *isomerization* of butenes, where the forms A, B, C are the *isomers*

(1-butene)   (trans-2-butene)   (cis-2-butene)

If we had to meet the demands of thermostatics alone, equilibrium could be sustained as follows. Besides a certain number of backward and forward transitions, balancing each other individually, i.e.,

$$A \rightleftharpoons B, \qquad B \rightleftharpoons C, \qquad C \rightleftharpoons A, \tag{58}$$

one could imagine transitions taking place around the cycle

$$
\begin{array}{ccc}
A & \longrightarrow & B \\
 & \nwarrow \quad \swarrow & \\
 & C &
\end{array}
\tag{59}
$$

The principle of detailed balancing now rules out the possibility of an equilibrium maintained entirely or in part by a device such as (59). Only the scheme (58) remains, as we anticipated when putting down (57).

It is instructive to examine exactly at what juncture chemists need to invoke the idea of detailed balancing. Let it be assumed that each of the six reactions involved in (57) obeys a simple mass-action law. In other words, the fraction of molecules of one kind changing into molecules of another kind is a time-independent constant. This so-called *velocity constant* will be denoted by k_{BA} for the reaction $A \rightarrow B$, by k_{AB} for the reaction $B \rightarrow A$, and so on. The law of mass action then asserts that the mole numbers n_A, n_B, n_C for A, B, C molecules increase at the rates

$$\frac{dn_A}{dt} = -(k_{BA} + k_{CA})n_A + k_{AB}n_B + k_{AC}n_C, \tag{60a}$$

$$\frac{dn_B}{dt} = k_{BA}n_A - (k_{AB} + k_{CB})n_B + k_{BC}n_C, \tag{60b}$$

$$\frac{dn_C}{dt} = k_{CA}n_A + k_{CB}n_B - (k_{AC} + k_{BC})n_C. \tag{60c}$$

At equilibrium, these derivatives all become zero, and Eqs. (60a, b, c) reduce to two independent equations for the equilibrium mole numbers $\bar{n}_A$, $\bar{n}_B$, $\bar{n}_C$, viz.,

$$0 = -(k_{BA} + k_{CA})\bar{n}_A + k_{AB}\bar{n}_B + k_{AC}\bar{n}_C, \tag{61a}$$

and

$$0 = k_{BA}\bar{n}_A - (k_{AB} + k_{CB})\bar{n}_B + k_{BC}\bar{n}_C. \tag{61b}$$

Equations (61a,b) can be solved for the equilibrium ratios $\bar{n}_A : \bar{n}_B : \bar{n}_C$ for any set of positive velocity constants. One finds readily

$$\frac{\bar{n}_B}{\bar{n}_C} = \frac{k_{BC}(k_{BA} + k_{CA}) + k_{BA}k_{AC}}{k_{CB}(k_{BA} + k_{CA}) + k_{AB}k_{CA}}, \tag{62}$$

and similar expressions for $\bar{n}_C/\bar{n}_A$ and $\bar{n}_A/\bar{n}_B$. These equations for the ratios, together with the equation

$$\bar{n}_A + \bar{n}_B + \bar{n}_C = n_A + n_B + n_C = n, \tag{63}$$

stating the conservation of the total number n of moles, may be solved, if one so desires, for the equilibrium mole numbers themselves.

The result (62) and its analogues are now compared with the consequences of the thermostatic criterion for chemical equilibrium, according to which the chemical potentials μ_A, μ_B, μ_C of the A, B, C molecules are equal at equilibrium. That is, if one denotes equilibrium values by horizontal bars, then

$$\bar{\mu}_A = \bar{\mu}_B = \bar{\mu}_C. \tag{64}$$

For simplicity, and in agreement with the mass-action formulas (60), let the triangular reaction take place in an ideal system, so that the chemical potentials vary linearly with the mole fractions:

$$\mu_A = \mu_A^0(T,p) + RT \log \frac{n_A}{n}, \tag{65}$$

and similarly for μ_B and μ_C. [Note that in Eq. (65) and subsequently, μ denotes once again the chemical potential per *mole*, not per unit mass.] On insertion of these values in Eqs. (64), the equilibrium ratios of any two mole numbers are seen to be (different) constants, dependent merely on T and p:

$$\frac{\bar{n}_B}{\bar{n}_C} = K_1, \qquad \frac{\bar{n}_C}{\bar{n}_A} = K_2, \qquad \frac{\bar{n}_A}{\bar{n}_B} = K_3. \tag{66}$$

The quantities $K_i(T,p)$ $(i = 1, 2, 3)$ are the *equilibrium constants* of the reactions $B \rightarrow C$, $C \rightarrow A$, $A \rightarrow B$, respectively.

Comparison of Eqs. (62) and (66) finally exhibits that each constant K_i equals a rather cumbersome function of the k's. One can proceed just so far on appealing to thermostatics alone. But chemists are wont to go a step further. They postulate that the equilibrium constant for a reaction can be set equal to the ratio of the velocity constants of the forward and backward reactions, i.e.,

$$K_1 = \frac{k_{BC}}{k_{CB}}, \qquad K_2 = \frac{k_{CA}}{k_{AC}}, \qquad K_3 = \frac{k_{AB}}{k_{BA}}. \tag{67}$$

Now, it clearly *is* possible to reconcile Eqs. (67) with equations such as (62), if one demands that $k_{BA}k_{AC}/k_{BC} = k_{AB}k_{CA}/k_{CB}$, or

$$k_{AC}k_{CB}k_{BA} = k_{AB}k_{BC}k_{CA}. \tag{68}$$

It should be stressed, however, that this connection between the k's is not necessary for the fulfillment of thermostatic requirements; those are secured by any set of positive k's. The additional assumption, implicit in Eqs. (67), is none other than the detailed balancing of each one of the reactions $B \to C$, $C \to A$, $A \to B$, so that the transition $B \to C$ is supposed to occur just as frequently as the reverse transition $C \to B$, and so on for the remaining reactions. For, symbolically this postulate reads:

$$k_{CB}\bar{n}_B = k_{BC}\bar{n}_C, \qquad k_{AC}\bar{n}_C = k_{CA}\bar{n}_A, \qquad k_{BA}\bar{n}_A = k_{AB}\bar{n}_B; \tag{69}$$

and these, in conjunction with Eqs. (66), at once yield the postulated Eqs. (67).

After having exposed the tacit or manifest (as the case may be) supposition of detailed balancing in chemical practice, Onsager goes on to show that detailed balancing is capable of furnishing reciprocity relations for a triangular reaction in an ideal system close to equilibrium. To pursue his argument, let us define y_A as the difference between the values of the mole number n_A at the time t and at equilibrium. Thus, on denoting time derivations by dots,

$$y_A = n_A - \bar{n}_A \tag{70}$$

and

$$\dot{y}_A = \dot{n}_A, \tag{71}$$

Substitution of Eqs. (70) and (71), together with the corresponding expressions for y_B and y_C in Eq. (60a) gives, with the aid of Eq. (61a),

$$\dot{y}_A = -(k_{BA} + k_{CA})y_A + k_{AB}y_B + k_{AC}y_C. \tag{72}$$

From Eq. (65) one sees that

$$\mu_A - \bar{\mu}_A = RT \log \frac{n_A}{\bar{n}_A} = RT \log \left(1 + \frac{y_A}{\bar{n}_A}\right). \tag{73}$$

For small departures from equilibrium, when $y_A/\bar{n}_A$ is negligible compared with unity, $\log(1 + y_A/\bar{n}_A) \approx y_A/\bar{n}_A$, and Eq. (73) can be written approximately as

$$y_A = -\frac{(\bar{\mu}_A - \mu_A)\bar{n}_A}{RT}. \tag{74}$$

If one inserts Eq. (74) in Eq. (72) and carries out a similar procedure for $\dot{y}_B$ and $\dot{y}_C$, one obtains in total:

$$RT\ddot{y}_A = (k_{BA} + k_{CA})\bar{n}_A(\bar{\mu}_A - \mu_A) - k_{AB}\bar{n}_B(\bar{\mu}_B - \mu_B) - k_{AC}\bar{n}_C(\bar{\mu}_C - \mu_C), \tag{75a}$$

$$RT\ddot{y}_B = -k_{BA}\bar{n}_A(\bar{\mu}_A - \mu_A) + (k_{AB} + k_{CB})\bar{n}_B(\bar{\mu}_B - \mu_B) - k_{BC}\bar{n}_C(\bar{\mu}_C - \mu_C), \tag{75b}$$

$$RT\ddot{y}_C = -k_{CA}\bar{n}_A(\bar{\mu}_A - \mu_A) - k_{CB}\bar{n}_B(\bar{\mu}_B - \mu_B) + (k_{AC} + k_{BC})\bar{n}_C(\bar{\mu}_C - \mu_C). \tag{75c}$$

Onsager's theorem presupposes the existence of linear relations of the kind in Eq. (49) between the thermodynamic forces and fluxes; these, it should be emphasized, are not chosen at will, but discovered on inspection of the relevant expression for the entropy production σ. In the instance before us, σ is easily ascertained. A triangular reaction obviously contributes the amount $-\mu_A \, dn_A - \mu_B \, dn_B - \mu_C \, dn_C$ to TdS [cf. Eq. (1)], so that, on differentiation, the corresponding entropy production is supplied by

$$TV\sigma = -\mu_A\dot{n}_A - \mu_B\dot{n}_B - \mu_C\dot{n}_C. \tag{76}$$

By virtue of $\dot{n}_A + \dot{n}_B + \dot{n}_C = \dot{n} = 0$, $\dot{y}_A = \dot{n}_A$, $\dot{y}_B = \dot{n}_B$, $\dot{y}_C = \dot{n}_C$, and Eqs. (64), the result (76) can be written as

$$TV\sigma = (\bar{\mu}_A - \mu_A)\dot{y}_A + (\bar{\mu}_B - \mu_B)\dot{y}_B + (\bar{\mu}_C - \mu_C)\dot{y}_C. \tag{77}$$

Thus, it is legitimate to regard σ as a bilinear form in the *forces*

$$X_A = \frac{\bar{\mu}_A - \mu_A}{T}, \qquad X_B = \frac{\bar{\mu}_B - \mu_B}{T}, \qquad X_C = \frac{\bar{\mu}_C - \mu_C}{T}, \tag{78}$$

and in the *fluxes*

$$J_A = \frac{\dot{y}_A}{V}, \qquad J_B = \frac{\dot{y}_B}{V}, \qquad J_C = \frac{\dot{y}_C}{V}. \tag{79}$$

With this choice of forces and fluxes, Eqs. (75) are recognized as the phenomenological equations appropriate to the chemical reaction:

$$J_A = L_{11}X_A + L_{12}X_B + L_{13}X_C, \tag{80a}$$
$$J_B = L_{21}X_A + L_{22}X_B + L_{23}X_C, \tag{80b}$$
$$J_C = L_{31}X_A + L_{32}X_B + L_{33}X_C, \tag{80c}$$

where $L_{11} = (k_{BA} + k_{CA})\bar{n}_A/RV$, $L_{12} = -k_{AB}\bar{n}_B/RV$, and so on. Now, when the purely thermostatic results, Eqs. (80), are combined with the extrathermostatic assumption of detailed balancing, as expressed by Eqs. (69), the reciprocity relations $L_{23} = L_{32}$, $L_{31} = L_{13}$, $L_{12} = L_{21}$ immediately ensue.

The above proof of the reciprocity relations suffers from the drawback that it starts out from a particular molecular picture: a chemical reaction is explained as the aggregate manifestation of many elementary transitions. We saw, however—and this is the heuristic value of the demonstration—that this model in itself is not sufficient to provide the reciprocity relations. Still, it is useful in that it permits us to invoke the condition of detailed balancing. From this fact we gather that any mechanism picturing a process as the net result of many elementary transitions will tend to yield reciprocity relations. But obviously one is called upon to deal with many instances where no such device can reasonably be assumed. For each of these cases we could conceivably design a special kinematic model and state a principle analogous to the condition of detailed balancing, so that the reciprocity relations follow once the principle is applied to the model. Hence instead of a single proof one would have many proofs, but each of them would be valid for a particular class of processes only. The reader will appreciate that a general demonstration, applicable to all kinds of irreversible phenomena, should make no reference whatsoever to any imagined microscopic mechanism. On the contrary, the proof must rely upon some macroscopic phenomenon common to all systems; if an auxiliary assumption of a microscopic nature is imperative, it ought to claim universal validity.

Onsager had the profound insight to realize that there exists a unique approach which will meet these demands: one must examine the *fluctuations* present in any isolated system, and discover the limitations imposed on them by the so-called *principle of microscopic reversibility*. It transpires that these considerations need to be supplemented by a hypothesis prescribing the manner in which a fluctuation regresses. By reason of this, Onsager's derivation falls into three parts, which we are now going to enumerate and discuss at some length.

FLUCTUATION THEORY

In thermostatics one supposes that a thermophysical system, when left isolated for a sufficient period of time, will ultimately settle down into a state of equilibrium, where all observable properties remain constant with the passage of time; the approach to equilibrium is one-directional, or irreversible. Statistical mechanics, on the other hand, teaches that the state of rest associated with equilibrium is only apparent, and that *absolute* irreversibility is a fiction. In reality, all observable properties, except the total mass and total energy—both of which are invariable owing to the postulated isolation of the system—are liable to undergo accidental deviations from, or *fluctuations* about, their thermostatic (equilibrium) values. There are good reasons for neglecting these fluctuations in thermostatic theory. The comparatively crude thermophysical instruments respond solely to sizable (long-lived) fluctuations; but the probability (relative frequency) of a fluctuation decreases very sharply with an increase in its size and duration. For example, the probability that a gas of N molecules contained in a vessel of volume V spontaneously deviates from the uniform (equilibrium) distribution to such an extent that the gas becomes confined to a volume $\frac{1}{2}V$, is evidently $(\frac{1}{2})^N$. Since N is usually of the order 10^{23}, this means that one would expect never to observe such an event. While large deviations from equilibrium are exceedingly rare, smaller fluctuations will happen more frequently. To illustrate: the most commonly occurring fluctuations in the number of molecules per unit volume of the vessel about its equilibrium value N/V are of the order $(N/V)^{1/2}$. The small and rapid fluctuations cannot, however, be registered by thermostatic instruments, because they average out over the macroscopic space and time intervals presupposed in macroscopic measurements.

Observable effects can be expected to manifest themselves only under very favorable conditions. Such conditions do, in fact, exist and are responsible, *inter alia*, for *Brownian movement* of small particles suspended in a liquid and of a mirror in delicate elastic suspension, the *opalescence* of liquids near the critical point, and in everyday life the blue color of the sky. About fifty years ago, Einstein (1905–10), Smoluchowski (1906–10), and other physicists demonstrated very convincingly that these phenomena admit quantitative explanations only with recourse to the idea of fluctuations. Since that time nobody could seriously doubt that the concept of a fluctuation is more than a theoretical construct.

A quantitative treatment of fluctuations must commence with Boltzmann's classic relation between the entropy S and the thermodynamic probability W of a thermodynamic state, viz., $S = k \log W + \text{const.}$ [Eq. (2)], an equation whose supreme usefulness derives from its validity even outside thermostatic equilibrium. From a discussion of the premises and consequences of Boltzmann's relation given by Einstein in 1910, we borrow some arguments that are relevant in the present context.

To start with, let us inquire into the meaning of the probability W. It is essential to apprehend that a thermodynamic state, specified in terms of macroscopic variables such as energy, volume, local temperatures, and so on, is incompletely defined from a microscopic (molecular) point of view; the quantity W measures the number of different microscopic possibilities for realizing a given thermodynamic state. In order to calculate W, one needs a molecular theory of the system in question. It will, for instance, make a big difference to the computation whether the molecules are assumed to behave in agreement with classical or with quantum mechanics. For this reason it is debatable whether or not the Boltzmann equation on its own—that is, unsupported by a molecular theory—conveys any information at all. If Eq. (2) were indeed a vacuous statement, it would lose its value for any kind of phenomenological discussion. Fortunately, as Einstein observes, Boltzmann's equation *can* be endowed with a content independent of a molecular theory, when one adopts the view that physical processes are irreversible in appearance only.

To be exact, let the phenomenological state of the system be described by the thermodynamic parameters $a_1, a_2, \ldots, a_n$. Each state Z then corresponds to a combination of values of these variables. When the system is isolated, the energy and the number of atoms, and in general no other functions of the a's, are fixed. Consider all the states compatible with the conditions of isolation, and denote them by $Z_1, Z_2, \ldots, Z_k$. If now irreversibility is not an inexorable requirement, it is plausible to posit that an *aged* system—a system that has been subjected to isolation for a length of time which is normally adequate to ensure thermostatic equilibrium—will in the course of time pass through *all* the states Z_1, Z_2, etc. Granted this assumption, one may speak in the following sense of the probability of the separate states. Over a long period of time t the system will be observed to spend a time t_1, say, in the state Z_1; the fraction $W_1 = t_1/t$ is then the probability of the state Z_1. Similarly, we may define the probabilities W_2, W_3, etc., for the remaining states Z_2, Z_3, etc.

According to Boltzmann, the seeming irreversibility of natural changes is attributable to the fact that the probabilities W_1, W_2, etc., are different, and that the system will probably proceed to states of greater probability when it happens to be in states of lesser probabilities. The inescapable irreversibility canonized in the second law is only apparent and should be ascribed to the circumstance that the probabilities not only differ but are of different orders of magnitude, so that of all the states bordering on a particular state Z, one state will virtually for certain succeed the state Z because it is so very much more probable than any other.

It is the probability as defined above, without an appeal to molecular theory, that is regarded to be connected with the entropy S through Boltzmann's equation. So far we have assumed that the parameters a_i determine the state of the system *completely* from the thermodynamic, or phenomenological, point of view. But, as Einstein avers, Eq. (2) stays valid even in the cases where the specification is incomplete, provided one subscribes to the following convention. Let a state be defined by special values of the parameters $a_1, a_2, \ldots, a_n$, while the values of the remaining variables $a_{n+1}, a_{n+2}, \ldots, a_{n+m}$ are left unspecified; next, keeping $a_1, a_2, \ldots, a_n$ constant, we search for the set of values of $a_{n+1}, a_{n+2}, \ldots, a_{n+m}$ that will maximize the entropy. Boltzmann's relation will then hold between this maximum entropy and the probability of the state $Z(a_1, a_2, \ldots, a_n)$. This conclusion depends again on the probabilities of various states being of different orders of magnitude, so that the chosen set of values of $a_{n+1}, a_{n+2}, \ldots, a_{n+m}$ will be realized much more frequently than all other sets taken together.

Equation (2) indicates that the state of thermostatic equilibrium has by far the greatest probability of all the states compatible with the conditions of equilibrium, and that a fluctuation of appreciable size will be a very rare event indeed. For, suppose W to be the probability and S the entropy of a state Z deviating from the state of equilibrium, the latter having the probability W_0 and an entropy S_0. Then, $S - S_0 = k \log (W/W_0)$, or

$$W = W_0 e^{\Delta S/k}. \tag{81}$$

$\Delta S = S - S_0$ represents the excess of the entropy S over its equilibrium value; it is necessarily negative or zero because the entropy is a maximum in the equilibrium state. If it is further borne in mind that k, the gas constant per molecule, is an extremely small quantity (of the order 10^{-16}), one notices immediately that W is bound to decline very sharply with an increase of $|\Delta S|$; and that, as a result, the relative frequency of a fluctuation accompanied by an entropy change ΔS is practically nonzero only when ΔS is, at the utmost, of the order 10^{-16}.

The interpretation of Boltzmann's equation up to this point might be adequate for qualitative and order-of-magnitude considerations, but a moment's reflection reveals that it is open to a fundamental objection. Obviously, each parameter a_i is capable of taking on a continuous set of values, and correspondingly a continuous set of states $Z(a_1, a_2, \ldots, a_n)$ exists. Once this is conceded, it does not make sense to speak, as was done above, of the probability of a precisely defined state $Z(a_1', a_2', \ldots, a_n')$; in fact, this probability is seen to be zero. It is clear that from a statistical standpoint a nonzero probability can attach only to a state in whose specification one allows the latitudes $\Delta a_1, \Delta a_2, \ldots, \Delta a_n$ or, what is the same, to a *region* of extension $\Delta a_1, \Delta a_2, \ldots, \Delta a_n$ in the n-dimensional space of the a_i $(i = 1, 2, \ldots, n)$. Mathematically, one deals with this situation by introducing a *distribution function* $f(a_1, a_2, \ldots, a_n)$ such that the probability for the state $Z(a_1', a_2', \ldots, a_n')$

becomes the n-dimensional integral of $f \exp (\Delta S/k)$ over the region $a'_1 < a_i < a'_i + \Delta a_i$ $(i = 1, 2, \ldots, n)$ of a-space. From this it follows that the probability dW of the parameters a_i to have values lying inside the infinitesimal intervals da_i is given by the equation

$$dW = e^{\Delta S/k} f \, da_1 \, da_2 \ldots da_n. \tag{82}$$

In concordance with the interpretation of dW as the time fraction spent by the system in the element $da_1, da_2, \ldots, da_n$ of a-space, the size of the function f must be chosen so that the integral of dW over all physically realizable values of the a_i amounts to unity. We further tacitly assumed that the variables $a_1, a_2, \ldots, a_n$ do *not* suffice to define the phenomenological state of the system completely; because, if they did, the existence of the equation $U(a_1, a_2, \ldots, a_n) = $ const., expressing the conservation of energy, would reduce the dimensionality of the states, accessible to the system, from n to $n - 1$.

We now specialize Eq. (82) for the immediate vicinity of an equilibrium state. The parameters a_i, the reader is reminded, are of the nature of local temperatures, local pressures, and so on. Without detracting from the generality of our argument, we shall presently require that the a_i, instead of standing for the local quantities themselves, designate rather the deviations of these properties from their equilibrium values. Hence, if A_i is the local parameter, and A_i^0 its equilibrium value, then $a_i = A_i - A_i^0$. The advantage of this choice of the so-called *Onsager coordinates* a_i is that each a_i will have the value zero in the equilibrium condition. The functions $S(a_1, a_2, \ldots, a_n)$ and $f(a_1, a_2, \ldots, a_n)$ may then be expanded for a neighborhood of the equilibrium state in a Taylor series, as follows:

$$S = S_0 + \sum_{i=1}^{n} \left(\frac{\partial S}{\partial a_i} \right)_0 a_i + \frac{1}{2} \sum_{i=1}^{n} \sum_{j=1}^{n} \left(\frac{\partial^2 S}{\partial a_i \partial a_j} \right)_0 a_i a_j + \cdots \tag{83}$$

and

$$f = f_0 + \sum_{i=1}^{n} \left(\frac{\partial f}{\partial a_i} \right)_0 a_i + \cdots. \tag{84}$$

Because the entropy is a maximum in the equilibrium state, the linear terms in Eq. (83) vanish separately, and the sum of the quadratic terms is negative. Furthermore, if the neighborhood under consideration is sufficiently small, the series for S can be broken off after the quadratic terms and that for f after the linear terms. Thus, Eqs. (83) and (84) simplify to

$$\Delta S = -\frac{1}{2} \sum_i \sum_j g_{ij} a_i a_j, \tag{85}$$

with

$$g_{ij} = \left(\frac{\partial^2 S}{\partial a_i \partial a_j}\right)_0,\tag{86}$$

and to

$$f = f_0 + \sum_i \left(\frac{\partial f}{\partial a_i}\right)_0 a_i.\tag{87}$$

The abridged expressions (85) and (87) are now inserted in Eq. (82). One notices then that the exponent $\Delta S/k$ is negative and contains the immensely large number $1/k$ as a factor. Hence, the factor $\exp(\Delta S/k)$ of dW will decline rapidly with an increase of the a_i and for practical purposes start vanishing even for small values of the a_i. In the remaining region of the still smaller values of the a_i, one is entitled to substitute for the factor f its equilibrium value f_0—on the assumption that the derivatives of f agree with f_0 *qua* order of magnitude. Consequently, for all states not far removed from equilibrium (such as those involved in the great majority of fluctuations) we can finally replace Eq. (82) by the formula

$$dW = f_0 e^{\Delta S/k}\, da_1\, da_2 \ldots da_n = f_0 e^{-(1/2k)\Sigma\Sigma g_{ij}a_i a_j}\, da_1\, da_2 \ldots da_n.\tag{88}$$

This equation, derived by Einstein, will serve as the basis for the computation of time averages of the products $a_i a_j$ as well as that of other special functions of the a_i which we are now going to introduce.

For reasons soon to become plain, Onsager defines the functions

$$F_i = \frac{\partial \Delta S}{\partial a_i} = -\sum_j g_{ij} a_j.\tag{89}$$

The so-called *Onsager forces* F_i, like the Onsager coordinates a_i, obviously vanish at equilibrium. One also notices that the entropy production $\dot{S} = \dot{\Delta S}$ may be expressed as a bilinear form in the F_i and the time derivatives of the a_i:

$$\dot{S} = \sum_i \dot{a}_i F_i.\tag{90}$$

For the sake of future application it is essential to know the average of the product $a_i F_j$ over a long period of time. By reason of the physical meaning of Eq. (88), this quantity is given by

$$\langle a_i F_j \rangle = f_0 \int_{-\infty}^{\infty} \cdots \int_{-\infty}^{\infty} a_i \frac{\partial \Delta S}{\partial a_j} e^{\Delta S/k}\, da_1\, da_2 \ldots da_n$$

$$= k f_0 \int_{-\infty}^{\infty} \cdots \int_{-\infty}^{\infty} a_i \frac{\partial e^{\Delta S/k}}{\partial a_j}\, da_1\, da_2 \ldots da_n.\tag{91}$$

Since $a_i \exp(\Delta S/k)$ vanishes at the upper and lower limits of integration,

integration by parts with respect to a_j merely shifts the operator $\partial/\partial a_j$ from the exponential function to the factor a_i of the integrand while changing its sign. Noting that $\partial a_i/\partial a_j$ is unity for $i = j$, and zero otherwise, and that the integral of $f_0 \exp(\Delta S/k)$, i.e., the total probability, is unity, one finally obtains

$$\langle a_i F_i \rangle = -k \quad \text{and} \quad \langle a_i F_j \rangle = 0. \quad (i \neq j) \tag{92}$$

MICROSCOPIC REVERSIBILITY

The second major idea underlying Onsager's proof is a postulate called the *principle of microscopic reversibility*, which states that under equilibrium conditions, any molecular process and its reverse take place on the average with the same frequency. The detailed balancing of independent chemical reactions cited before is a special instance of the functioning of this principle. In parenthesis, the molecular processes involved there, are the transition of A- into B-molecules, of B- into C-molecules, and so on. As a matter of fact, it was the idea of detailed balancing which suggested to Onsager the possibilities of the more generally valid principle of microscopic reversibility.

This principle has its foundation in the following circumstance: barring certain exceptional cases that we shall identify and sort out later on, the force F_i acting on any body i of a system of n ordinary bodies depends only on the coordinates $r_1, r_2, \ldots, r_n$ of the n bodies or—if it depends on the velocities $\dot{r}_1, \dot{r}_2, \ldots, \dot{r}_n$ as well—it is an even function of the velocities. As a consequence —since each velocity $\dot{r}_1 = dr_i/dt$ goes over into $-\dot{r}_i$ and each acceleration $\ddot{r}_i = d^2 r_i/dt^2$ is not affected at all when one substitutes $-t$ for $+t$—the equations of motion $F_i = m_i \ddot{r}_i$ $(i = 1, 2, \ldots, n)$ remain unchanged on replacing $+t$ by $-t$. In physical language this means that, if the velocities $\dot{r}_1, \dot{r}_2, \ldots, \dot{r}_n$ of all the bodies are reversed at a given instant $t = t_0$, the bodies will retrace their paths backwards, thereby transposing the entire sequence of configurations traversed by the system prior to $t = t_0$. Thus, to every *direct* solution of the equations of motion corresponds a *reverse* solution; the equations of motion are said to be *reversible*. The situation may be mentally depicted by representing each solution, i.e., succession of system configurations, with the aid of a curve, or path, in $(3n + 1)$-dimensional space of the $3n$ coordinates and the time. In this space each direct path and its reverse will be mirror reflections of one another in the plane $t = t_0$.

The reversibility characterizing the motion of ordinary bodies need not necessarily apply to bodies of atomic size. In fact, it is known that the classical equations of motion break down in the atomic domain, and must be replaced by quantum-mechanical equations of motion. Fortunately, these too are invariant under the substitution of $-t$ for $+t$, so that direct and reverse solutions are features of atomic dynamics as well. Now, it is one thing to show the existence of reverse paths, and quite another to allege that both a given path and its reverse are actually traversed by a physical system with equal probabilities. The assumption that this is indeed the case in equilibrium situations, constitutes the principle of microscopic reversibility.

We next ask what consequences issue from the stated principle for the coordinates a_i describing fluctuations about equilibrium in an isolated system. Assume for simplicity that the a_i are even functions of the atomic velocities, as, for example, the specific properties $u - u_0$, $v - v_0$, $w - w_0$, so that the values of the a_i are not affected when the time t is reversed. The principle of microscopic reversibility may then be expressed by the formula

$$\langle a_j(t + \tau)\rangle_{a_1(t), \ldots, a_n(t)} = \langle a_j(t - \tau)\rangle_{a_1(t), \ldots, a_n(t)}. \tag{93}$$

In words: if one observes fluctuations about equilibrium, and considers all the situations for which simultaneously the values of the coordinates are given by $a_1, \ldots, a_j, \ldots, a_n$, then on the *average* the value of a_j, computed in each case at a time τ after the situation $a_1, \ldots, a_j, \ldots, a_n$ has occurred, will agree with the value of a_j calculated at a time τ before.

Starting from Eq. (93), one may deduce a valuable symmetry relation for the correlation function $\langle a_i(t)a_j(t + \tau)\rangle$. In pursuit of this, we multiply both members of Eq. (93) by $a_i(t)$, and average the products over all possible values of $a_1(t), a_2(t), \ldots, a_n(t)$, to get

$$\langle a_i(t)a_j(t + \tau)\rangle = \langle a_i(t)a_j(t - \tau)\rangle. \tag{94}$$

According to the postulates of statistical mechanics, each average employed here can be regarded as either a time-average over a great period of time for the system in question, or a crowd-average for a large set of macroscopically exact replicas of our system distributed over all the accessible states in a time-independent manner. Whichever of the two interpretations is adopted, the averages in Eq. (94) do not depend on the value of t. It is therefore permissible to substitute $t + \tau$ for t in the right-hand member of Eq. (94), to obtain the symmetry relation

$$\langle a_i(t)a_j(t + \tau)\rangle = \langle a_j(t)a_i(t + \tau)\rangle. \tag{95}$$

REGRESSION OF FLUCTUATIONS

As a final point in the derivation of the reciprocity relations, Onsager submitted the following contention. A deviation from equilibrium, which occurs spontaneously as the result of a fluctuation, decays on the average in the same way as a deviation that has been artificially induced by outside interference.

If, for example, a charge appears on a condensor of an electric RC-circuit as the result of a fluctuation, this charge will on the average leak away like an ordinary macroscopic charge, i.e., in agreement with the linear law $\dot{q} = -(1/RC)q$. The mode of decay—to put it differently—is independent of the charge's history.

We may quote another instance. If a metal block of heat capacity C, coated with a poorly conducting layer of heat transfer coefficient K, is immersed in a liquid heat reservoir, it is known experimentally that the energy U of the block will relax to its equilibrium value with a linear time rate $\dot{U} = (-C/K)(U - U_0)$. By Onsager's contention, the average decay rate of energy fluctuations will also be linear with the same coefficient of proportionality, so that an observer who is ignorant of the past history of the block would be unable to decide whether its initial state was produced artificially or spontaneously.

Now it is a well-known fact that the recovery of an equilibrium state obeys a linear law in a large class of phenomena besides the two cases cited here, so that one is tempted to write more generally

$$\dot{a}_i = \sum_j p_{ij} a_j, \tag{96}$$

where the inclusion of terms other than a_i on the right-hand side allows for the possibility of coupling among different fluctuations. On taking into consideration that the coordinates a_i are linearly related to the forces F_j through the definitions (89), Eq. (96) is seen to be equivalent to the equation

$$\dot{a}_i = \sum_j L_{ij}^* F_j, \tag{97}$$

in which the coefficients L_{ij}^* are determinable directly from the empirical macroscopic equations of regression.

The time derivative entering into Eq. (97) calls for some comment, as it is not a derivative in the strict mathematical sense. Instead, the quantity $\dot{a}_i$ is to be interpreted as the difference quotient

$$\dot{a}_i = \frac{1}{\tau} \langle a_i(t + \tau)_{a_1(t),\ldots,a_n(t)} - a_i(t) \rangle; \tag{98}$$

the time interval τ employed here is not subject to arbitrary choice, but must satisfy the condition $\tau_0 \ll \tau \ll \tau_r$, where τ_0 is a time characteristic for the mechanism of the molecular interaction, and τ_r the regression time of a fluctuation, i.e., the time it takes a fluctuation to diminish appreciably in size. τ_0 may, for example, be the time between collisions of molecules, and τ_r for the RC-circuit mentioned earlier will be RC.

Before pursuing Eq. (97) any further, it should be clearly understood that this regression formula has not been proved rigorously, although it represents a plausible extrapolation of macroscopic equations of regression to very small deviations. In this sense Eq. (97) is really an independent new hypothesis, a fact to which Casimir (1945) in particular called attention. Be that as it may, surmising the validity of formula (97) we can now derive Onsager's relations in a few steps. To this end, multiply Eq. (97) by $a_j(t)$, observe the definition of Eq. (98), and average over all values of $a_1, a_2, \ldots, a_n$. Then, invoking the results of Eq. (92), one gets

$$\langle a_j(t)a_i(t + \tau)\rangle - \langle a_j(t)a_i(t)\rangle = -\tau k L_{ij}^*. \tag{99}$$

Analogously,

$$\langle a_i(t)a_j(t + \tau)\rangle - \langle a_i(t)a_j(t)\rangle = -\tau k L_{ji}^*. \tag{100}$$

Because of Eq. (95), the left-hand sides of Eqs. (99) and (100), and therefore their right-hand sides, are equal, so that we finally obtain:

$$L_{ij}^* = L_{ji}^*. \tag{101}$$

Equation (101) will be the wanted reciprocity relation provided one identifies the fluxes J_i with the $\dot{a}_i$, the forces X_i with the F_i, and the L_{ij} with the L_{ij}^*. For, if one performs this substitution, Eq. (90) goes over into $\dot{S} = \sum J_i X_i$ and Eq. (97) into $J_i = \sum L_{ij}X_j$, which may be compared with Eqs. (52) and (49) respectively.

Having reached this stage of exposition, one becomes aware of the need to supplement the tentative formulation of Onsager's theorem given at the beginning of this section, lest the statement $L_{ij} = L_{ji}$ [Eq. (54)] becomes devoid of all physical content. The issue centers around the proper selection of the fluxes J_i and the forces X_i to which the reciprocity relations are supposed to apply. In our original formulation, the J_i and X_i are identified only by their appearance in the bilinear form $\sigma = \sum J_i X_i$ [Eq. (52)] and by the fact that they are linearly connected through the equations of motion $J_i = \sum L_{ij}X_j$ [Eq. (49)]. Now, it is obvious that if no other criteria are to be complied with, one still has considerable latitude in the choice of fluxes and forces. Indeed, one can make this selection without end. To be specific, it is possible to combine linearly the J_i and X_i in an infinite number of ways to get new linearly connected fluxes J_i' and forces X_i', which give, on bilinear combination, the same entropy production as the unprimed fluxes and forces.

Once this is realized it becomes urgent to decide whether or not an arbitrary set of forces and fluxes selected on the basis of Eqs. (49) and (52) will still lead to the reciprocity relations of the type (54). It is disturbing to discover that the answer to this question is negative (Coleman and Truesdell, 1960). In other words, Eqs. (49) and (52) alone do not imply Eq. (54). Stated explicitly: it turns out that by linear combination of fluxes and forces satisfying Eqs. (49), (52), and (54), new fluxes and forces may always be constructed that obey Eqs. (49) and (52), but not Eq. (54); conversely, given any set of fluxes and forces satisfying Eqs. (49) and (52) but not Eq. (54), it is always possible by sheer linear combination of fluxes and forces to find another set that obeys Eqs. (49), (52), and (54).

Thus it seems clear that unless and until the forces and fluxes in any particular physical situation are identified by some property more definite than their mere occurrence in the bilinear form Eq. (52) and their linear interrelation through Eq. (49), the statement $L_{ij} = L_{ji}$ is false, or at best true but trivial. The extra conditions that elevate the reciprocity theorem to the status of a significant pronouncement have been uncovered in the course of the above demonstration of Onsager's relations: they are essentially contained in the propositions $J_i = \dot{a}_i$ and $X_i = F_i$. On this showing, a proper formulation of Onsager's theorem should read as follows.

Consider a set of n thermodynamical fluxes J_i linearly related to n thermodynamical forces X_i, i.e., $J_i = \sum L_{ij} X_j$. If (i) the equations of motion are reversible; (ii) the fluxes J_i are time-derivatives of independent Onsager coordinates a_i, i.e., $J_i = \dot{a}_i$; (iii) the a_i are even functions of the particle velocities; (iv) the a_i enter the equation $\Delta S = \frac{1}{2} \sum \sum g_{ij} a_i a_j$; and (v) the forces X_i are chosen to be $X_i = \partial \Delta S / \partial a_i = -\sum g_{ij} a_j$: *then* the coefficients L_{ij} are symmetric in their subscripts, i.e., $L_{ij} = L_{ji}$.

If any one of the conditions (i) to (v) is ignored, the symmetry relations will no longer hold. It is however possible to relax somewhat the restrictions (i) and (iii), and still obtain equations closely allied to the simple reciprocity relations $L_{ij} = L_{ji}$. We shall examine (i) and (iii) in turn.

Physical systems are known for which the equations of motion are not reversible as defined in our discussion of the principle of microscopic reversibility. Two important instances may be mentioned here.

When an external magnetic field **B** is imposed on a system, this field gives rise to a *Lorentz force* $e\mathbf{v} \times \mathbf{B}$ acting on each particle with charge e and velocity **v**. (If θ is the smaller angle included between **v** and **B**, the *vector product* $\mathbf{v} \times \mathbf{B}$ signifies a vector of magnitude $vB \sin \theta$ that stands perpendicular to the plane of **v** and **B**, and forms with them a right-handed triad.) This force, being an odd function of the particle velocity **v**, will on reversal of

v remain unchanged and the particles will retrace their former paths backwards, only if the field **B** is reversed at the same time. Therefore, the simple relation $L_{ij} = L_{ji}$, based on supposition (i), is no longer valid but must be replaced by $L_{ij}(\mathbf{B}) = L_{ji}(-\mathbf{B})$, where now the L_{ij} are regarded as functions of the vector **B**.

A similar situation exists for a particle whose motion is described with respect to a coordinate system rotating with angular velocity **ω** relative to an inertial (fixed) frame of reference. To an observer in the rotating frame, a free particle of mass m moves as if it were subjected to a transverse force $m\mathbf{v} \times \boldsymbol{\omega}$, the so-called *Coriolis force*. This force agrees with the *Lorentz force* except for the replacement of e by m and of **B** by **ω**. Hence by analogy we can immediately conclude that the desired reversal of system configurations will obtain only if the angular velocity and the particle velocities are reversed simultaneously; that is, the appropriate reciprocity relations are $L_{ij}(\boldsymbol{\omega}) = L_{ji}(-\boldsymbol{\omega})$.

Passing on to supposition (iii), we allow some of the a's to be odd, instead of even, functions of the particle velocities. It is then not difficult to appreciate that the reciprocity relations will remain $L_{ij} = L_{ji}$ provided a_i and a_j are both even or both odd functions, but they will change to $L_{ij} = -L_{ji}$ if one of the a's is even and the other odd (Casimir and Tellegen, 1945).

The findings of the last few paragraphs may be summarized concisely in a single formula, viz.,

$$L_{ij}(\mathbf{B},\boldsymbol{\omega}) = \varepsilon_i\varepsilon_j L_{ji}(-\mathbf{B}, -\boldsymbol{\omega}), \tag{102}$$

where ε_i is defined as $+1$ for a_i even and -1 for a_i odd. Equation (102) constitutes the analytic statement of the reciprocity theorem in its most general form.

Since the physically interesting violations of premises (i) and (iii) of Onsager's theorem can be dealt with by a suitable generalization of the simple relations $L_{ij} = L_{ji}$, (i) and (iii) do not limit appreciably the scope of validity of the reciprocity equations. By contrast, the requirement (ii), namely $J_i = \dot{a}_i$, does seem on first sight to represent a severe impediment to the applicability of the reciprocal relations. In fact, of all the fluxes defined explicitly so far, only the chemical reaction rate v is the time derivative of an Onsager coordinate, whereas the heat flux vector, for example, is not. Onsager's theorem is then evidently not directly applicable to these fluxes. One should instead analyze the physical situation more cautiously in the hope of finding fluxes which are indeed the time derivatives of Onsager coordinates. We shall here indicate how this objective can be realized in the special case of heat conduction in an anisotropic crystal.

The flow of heat in such a crystal is described by Fourier's law (56), which we rewrite for the present purpose more briefly:

$$J_i = \sum_i L_{ij} \frac{\partial T}{\partial x_j}. \qquad (i = 1, 2, 3) \qquad (103)$$

As Casimir first pointed out (1945), the components J_i of the heat flux vector are *not* time derivatives of Onsager coordinates, so that it is not permissible to adduce Onsager's theorem in justification of the conclusion $L_{ij} = L_{ji}$. In truth, the vector with components J_1, J_2, J_3 is not even uniquely defined, for only its divergence is observable and therefore physically meaningful. This entails that one may add to L_{ij} any quantity M_{ij}, as long as

$$\text{div} \sum_j M_{ij} \frac{\partial T}{\partial x_j}$$

is zero, i.e.,

$$0 = \sum_i \sum_j \left(\frac{\partial T}{\partial x_j} \frac{\partial M_{ij}}{\partial x_i} + M_{ij} \frac{\partial^2 T}{\partial x_i \partial x_j} \right).$$

This equation is satisfied for an arbitrary distribution of temperature provided $M_{ij} = -M_{ji}$, and

$$\frac{\partial M_{ij}}{\partial x_i} = 0. \qquad (104)$$

Thus, the addition of a quantity M_{ij}, obeying $M_{ij} = -M_{ji}$ rather than $M_{ij} = M_{ji}$, to L_{ij}, has no physical consequences (if condition (104) is also fulfilled). Due to the resulting freedom in the choice of the L_{ij}, the coefficients L_{ij} of Eq. (103) will in general not be expected to be symmetric in their subscripts; and the experimentally verified equality $L_{ij} = L_{ji}$ can obtain only if the unwanted L_{ij}'s are eliminated by some additional restrictions. We shall not pursue this aspect any further, but simply carry on with our search for the correct fluxes and forces in the sense of Onsager's theory.

Let the crystal be divided into a number of small cells having volumes V_i and temperatures $T_i = T_0 + \Delta T_i$, where T_0 is the temperature of the crystal in thermostatic equilibrium. One can then write for the deviation of the entropy from its equilibrium value, with disregard of thermal expansion,

$$\Delta S = C \sum_i V_i \int_{T_0}^{T_i} \frac{1}{T} dT, \qquad (105)$$

where C is the heat capacity per unit volume of the crystal (taken to be constant for the given temperature ranges) and the summation extends over all the cells. If one expands the integrand $1/T$ about $T = T_0$ as origin in a power series $(1/T) = (1/T_0) - (1/T_0^2)\Delta T + \cdots$, the zero-order term is seen to contribute nothing to ΔS, since $(C/T_0) \sum V_i \Delta T_i = 0$. Hence, if the power series is broken off after the first-order term, Eq. (105) yields the entropy deviation

$$\Delta S = -\frac{C}{2T_0^2} \sum V_i (\Delta T_i)^2,$$ (106)

and, on differentiation, the entropy production

$$\Delta \dot{S} = -\frac{C}{T_0^2} \sum V_i \Delta T_i \dot{\Delta T_i}.$$ (107)

Given the expression (106), which has the desired form

$$\Delta S = -\frac{1}{2} \sum \sum g_{ij} a_i a_j$$

in terms of the Onsager coordinates $a_i = \Delta T_i$, one is entitled to choose for the heat conducting crystal the $\dot{a}_i = \dot{\Delta T_i}$ and $-(C/T_0^2)V_i\Delta T_i$ to represent the fluxes and forces respectively. These fluxes now are indeed time derivatives of Onsager coordinates ΔT_i, and the fluxes and forces moreover satisfy the premises (iv) and (v) of his theorem; so that if the phenomenological coefficients L'_{ij} are introduced through the postulated equations of motion

$$\dot{\Delta T_i} = -\frac{C}{T_0^2} \sum_j L'_{ij} V_j \Delta T_j,$$ (108)

we may cogently maintain that the Onsager relations

$$L'_{ij} = L'_{ji}$$ (109)

are valid. One may, if one so wishes, develop the consequences of Eqs. (109) for the coefficients L_{ij} appearing in Eq. (103); since the mathematics involved is rather exacting, we shall rest content to simply quote the final result:

$$\sum_i \frac{\partial L_{ij}}{\partial x_i} = \sum_i \frac{\partial L_{ji}}{\partial x_i}.$$ (110)

An analysis similar to that carried out above applies not only to heat conduction, but to all instances where a current density with an observable divergence is expressed as the gradient of a thermodynamic parameter.

On the whole, given a particular physical system, one will experience that it calls for some ingenuity to uncover the coordinates a_i to which Onsager's theorem may properly be related. A detailed discussion of this problem, however, does not come within the purview of an introductory treatise.

In summary of this section, we should like to put forward a few evaluative comments on the nature of Onsager's theory and the place of his reciprocity relations in thermodynamics. Onsager's formalism as elucidated here is founded on the notion of atoms and statistical-mechanical assumptions about their behavior. It might seem that for this reason, Onsager's theorem should not be adopted as a principle of thermodynamics which is, by common consent, a macroscopic discipline.

Two objections may be raised against this point of view. First, the boundary between the macroscopic and the microscopic domains is not always sharply defined, and it is more or less a matter of predilection where the line of division should be drawn. Thus, while the principle of microscopic reversibility is irrevocably phrased in the language of atoms and probabilities, the theory of fluctuations can be brought within the province of thermodynamics by a revision of the traditionally respected border between statistical mechanics and thermodynamics.

In the second place, although Onsager's theory starts from a priori ideas about hypothetical atomic motions, it leads finally to observable limitations of the coupling of two or more macroscopic processes. One may, of course, reverse the logical order of the approach, that is, accept Onsager's theorem as an experimentally corroborated hypothesis and attempt a posteriori to discover a statistical-mechanical justification for it. The attraction of such a method is that the reciprocity relations derive their validity from incontrovertible empirical evidence rather than from current statistical-mechanical theories whose foundations are still a subject of controversy. Onsager's theorem established on this basis will be endowed with a credibility comparable with that of the first and second laws, which are, after all, also understood only retrospectively in terms of the mechanics of atoms and probability considerations. But we should caution that the empirical procedure is more liable to result in an indiscriminate selection of forces and fluxes—encountered even in recent literature.

The theorem of Onsager might be called the *fourth law* of thermodynamics in recognition of its prominent theoretical and experimental status. One should bear in mind though that the reciprocity relations can in no way claim the universal validity of the first and second laws.

1–5. Applications of Onsager's Theorem to Thermoelectric Phenomena

For nearly eighty years preceding the publication of Onsager's theory, various other conceptions about irreversible processes rivalled to gain acceptance. It was customary to assess these attempts according to their ability to explain an important group of phenomena commonly denoted as *thermoelectric effects*. The oldest and most widely discussed theory of

thermoelectricity was proposed in 1854 by W. Thomson (Lord Kelvin) who
derived quantitative results in accord with experiment; but he introduced a
hypothesis which he was unable to justify on the basis of thermostatic ideas.
Onsager's formalism succeeded for the first time in accounting for all the
thermoelectric occurrences from a unified standpoint.

Thermoelectric phenomena may be defined as the cross-effects associated
with the simultaneous flows of heat and electricity. Their number increases
with the complexity and degree of anisotropy of the system. We shall confine
our attention to an isotropic system and analyze only three well-known effects
to be enumerated below.

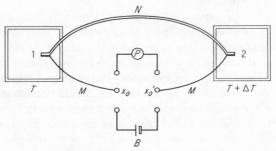

FIGURE 1–1. Thermocouple circuit.

Figure 1–1 is a schematic representation of a *thermocouple*, that is, a system
consisting of two dissimilar metals such as platinum and rhodium or copper
and silver arranged in series to form an electric circuit. The junctions of the
two metallic wires M and N are embedded in, and kept at fixed temperatures
T and $T + \Delta T$ by, two heat reservoirs 1 and 2. The circuit is interrupted in the
metal M and its loose ends x_0 and x_0' can be connected with the terminals of
either a potentiometer P or a battery B, depending on the effect that is being
examined.

Seebeck effect.   If $\Delta T \neq 0$, a conduction of heat takes place along the wires
M and N; in addition, it is found (Seebeck, 1821) that an emf $\Delta \phi$ is set up
between the points x_0 and x_0', whose value varies with ΔT and the nature of the
metals M and N. The so-called Seebeck emf $\Delta \phi$ is measured under conditions
of zero current I with the aid of the potentiometer P. Furthermore, the terminals x_0 and x_0' are maintained at the same temperature T_0, say, to prevent
them from becoming unwanted seats of emf's. For small ΔT, the quantity

$$\varepsilon = \left(\frac{\Delta \phi}{\Delta T}\right)_{I=0} \tag{111}$$

is referred to as the *thermoelectric power* of the thermocouple.

Peltier effect. Alternatively, let $\Delta T = 0$, but force a constant electric current I through the circuit by connecting x_0 and x'_0 to the poles of the battery B. It is then observed (Peltier, 1834) that at each junction the familiar Joule heat is developed which is proportional to I^2; over and above this, a quantity of heat proportional to I is absorbed at one of the junctions and an equal amount is given off at the other. The sign of this heat changes with the direction of the current, so that one may define the Peltier heat Π as the heat J absorbed at junction 1 (or 2) when unit current I passes from metal M to metal N across junction 1 (or 2), i.e.,

$$\Pi = \Pi_{MN} = \left(\frac{J}{I}\right)_{\Delta T = 0}. \tag{112}$$

Thomson effect. Consider lastly a conductor composed of a single homogeneous metal in which a temperature gradient exists. Naturally, there will be a flow of heat, but one will also find that an emf arises between separate points of the metal kept at different temperatures. Conversely, if an electric current is forced through a metal exhibiting a temperature gradient, a development of heat occurs that is greater or smaller than the Joule heat. The excess over the Joule heat will depend on the magnitude and direction of the current, the temperature, and on the nature of the metals; and like the Peltier heat it will alter its sign when the current is reversed. This phenomenon is the Thomson effect; its quantitative measure is the Thomson heat σ which is defined such that σdT is the heat absorbed by the metal when a unit charge passes from a point at the temperature T to a point at the temperature $T + dT$.

All three aforementioned effects can now be treated immediately—in a method due to D. Polder (1944)—within the framework of Onsager's formalism. As in all applications of his theory, the crucial result of our present discussion is the expression for the entropy production. To facilitate the derivation of this quantity, we imagine that the potential difference $\Delta\phi$ exists between the plates of an electric condenser whose terminals are attached to the points x_0 and x'_0. The condenser should have zero heat capacity and must not arrest the flow of heat. Then, the entropy increase of our system due to any change is composed additively of the increases ΔS_1, ΔS_2, ΔS_c for the reservoirs 1 and 2 and the condenser, respectively. Suppose the process in question entails simply the transfer of the energy dU from the reservoir 1 to the reservoir 2 and the introduction of the charge de on the condenser. On applying Gibbs' relation $TdS = dU + pdV - \phi de$ to each part of the system, one sees that $TdS_1 = -dU$, $(T + \Delta T)dS_2 = dU$, $T_0 dS_c = -(\Delta\phi)de$;

thus, addition of these equations and subsequent division by the time interval dt yields, with neglect of second-order quantities in ΔT,

$$\frac{dS}{dt} = -\frac{dU}{dt}\frac{\Delta T}{T^2} - \frac{de}{dt}\frac{\Delta\phi}{T}. \tag{113}$$

The approximation utilized here is adequate, provided ΔT is very small compared with T.

The entropy production, Eq. (113), has the bilinear form—required by Onsager's theory—in the fluxes

$$I = \frac{de}{dt}, \quad J = \frac{dU}{dt} \tag{114}$$

and the forces

$$X = -\frac{\Delta\phi}{T}, \quad Y = -\frac{\Delta T}{T^2}. \tag{115}$$

As equations of motion one postulates the linear relations

$$I = -L_{11}\frac{\Delta\phi}{T} - L_{12}\frac{\Delta T}{T^2} \tag{116}$$

and

$$J = -L_{21}\frac{\Delta\phi}{T} - L_{22}\frac{\Delta T}{T^2}, \tag{117}$$

where, in virtue of Onsager's theorem,

$$L_{12} = L_{21}. \tag{118}$$

The phenomenological Eqs. (116) and (117) are generally valid; we now specialize them to conform to the particular physical situations accompanying the direct effects and cross-effects.

The *direct* effects are heat conduction and electric conduction. If $\Delta\phi = 0$, the heat current J is proportional to $-\Delta T$, and if $\Delta T = 0$, the electric current is proportional to $-\Delta\phi$; from Eqs. (117) and (116), the proportionality factors are seen to be $-(J/\Delta T)_{\Delta\phi=0} = L_{22}/T^2$ and $-(I/\Delta\phi)_{\Delta T=0} = L_{11}/T$, respectively.

The cross-effects can similarly be related to the coefficients L_{ij} and the temperature T. The Seebeck effect is observed when ΔT is held at a fixed nonzero value and $I = 0$. Equation (116) then asserts that the thermoelectric power is

$$\varepsilon = \left(\frac{\Delta\phi}{\Delta T}\right)_{I=0} = -\frac{L_{12}}{TL_{11}}. \tag{119}$$

The Peltier effect corresponds to the isothermal state $T = 0$; and by Eqs. (116) and (117), the Peltier heat is

$$\Pi = \left(\frac{J}{I}\right)_{\Delta T = 0} = \frac{L_{21}}{L_{11}}. \tag{120}$$

One may rewrite Eqs. (119) and (120) respectively as $\dfrac{L_{12}}{L_{11}} = -T\varepsilon$ and $\dfrac{L_{21}}{L_{11}} = \Pi$. Since $L_{12} = L_{21}$, comparison gives

$$\Pi = -T\varepsilon. \tag{121}$$

This formula is called *Thomson's second relation*; it connects the Peltier heat Π with the thermoelectric power ε.

A correspondence can also be established between the Thomson heat σ and the thermoelectric power ε. Let a unit charge flow from metal M to metal N across the junction 1. Then, as $\Pi = (dU/de)_{\Delta T = 0}$ by Eq. (114) and invoking the definition of σ in (iii), one has, by the conservation of energy, for small $\Delta T = dT$,

$$\Pi - (\Pi + d\Pi) + (\sigma_N - \sigma_M)dT = d\phi$$

or

$$-d\Pi + (\sigma_N - \sigma_M)dT = d\phi. \tag{122}$$

If Eq. (122) is divided by dT and $d\phi/dT = \varepsilon$ replaced by its value (121), we obtain

$$\sigma_N - \sigma_M + \frac{\Pi}{T} - \frac{d\Pi}{dT} = 0, \tag{123}$$

or, owing to $\Pi = -T\varepsilon$,

$$\sigma_M - \sigma_N = T\frac{d\varepsilon}{dT}. \tag{124}$$

This result is *Thomson's first relation*.

Both Eqs. (121) and (124) have been verified within experimental error for many metal pairs. They were derived for the first time by W. Thomson in

1854 on the basis of this hypothesis: the absorption of Peltier and Thomson heats can be divorced completely from the irreversible evolution of Joule heat and heat conduction, and be treated as reversible processes. Thomson's method led to the correct results because his assumption, as one may easily show, is equivalent to applying the Onsager relation $L_{12} = L_{21}$.

1–6. Stationary States and Biological Systems

In thermodynamics a special position is occupied by a class of states customarily designated as *stationary states*, because they are readily amenable to mathematical analysis and faithfully represent many situations of practical interest.

A system is said to be in a stationary state if its macroscopic parameters—such as temperature, pressure, composition, and entropy—do not depend on the time, notwithstanding the possible occurrence of irreversible processes; of the macroscopic parameters, the intensive ones, though unchanged in time, will generally still vary from point to point in the system.

The concept of a stationary state is illustrated by the following examples. If heat is added at a constant rate to one end of a metal bar and withdrawn at an equal rate from its other end, the temperature at each point of the bar approaches a time-independent value. All the same, the temperature varies along the length of the bar, and entropy is produced continually as a result of heat conduction. And similarly, if an electric current flows through a metal wire embedded in a heat reservoir, the temperature of the wire as a whole and the electric potential at each point, remain constant in time despite the irreversible generation of Joule heat.

In the simplest realizations of stationary states, the macroscopic variables have lost their dependence on position too and become uniform throughout the system. The states so defined are the familiar situations of thermostatic equilibrium, which therefore constitute a subclass of the class of stationary states. Whereas equilibrium can obtain only in an isolated system or a system in contact with a uniform environment, nonequilibrium stationary states cannot endure unless the entropy-producing processes are sustained by a continual flux of energy, or matter and energy, between the system and its surroundings.

Our further exposition will be facilitated by first classifying stationary states in the following manner. Consider a system characterized by n independent forces $X_1, X_2, \ldots, X_n$, and let a number k of them, say $X_1, X_2, \ldots,$

X_k, be kept at fixed values through the operation of external constraints. It is then found empirically that the system will sooner or later reach a stage where the remaining forces X_{k+1}, X_{k+2}, ..., X_n as well remain constant with the passage of time. In the end, therefore, all the forces X_i, and as a result all the fluxes J_i composed linearly of them, become independent of time; the stationary condition prepared by this method is known as a *stationary state of order k.*

Now it turns out that when the stationary state of order k is established, the fluxes J_{k+1}, J_{k+2}, ..., J_n conjugate to the nonconstrained forces X_{k+1}, X_{k+2}, ..., X_n are not only constant, but individually zero. For instance, the conditions under which the Seebeck effect is measured, determine a stationary state of the first order ($k = 1$): while ΔT is held fixed and the heat flux persists, i.e., $J \neq 0$, the potential difference assumes a value $\Delta\phi$ compatible with zero electric current, i.e., $I = 0$. Likewise, if flows of both energy and matter can occur, a stationary state of the first order will result when a constant temperature gradient is maintained and the chemical potential gradient allowed to adjust itself to a value causing the flow of mass, but not of energy, to become zero.

In the special case that no forces X_i are held fixed ($k = 0$), the system will continue to evolve until all the fluxes, and consequently all the forces, have vanished. Thus, the stationary state of order zero is identical with the state of thermostatic equilibrium.

Any stationary state represents a *stable* situation, that is to say, if a transient interference has caused a small displacement from the stationary state, the system will return of its own to the initial stationary condition. In order to justify this statement, suppose that one is dealing with a stationary state for which the forces X_1, X_2, ..., X_k are constrained to have constant values. Once the system has attained a stationary state, one applies a virtual perturbation δX_m to one of the unconstrained forces X_m ($m > k$). This will make the flux $J_m = \sum L_{mj}X_j$, which is zero in the unperturbed state, assume the nonzero value $\delta J_m = L_{mm}\delta X_m$ in the perturbed state. By virtue of Eqs. (28) and (53) combined,

$$\sigma = \sum \sum L_{ij}X_iX_j \geqslant 0, \tag{125}$$

the coefficient L_{mm} is positive, so that $(\delta J_m)(\delta X_m) = L_{mm}(\delta X_m)^2 > 0$; hence, if the force X_m increases, the flux J_m will increase too. It is a fact, however, that the increase of a flux is always attended by a diminution of the force conjugate to it, so that the flux δJ_m will tend to nullify the perturbation δX_m, and thus restore the unperturbed stationary state. This conclusion was first formulated by Le Chatelier (1888) for thermostatic equilibrium ($k = 0$);

the extension of his *principle* to $k = 1$ was made by Prigogine (1947) and to stationary states of higher order by de Groot (1951).

Thermostatic equilibrium may be defined as the state for which entropy reaches its maximum value compatible with the restriction of adiabatic isolation. Naturally, the question then arises—which state parameter, if any, has an extremum for a stationary state? The answer is furnished by an examination of Eq. (125). According to this formula, σ is a *positive quadratic form* in the forces X_i, that is, σ is zero when all the X_i are zero, and positive otherwise. Therefore, on keeping the k forces $X_1, X_2, \ldots, X_k$ fixed, the function σ displays a minimum when the remaining X_i assume values satisfying the equations

$$
\begin{aligned}
0 = \frac{\partial \sigma}{\partial X_i} &= \sum_j (L_{ij} + L_{ji})X_j \\
&= 2\sum_j L_{ij}X_j = 2J_i, \qquad (i = k + 1, k + 2, \ldots, n) \quad (126)
\end{aligned}
$$

where use has been made of the reciprocity relations $L_{ij} = L_{ji}$. Equations (126) assert the vanishing of the fluxes corresponding to the forces which are not held fixed. In other words: the situation of minimum entropy production is identical with the stationary state of order k! This theorem was proved for the special case $k = 1$ by Prigogine (1947) and for arbitrary k by de Groot (1951).

The conception of stationary states as situations of minimum entropy production suggests an instructive geometrical method for viewing stationary states of various orders, which will here be exemplified for two independent forces X_1 and X_2 only. For $n = 2$, Eq. (125) reduces to

$$
\sigma = L_{11}X_1^2 + 2L_{12}X_1X_2 + L_{22}X_2^2 \geqslant 0, \quad (127)
$$

and this equation may be described by an elliptic paraboloid with its vertex at the origin $X_1 = X_2 = \sigma = 0$ in the space of X_1, X_2, σ. The approach toward the stationary state for the possible orders $k = 0, 1, 2$, respectively, can then be pictured as follows. When both X_1 and X_2 (and hence σ) are prescribed, the stationary state $k = 2$ is realized immediately and represented by a point lying on the paraboloid, Eq. (127). If now the constraint fixing, for example, X_1, is lifted, then the point representing the system moves downward along the parabolic intersection of the paraboloid (127) with the plane $X_2 = $ constant until the vertex of the parabola is reached; this point corresponds to the stationary state $k = 1$. Finally, if we lift the constraint on X_2 too, the system becomes free to pass toward the vertex of the paraboloid at $X_1 = X_2 = \sigma = 0$; this point represents the state of thermostatic equilibrium.

The theory of stationary states related to open systems has applications of considerable importance to living phenomena. In 1932 von Bertalanffy advanced the hypothesis that living organisms and cells should be treated as open thermodynamic systems. The theory of such systems was developed by Prigogine and Wiame in 1946. They arrived at conclusions that were essentially novel. In the first place, their theory accounts for many features of life which previously appeared to be inconsistent with the laws of physics, and for which explanations were sought in terms of ideas foreign to physical science. Secondly, the theory of open systems provides quantitative laws regulating basic biological phenomena, such as metabolism and growth.

A seeming violation of a physical principle is encountered if one erroneously regards a living organism as an isolated system. When an inanimate system is isolated or placed in uniform surroundings, an evolution of the system takes place during which all gradients in thermodynamic parameters are leveled out, all permissible chemical reactions occur, and all higher forms of energy become completely degraded to internal energy. Ultimately, equilibrium reigns when every macroscopic property is uniform throughout the system and all observable events have come to end. The system has reached the state of maximum entropy, or maximum disorder; in general, this state or a nearly inert state (for which the entropy is not yet a maximum) is attained very rapidly. Exceptions to the development here described may happen in the microphysical domain—compare the synthesis of helium atoms from hydrogen atoms in the interiors of stars and in hydrogen bombs— but on the macrophysical level, the requirement that any transition should be directed toward maximum disorder seems always to be fulfilled when lifeless matter alone is affected. For animate systems, the situation appears to be quite the opposite! The growth of a living organism or cell is characterized by transitions leading to states of ever greater order and increasing differentiation; and once the adult stage is reached, the organism successfully averts a speedy decay to the state of equilibrium, or death, for some time at least.

The apparent conflict between the principles governing the behavior of animate and inanimate bodies may easily be resolved if one treats a living organism as an open system, which exchanges both energy and matter with its environment. For a system of this kind, $ds = d_e s + d_i s$ according to Prigogine's equation (25), so that an increase of the entropy s (per unit mass) may be avoided by an importation from outside of the *negative* amount of entropy $d_e s/dt$ exceeding in absolute value the inescapable *positive* production of entropy, $\sigma = d_i s/dt$, inside the living object.

The main contribution to the entropy production σ arises from metabolism, that is, from the chemical and physical changes continuously going on in living organisms and cells. Metabolism comprises processes by which assimilated food is built up into protoplasm and broken down into simpler substances or waste matter, with the release of energy that is needed for vital functions. During the period of growth, $d_e s/dt$ exceeds $d_i s/dt$ in absolute value, so that (since $d_e s/dt < 0$) their sum ds/dt becomes negative; this decrease in the entropy s manifests itself in an improved organization and a greater differentiation of the protoplasmic structure.

One may adopt the viewpoint that while growth occurs, the organism is subjected to a number of fixed constraints, or constant forces in the thermodynamic sense, imposed on the system by its environment. If one accepts this idea, then the Prigogine-de Groot theorem on entropy production requires the development of the organism to be accompanied by a decrease in the entropy production. Thus, at the adult stage of growth the entropy production σ, as well as the entropy s itself, has attained its smallest value compatible with the imposed constraints. In connection with nonliving systems, the state of minimum entropy production is, as we know, referred to as a stationary state; for biological systems it is customary to employ the alternative designation *steady state*.

When the steady state is established, ds/dt is zero, so that the positive entropy production $d_i s/dt$ is exactly counterbalanced by the negative influx of entropy $d_e s/dt$. The withdrawal of *negative entropy* (a term favored by Schrödinger) from the environment is the device whereby a living organism succeeds in keeping alive, or postponing the final state of equilibrium which is the fate of inanimate matter in isolation. Contrary to popular belief, the essential purpose of eating, drinking, and breathing is therefore not to provide energy for vital functions, but to rid the system of the entropy it cannot avoid producing while being alive. As Schrödinger puts it: an organism feeds upon negative entropy, rather than on energy. Since negative entropy may be considered a measure of order, it is legitimate to say that an organism maintains a steady state by continually extracting order from its surroundings. In the case of human beings and higher animals it is clear how this process is realized. Foodstuffs consisting of highly organized, entropy-poor, organic molecules are taken in by the body, their energies partially utilized, and finally returned to the environment in a highly disorganized, or entropy-rich, form.

Prigogine and Wiame showed that the hypothesis according to which living systems evolve toward states of minimum entropy production, or minimum metabolism, is verified by the following observations: (1) among animals resembling one another closely, the intensity of metabolism per unit mass diminishes as the size of the animal increases; (2) migrant animals usually settle in environments allowing them to function with a minimum of metabolism; (3) the development of bacteria tends to proceed in the direction of states of minimum metabolism.

The theory of open systems and steady states has already been applied with success to many specific problems of biology, and the possibilities for further recourse to thermodynamic ideas are most promising. In the opinion of the biologist von Bertalanffy, thermodynamic principles related to open systems lie "near the very root of central biological problems," and seem "to point the direction and pave the way for biology to become an exact science."

REFERENCES

VON BERTALANFFY, L. *Theoretische Biologie*, Vol. I. Berlin: Borntraeger, 1932.

VON BERTALANFFY, L. *Science*, 111, 23 (1950).

CALLEN, H. B. *Thermodynamics*. New York: Wiley, 1960.

CASIMIR, H. B. G. *Rev. Mod. Phys.*, 17, 343 (1945).

CHAPMAN, S. *Phil. Trans. Roy. Soc.*, A216, 271 (1916); 217, 115 (1917).

CHAPMAN, S., and T. G. COWLING. *The Mathematical Theory of Non-Uniform Gases*. Rev. ed., 1953. New York: Cambridge U.P., 1939.

COLEMAN, B. D., and C. TRUESDELL. *J. Chem. Phys.*, 33, 28 (1960).

CURIE, P. *Oeuvres de Pierre Curie*. Paris: Gauthier-Villars, 1908.

DAVIES, R. O. *Reports on Progress in Physics*, 19, 326 (1956).

DENBIGH, K. G. *The Thermodynamics of the Steady State*. London: Methuen, 1951.

EINSTEIN, A. *Ann. Phys.*, 33, 1275 (1910).

ENSKOG, D. *Kinetische Theorie der Vorgänge in Mässig Verdünnten Gasen*. Inaugural Dissertation, Uppsala, 1917.

ENSKOG, D. *Kungl. Svenska Akad.*, 63, 4 (1922).

FITTS, D. D. *Nonequilibrium Thermodynamics*. New York: McGraw-Hill, 1962.

DE GROOT, S. R. *Thermodynamics of Irreversible Processes*. Amsterdam: North-Holland, 1951.

DE GROOT, S. R., and P. MAZUR. *Non-Equilibrium Thermodynamics*. Amsterdam: North-Holland, 1962.

HAASE, R. *Thermodynamik der irreversiblen Prozesse*. Darmstadt: Dietrich Steinkopff, 1963.

KIRKWOOD, J. G., and B. CRAWFORD. *J. Phys. Chem.*, 56, 1048 (1952).

MAXWELL, J. C. *Phil. Mag.*, 19, 22 (1860).

MEIXNER, J., and H. G. REIK. "Thermodynamik der irreversiblen Prozesse," in *Handbuch der Physik*. Vol. III/2. Berlin: Springer, 1959.

ONSAGER, L. *Phys. Rev.*, 37, 405 (1931); 38, 2265 (1931).

PRIGOGINE, I., and J. M. WIAME. *Experientia*, 2, 451 (1946).

PRIGOGINE, I. *Étude thermodynamique des phénomènes irréversibles.* Thesis. Liège, Desoer, 1947.

PRIGOGINE, I. *Physica,* **15**, 272 (1949).

PRIGOGINE, I. *Introduction to Thermodynamics of Irreversible Processes.* Springfield, Ill.: Thomas, 1955.

SCHRÖDINGER, E. *What is Life?* New York: Cambridge U.P., 1945.

VON SMOLUCHOWSKI, M. *Ann. Phys.,* **25**, 205 (1908).

TOLMAN, R. C., and P. C. FINE. *Rev. Mod. Phys.,* **20**, 51 (1948).

Termodinamica dei Processi Irreversibili. Rendiconti della Scuola Internazionale di Fisica Enrico Fermi, Corso X. Bologna: Nicola Zanichelli, 1960.

2

GENERAL PRINCIPLES OF STATISTICAL THERMODYNAMICS

THERMODYNAMICS is a phenomenological theory concerning itself exclusively with the macroscopic properties of physical systems. In the present context, macroscopic properties are those conditional on the concerted action of a great many atoms, molecules, electrons, or photons, as contrasted with the attributes pertaining to individual particles. Thus, for example, temperature and pressure are macroscopic quantities which are meaningful in terms of measurements on matter in bulk, but lose their significance when applied to individual molecules. Arguments of the kind favored in thermodynamics usually establish certain definite relationships between macroscopic properties of an arbitrary macrophysical system, and rely upon some general assertions about the behavior of the separate properties under specified conditions. Despite the undoubted usefulness of information gained in this manner, the discipline of thermodynamics suffers from serious deficiencies.

In the first place it fails to predict, for any physical system, either the equation of state or a formula for the computation of anyone of the quantities appearing in the thermodynamic relations alluded to above. Secondly, the phenomenological approach rests upon at least three seemingly unconnected principles—a fact suggesting that they themselves are not basic but rather derivable from a lesser number of fundamental axioms. Lastly, the mere restriction of thermodynamics to that which can be perceived does not alter the fact that there are unobserved occurrences. Some of these may give rise to objects capable of perception, which can nevertheless escape detection if they appear under very special circumstances to which phenomenological theory normally pays scant attention.

A need therefore exists for a new discipline that would not only succeed in deriving the facts of phenomenological thermophysics from postulates more fundamental than the laws of thermodynamics, but also provide numerical values for individual macroscopic properties, and finally alert us to the possibility of rarely occurring effects. A theory of this nature began to assume a clear form at the turn of the century as a result of the conceptual researches mainly of Boltzmann, Gibbs, and—it is frequently forgotten—Einstein. This branch of physics, called *statistical thermodynamics*, seeks to deduce the thermophysical properties of matter from the laws governing the behavior of its microscopic, or atomic, constituents. We proceed to express briefly the origins of the problems confronting us, and how statistical thermodynamics proposes to deal with them.

According to the atomic theory of matter, a macroscopic body is simply a mechanical system of, say, N particles of atomic dimensions. An idea of the size of N can be inferred from the fact that, under conditions prevailing in a living room, the number of atoms in 1 cm^3 of a substance is of the order 10^{20} for hydrogen and 10^{23} for copper. Thus, $N \sim 10^{20}$ or larger for ordinary systems of thermophysical interest. The astronomical size of N is the major reason why attempts to arrive at thermophysical results from a purely mechanical point of view are foredoomed to fail.

To render the explanation of this statement more concrete, and to supply a basis for subsequent mathematical analysis, we advance at this point the hypothesis that the atomic particles obey the classical laws of motion of Newton, which hold for the motions of everyday objects ranging from bullets to planets. This assumption will turn out to be a reckless extrapolation, but for the time being it will serve as the basic premiss underlying our reasoning. With the aid of the classical equations of motion, the positions and velocities of all particles contained in a system, that is, the *mechanical state* of the system, can be calculated for any time t. This is true in principle; in practice, however, such calculations are impossible, and for more than one reason. First, one is called upon to solve a gigantic number, say, approximately 10^{23}, of simultaneous differential equations—a task that is technically ruled out. Second, the forces acting on the particles might not be known, although they enter into the equations of motion. Finally, the most fundamental objection is that, in order to select from the mathematically possible solutions of the aforementioned equations those that are physically realized, one must insert in the general solutions the positions and velocities of all particles at some initial time t_0: and such data we do not possess for any given system!

The situation is, however, not beyond remedy. For although one does not know a system's detailed mechanical state at any particular time, its thermo-dynamic state is determinable at all times, and one may ask what configurations and velocities of the system are compatible with our partial knowledge.

It is at this point that one introduces statistical, or probabilistic, considerations to support those general arguments from mechanics that survive after a detailed description of individual particle motion has been shown to be an illusion. The use of statistical arguments becomes feasible because one is dealing with an exceedingly large number N of individual entities, that is, because of the very fact which, ironically, forced us to abandon a purely mechanical approach.

It might now be contended that the fusion of statistical ideas with those of mechanics is nothing new, since it has already been implemented in kinetic theory as developed by Maxwell and Boltzmann. This is of course true, but the program envisioned at present is different in emphasis and far more general in scope. In kinetic theory, one analyzes events involving single molecules, makes special assumptions about the nature of interparticle forces, and assigns to probability notions a mere subsidiary role. In statistical thermodynamics, on the other hand, we do not scrutinize separate happenings, we economize on ad hoc assumptions, and—the most typical feature—the remaining mechanical laws of general validity are supplemented by some far-reaching probability hypotheses of comparable importance.

Basically, one may distinguish two methods of statistical thermodynamics, corresponding to two possibilities of deciding upon the aggregate of individual entities to which statistical-mechanical arguments are applied. We shall mention both, but only one will be developed.

2–1. The Statistics of $µ$-Space and $γ$-Space

In the first method, which is associated with the name of Boltzmann (1877), one subjects the atomic particles themselves to statistical analysis. This choice was made by Maxwell too in kinetic theory, but his efforts were confined to an examination of the distribution of particles with respect to their velocity components only. Boltzmann generalized this procedure to encompass the distribution of particles in relation to position coordinates as well.

The simplest possible illustration of the Boltzmann method is provided by a physical system composed of monatomic molecules. Assuming that the dimensions of a monatomic molecule are negligible, one can define its state completely by its position vector $\mathbf{r}$ and linear momentum vector $\mathbf{p}$, or by the rectangular cartesian components x, y, z and p_x, p_y, p_z of these vectors. The mechanical state of the system as a whole will thus be known when both vectors $\mathbf{r}$ and $\mathbf{p}$ have been specified for every molecule. It facilitates the discussion to represent the state of a molecule in geometrical language by saying that its coordinates x, y, z and momentum components p_x, p_y, p_z together constitute the cartesian coordinates of a point in an abstract six-dimensional space, the so-called *phase space of a molecule*. P. and T. Ehrenfest (1912) coined the term *μ-space* to briefly denote the same concept. A point in μ-space representing the state, or *phase*, of a molecule, is known as a *phase point* or *image point*.

Obviously, one can also construct a μ-space that will allow the geometrical representation of the state of any polyatomic molecule. For a molecule with f degrees of freedom, this space will be $2f$-dimensional. Finally, one may represent each member of a system of N similar molecules by an image point in the same μ-space, and achieve thereby a representation of the mechanical state of the system as a whole by an assembly containing N image points. In geometrical terms, the statistical problem then reduces essentially to a determination of the manner in which the image points of the assembly will distribute themselves over μ-space. The solution of this problem was given by Boltzmann in a famous distribution law, called after him and Maxwell, which we shall derive later on employing a different method.

The formalism outlined above, or *μ-space statistics*, has the advantage of being mathematically simple and physically perspicuous. Yet it possesses only limited applicability. In fact, it strictly suffices only for those systems in which the interaction between molecules is vanishingly small. By reason of this inadequacy, we shall not make any further mention of this method.

The second approach to statistical thermodynamics is due to Gibbs. Crowning the achievements of Clausius, Maxwell, and Boltzmann with decisive researches of his own, he presented the first systematic exposition of the foundations of a general theory devoted to statistical thermodynamics in his well-known *Elementary Principles in Statistical Mechanics*, published in 1902. We prefer the method that has grown from this origin because it is elegant and lends itself readily to a treatment of all kinds of thermophysical systems.

Gibbs chose to apply statistical analysis not to the atomic constituents of a system but instead to a large assembly, or *ensemble*, of mental, or *virtual*, copies of the real system. The virtual systems are, of course, not identical in all respects. Indeed, the similarity extends only as far as the Hamiltonian functions of the systems; in relation to the configurations and velocities of their particles, the virtual systems may still differ vastly among themselves and from the real system. Some advantages of Gibbs' selection of a statistical aggregate might be mentioned immediately. Firstly, seeing that the ensemble is an imaginary one anyway, we are free to permit the number of systems to become as large as we please whenever it is required for mathematical reasons. Secondly, because the systems are macroscopic objects, the question as to their individualities can never arise, whereas it does occur, for instance, in connection with the molecules of a single chemical substance. The first advantage we shall exploit very soon; the relevancy of the second one will manifest itself much later.

From our present viewpoint, as in μ-space statistics, a geometrical representation of the mechanical states of the members constituting the statistical aggregate is conducive to succinct reasoning and suggests valuable ideas; in fact, without this device, little progress could be made. However, since the members are now the systems themselves, the contemplated phase space must be such that the state of a system, rather than that of any one of its molecules, is represented by a single image point. To distinguish this space from μ-space, P. and T. Ehrenfest proposed the use of the designation *gas space* or *γ-space*; the statistics based on γ-space might conveniently be called *γ-space statistics*. Because the phase of a system containing N monatomic molecules is defined by the values of the position coordinates x, y, z and momentum components p_x, p_y, p_z belonging to each of its molecules, γ-space in this case will be $6N$-dimensional. In general, however, a molecule has f degrees of freedom, and γ-space pertaining to a system of N such molecules will be $2fN$-dimensional, corresponding to its fN generalized coordinates $q_1, q_2, \ldots, q_{fN}$ and fN generalized momenta $p_1, p_2, \ldots, p_{fN}$, whose values together determine the mechanical state of the system. For the sake of convenience, the coordinate axes, along which the values of the coordinates $q_1, q_2, \ldots, q_{fN}, p_1, p_2, \ldots, p_{fN}$ of any given point in γ-space are read off, will be required to be perpendicular to one another.

In terms of an image point in γ-space, the temporal development of the mechanical system, whose state is represented by it, can be surveyed pictorially. The position of an image point at a given time t_0, corresponding to some initial state of the system, might be a matter for arbitrary decision. Once this choice has been made, however, Hamilton's equations of motion, viz.,

$$\dot{q}_j = \frac{\partial H}{\partial p_j}, \qquad \dot{p}_j = -\frac{\partial H}{\partial q_j}, \qquad (j = 1, 2, \ldots, fN) \qquad (1)$$

determine uniquely the position of the image point at any other time t. The image point therefore describes in the course of time a curve in γ-space, known as a *phase orbit* or *trajectory*; and due to the uniqueness of the solutions of Eqs. (1), each point in γ-space is traversed by only one trajectory—that is, trajectories cannot intersect or touch themselves or one another.

To actually plot a phase orbit passing through a given point of phase space, one would need to know the forces exerted on each molecule by all the remaining molecules (and by bodies outside the system). However, in γ-space it is our avowed aim, in contrast to that of kinetic theory, to make as few assumptions as possible concerning the intermolecular forces, and to develop instead laws whose validity would not depend on the nature of the interacting particles. To achieve this end we turn our attention from the individual image point and focus it on the assembly of points obtained if one represents every system of the virtual ensemble by an image point in γ-space. Because the systems in general differ in phase, their image points will correspondingly occupy different positions, so that the assembly of points will be spread out in a "cloud" over a finite region of γ-space. The diversity in phase reflects the extent of our ignorance about the phase of the real system that serves as a prototype for the construction of the virtual systems. To find the correct distribution of image points is a problem that will concern us later. At present, we wish simply to inquire how an assembly of phase points, initially arranged in phase space in an arbitrary manner, is going to behave with the passage of time. The answer to this question is given by a general law, which will be derived next.

2–2. Liouville's Theorem

We suppose that a region of γ-space is occupied by a very large number N^* of image points representing an equally large virtual ensemble. For the sake of brevity, the symbols q and p (without subscripts) shall henceforth stand for the set of all q_j and all p_j, respectively, and $dqdp = dq_1 dq_2 \ldots dq_{fN} dp_1 dp_2 \ldots dp_{fN}$ for the volume of an infinitesimal rectangular parallelepiped in phase space. If N^* is increased indefinitely, the number of image points per unit volume of γ-space, $dN^*/dqdp$, approximates a continuous function of the coordinates q,p; in this limit it becomes legitimate to define a function $\rho(q,p,t)$, called the *density-in-phase*, after Gibbs, by the equation

$$\rho = \frac{dN^*}{N^*dqdp}. \tag{2}$$

Thus ρ equals the ordinary density of phase points divided by N^*. The advantage of including N^* in the denominator is that ρ so defined is normalized—that is, the $2fN$-fold integral of ρ over all phase space (at fixed time t) amounts to unity.

As implied by the notation $\rho = \rho(q,p,t)$, the density-in-phase is in general an explicit function of the time t, as well as of the coordinates q and the momenta p. This means that at a fixed point (q,p) of γ-space, image points continually appear and disappear. The rate $\partial\rho/\partial t$ characterizing this process is however not an independent quantity, due to the fact that image points are conserved, i.e., that N^* is constant.

In hydrodynamics the conservation of the mass of a fluid in motion is expressed analytically by the familiar equation of continuity (Chapter 1)

$$\frac{\partial\rho}{\partial t} + \text{div } \rho\mathbf{v} = 0, \tag{3}$$

where ρ signifies the density of the fluid at time t and $\mathbf{v}$ the velocity of the fluid at the space point under consideration. When the term div $\rho\mathbf{v}$ in Eq. (3) is transposed to the right-hand side, Eq. (3) is seen to state simply that the net increase of fluid in an element of space in any time interval must be ascribed to the net inward flow of fluid across the element's boundaries.

Equation (3) and its foregoing interpretation hold literally for the motion in phase space of the "fluid" consisting of phase points, provided the symbols occurring in Eq. (3) are suitably redefined. The quantity ρ in (3) must now stand for the density-in-phase and $\mathbf{v}$ for the "velocity" of phase points—that is, the $2fN$-dimensional vector with components $\dot{q}(t)$, $\dot{p}(t)$; div $\rho\mathbf{v}$ is defined, in analogy to the three-dimensional case, by

$$\begin{aligned}
\text{div } \rho\mathbf{v} &= \sum_{j=1}^{fN} \left(\frac{\partial\rho\dot{q}_j}{\partial q_j} + \frac{\partial\rho\dot{p}_j}{\partial p_j} \right) \\
&= \sum_{j=1}^{fN} \left(\dot{q}_j \frac{\partial\rho}{\partial q_j} + \dot{p}_j \frac{\partial\rho}{\partial p_j} \right) + \rho \sum_{j=1}^{fN} \left(\frac{\partial\dot{q}_j}{\partial q_j} + \frac{\partial\dot{p}_j}{\partial p_j} \right).
\end{aligned} \tag{4}$$

The second sum on the far right-hand side of Eq. (4) is clearly ρ div $\mathbf{v}$. If in this definition of div $\mathbf{v}$, one replaces $\dot{q}_j$ by $\partial H/\partial p_j$ and $\dot{p}_j$ by $-\partial H/\partial q_j$, in agreement with Hamilton's equations (1), the result is

$$\text{div } \mathbf{v} = 0, \tag{5}$$

which implies that the "fluid" formed by image points is incompressible!

By virtue of Eq. (5), only the first sum on the far right-hand side of Eq. (4) remains, so that Eq. (3) reduces to

$$\frac{\partial\rho}{\partial t} = -\sum_{j=1}^{fN} \left(\dot{q}_j \frac{\partial\rho}{\partial q_j} + \dot{p}_j \frac{\partial\rho}{\partial p_j} \right). \tag{6}$$

Equation (6) for the change of density-in-phase at a fixed point (q,p) is known as *Liouville's theorem*; the mathematician Liouville (1838) was the first to derive this law, but Boltzmann (1868) applied it in the context of statistical-mechanical theory.

An alternative formulation of Liouville's theorem is found if one asks for the rate of change of ρ, not at a fixed point in γ-space, but at the positions of an image point traveling through that space. Since the coordinates $q(t)$ and $p(t)$ of an image point are definite functions of the time, $\rho(q,p,t)$ along a trajectory is a function of t alone, and

$$\frac{d\rho}{dt} = \frac{\partial \rho}{\partial t} + \sum_{j=1}^{fN} \left(\dot{q}_j \frac{\partial \rho}{\partial q_j} + \dot{p}_j \frac{\partial \rho}{\partial p_j} \right). \tag{7}$$

Formula (7) in combination with Eq. (6) gives

$$\boxed{\frac{d\rho}{dt} = 0}. \tag{8}$$

The physical meaning of Eq. (8) is that a hypothetical observer, accompanying an image point that pursues its trajectory, will at all times measure the same density-in-phase.

It is interesting to note that Liouville's theorem is valid only in a phase space constructed to represent the generalized coordinates q_j and their conjugate momenta p_j; it would not hold, for instance, in a phase space featuring the generalized velocities $\dot{q}_j$ in place of the momenta p_j. Herein lies the main reason for resorting to Hamilton's equations of motion as the starting point of statistical theory.

The law expressed by Eq. (6) or (8) is true for an arbitrary ensemble of independent systems with identical Hamiltonian functions. To proceed with the theory, it is necessary to restrict the ensemble further. In the first place, we require the virtual systems to be conservative, so that H does not depend explicitly on the time, i.e., $H = H(q,p)$. Thus $dH/dt = \partial H/\partial t = 0$, and H equals a constant, the energy E of the system. Our second restriction demands that the density-in-phase depends on the coordinates q and momenta p only in the combination $H(q,p)$, i.e., $\rho(q,p,t) = \rho(H,t)$. This stipulation has an important consequence, for it implies that

$$\dot{q}_j \frac{\partial \rho}{\partial q_j} + \dot{p}_j \frac{\partial \rho}{\partial p_j} = \frac{\partial \rho}{\partial H} \left(\dot{q}_j \frac{\partial H}{\partial q_j} + \dot{p}_j \frac{\partial H}{\partial p_j} \right) = \frac{\partial \rho}{\partial H} (-\dot{q}_j \dot{p}_j + \dot{p}_j \dot{q}_j) = 0,$$

where use has been made of Hamilton's equations in the second step. Hence, each of the fN summands in Eq. (6) vanishes, so that $\partial \rho/\partial t = 0$, or $\rho = \rho(q,p)$; which means that the density-in-phase does not vary with the time. The ensemble defined in this way is called a *stationary ensemble*, and it is said to be in *statistical equilibrium*. The equilibrium situation is thus guaranteed at all times t if the phase points at an arbitrary instant t_0 are distributed in γ-space with a density-in-phase $\rho(q,p,t_0) = \rho(H)$.

2–3. The Ergodic Problem

We now pass on to a consideration of the postulates that will establish a correspondence between a given real system and a suitable virtual ensemble.

For this purpose, let it be assumed that we have before us a closed thermophysical system, which we interpret as a conservative mechanical system of atomic particles. The system's phase orbit will then lie completely on the surface $H(q,p) = E$ in phase space. It is consistent with the atomic theory of matter to posit that each measurable property F of the system can be put into correspondence with some function $F(q,p)$ of the coordinates q and momenta p, called a *phase function*. To ascertain the exact form of the relationship between F and $F(q,p)$ will be our immediate object.

The reader will recall the statement that if the phase point of a system occupies the position (q^0,p^0) at the time t_0, it will occupy a uniquely determinable position $[q(t),p(t)]$ at any other time t. When indicated, we may stress the unique dependence of q and p on time, by writing $F(q^0,p^0,t)$ instead of $F(q,p)$. Since any measurement necessarily covers a finite interval of time τ, the measured value F_{mea} of F at the time t_0 should obviously not be equated to $F(q^0,p^0,t_0)$, but rather to the average of $F(q^0,p^0,t)$ over the interval τ, that is, to

$$F_\tau = \frac{1}{\tau} \int_{t_0}^{t_0+\tau} F(q^0,p^0,t)dt. \tag{9}$$

Regarding a system in equilibrium, to which we confine our further considerations, we make the assumption that F_τ can be replaced by the *time average* $\bar{F}$ of $F(q,p)$, defined by

$$\bar{F} = \lim_{\tau \to \infty} F_\tau = \lim_{\tau \to -\infty} F_\tau. \tag{10}$$

Thus, finally,

$$F_{\text{mea}} = \bar{F} \tag{11}$$

for a system in equilibrium.

The replacement of the average over a short interval of time τ by the average over an infinite period of time can be defended strictly only if it is contended, in contradiction to known facts, that the deviations of macro-scopic properties from their equilibrium values are unobservable. Conse-quently it is evident that the conceptual structure erected on the basis of Eq. (11) will not automatically suggest a theory of fluctuations.

After having registered this limitation, we consider a more urgent question arising in connection with Eq. (11). Obviously, the identification of F_{mea}, which is a unique quantity, with $\bar{F}$, makes sense only if (i) the limit $\bar{F}$ exists for all trajectories of interest, and (ii) for a given trajectory, $\bar{F}$ is independent of the initial time t_0. Von Neumann and Birkhoff (1931–32) proved, in two celebrated theorems called after them, that these conditions are indeed fulfilled, at least for the vast majority of phase orbits lying on the surface $H(q,p) = E$; for the details of their demonstrations, the reader is referred to the relevant publications.

The foregoing analysis has drawn our attention to quantities of the type $\bar{F}$, and explains why any valid theory of statistical thermodynamics must be able to ascribe correct numerical values to them. Definitions (9) and (10)—we need hardly say—do not furnish any practical prescription for calculating $\bar{F}$. After all, one does not know the orbit of the phase point in question, and even if one did, the evaluation of the integral of $F(q,p)$ along this orbit would not be feasible. In search of a procedure that *can* be realized, we turn again to the ensemble composed of imagined replicas of the real system.

With respect to the ensemble, the key quantity is found to be the *phase average* $\langle F \rangle$ of $F(q,p)$, defined as

$$\langle F \rangle = \int \int F(q,p)\rho(q,p,t)\, dqdp; \tag{12}$$

$dqdp$, it should be remembered, denotes a volume element in γ-space, so that the integral (12) is $2fN$-dimensional. Since $\rho\, dqdp$ equals the fraction dN^*/N^* of image points situated in the element $dqdp$, $\langle F \rangle$ is none other than the average of $F(q,p)$ for the members of the ensemble. If $\langle F \rangle$, like $\bar{F}$, is to be constant in time, one must obviously require the ensemble to be distributed in γ-space with a density-in-phase ρ that is not an explicit function of the time—i.e., the ensemble must be stationary. By virtue of the corollary of Liouville's theorem deduced before, a stationary ensemble automatically obtains if ρ at any time is a function of $H(q,p)$. A simple choice of ρ that will clearly satisfy this condition, is

$$
\begin{aligned}
\rho(q,p) &= C^{-1} & &\text{in the shell of volume } C \text{ lying between} \\
& & &\text{the surfaces } H = E \text{ and } H = E + dE, \\
& & &\text{where } dE \text{ tends to zero;} \\
\rho(q,p) &= 0 & &\text{outside this shell.}
\end{aligned}
\tag{13}
$$

Gibbs invented the term *microcanonical* to denote the distribution in phase (13) and the ensemble associated with it.

Employing the concepts just introduced, we may now establish a connection between a real system and an ensemble by the following crucial postulate: the time average of any phase function $F(q,p)$ equals its phase average computed with respect to a microcanonical ensemble; in symbols,

$$\bar{F} = \langle F \rangle, \tag{14}$$

where ρ in the definition (12) of $\langle F \rangle$ is the function (13).

Equation (14) expresses the central assumption of classical statistical thermodynamics. Attempts to prove it have given rise to the renowned *ergodic problem*, which has bedeviled eminent physicists and mathematicians for the past eighty years. The first endeavor to justify Eq. (14) was made on the basis of the so-called *ergodic hypothesis*, advanced by Boltzmann (1887) and asserting that the orbit of any phase point traverses each point of the surface $H(q,p) = E$. (The term "ergodic" is a combination of the Greek words for "energy" and "path.") Using this conjecture, one can derive Eq. (14) in three steps. First, because only one orbit passes through any point in γ-space, the ergodic hypothesis implies that the surface of constant energy consists of a single-phase orbit. Thus, all image points cover in total the same trajectory, and systems differ from one another solely in relation to the time t_0 when the image points traverse a particular point in phase space. As a result, the time average of $F(q,p)$, which depends only upon the orbit, not on the value of the initial time t_0, will be the same for all members of the ensemble, or $\langle \bar{F} \rangle = \bar{F}$. Second, since we are dealing with a stationary ensemble, the time average of the phase average is the same as the phase average at an arbitrary time, or $\overline{\langle F \rangle} = \langle F \rangle$. Third, one makes the plausible assumption—which can also be proved—that it is immaterial whether the averaging over time precedes or succeeds the averaging over phase, i.e., $\langle \bar{F} \rangle = \overline{\langle F \rangle}$. It follows then that $\bar{F} = \langle F \rangle$, as maintained by Eq. (14). The ergodic hypothesis therefore suffices to justify the theorem (14). Unfortunately, however, this hypothesis cannot be upheld, as mathematicians soon pointed out. Indeed, as no trajectory can cross itself, it is incapable of filling the whole multidimensional space $H(q,p) = E$.

P. and T. Ehrenfest (1912) suggested that the ergodic hypothesis be replaced by their so-called *quasi-ergodic hypothesis*, according to which the trajectory approaches arbitrarily closely each point of the energy surface $H(q,p) = E$, without actually traversing each point. This suggestion does not solve the problem, though; for the inner consistency of the quasi-ergodic hypothesis has not been established—and besides it seems that no one has furnished a demonstration of Eq. (14), satisfying all the experts, on the basis of this hypothesis alone.

Von Neumann and Birkhoff (1931–32) were responsible for a new attack of the ergodic problem, in their publications referred to earlier. Shunning the quasi-ergodic hypothesis, they succeeded to formulate a single necessary and sufficient condition for the validity of Eq. (14), pertaining to the nature of surfaces of constant energy. Lately, Khinchin (1949) managed to dispense with this condition, but his proof of Eq. (14) applies to a limited class of systems only, and thus lacks the generality commending the von Neumann-Birkhoff proof.

At present, therefore, the ergodic problem appears to have been reduced to the problem of demonstrating that the von Neumann-Birkhoff condition is fulfilled. In the absence of a universally accepted proof of Eq. (14), it seems wisest to us simply to postulate as *ergodic hypothesis* the very identification of the time average $\bar{F}$ with the phase average $\langle F \rangle$, and to appraise the cogency of this step by the practical consequences of the theory founded on it.

2–4. Phase Averages and the Canonical Distribution

The foregoing discussion has shown the microcanonical distribution in phase to be an indispensable concept in a search for a logical point of contact between the real system and the ensemble describing it. Once this quest has ended in the ergodic hypothesis as defined above, we are motivated by new considerations to deemphasize the relevancy of the microcanonical distribution and examine the importance of other possible distributions.

The first argument affecting the popularity of the microcanonical distribution is a practical one: since the function (13) is discontinuous, it becomes difficult to perform calculations with it. Partly for this reason, one introduces a related distribution determined by the density-in-phase

$$\rho(q,p) = Ce^{-\beta H}. \tag{15}$$

From the requirement that ρ should be normalized, it follows that the reciprocal of the constant C, appearing here, must be equated to the integral over all phase space of $\exp -\beta H(q,p)$. The constant β, on the other hand, does not allow an immediate interpretation. Physical arguments would show, however, that β^{-1} equals Boltzmann's constant k times the temperature T. Because the density (15) is a function only of the Hamiltonian H, the ensemble it defines is stationary, and can for this reason claim to describe a real system in equilibrium. Moreover—and this is decisive in the present context— Eq. (15) gives practically the same numerical results as the microcanonical distribution, provided the number of atomic particles N is sufficiently large. Since this prerequisite is fulfilled in regard to macrophysical systems, the microcanonical distribution may be replaced by the distribution (15) for computational purposes.

The main objection against the widespread use of the microcanonical ensemble is however dictated by physical reality rather than by mathematical convenience. For, underlying the use of a microcanonical ensemble is the supposition that a closed thermophysical system is a conservative mechanical system. This assumption is certainly not strictly true. Indeed, every thermophysical system interacts with weak radiation fields and the walls of some kind of container, and both types of interaction elude description in terms of conservative forces. Furthermore, the very act of measuring a system's properties represents a nonconservative form of interaction. Apart from these components of interaction, which usually are or can be made negligible, many a system of thermophysical interest exhibits significant interaction with its environment, which is appreciable as well as nonconservative. In fact, the interaction might have been introduced by the experimenter on purpose to ensure the constancy of one or more thermodynamic parameters. Now, a system capable of exchanging energy with its surroundings should obviously not be related to an ensemble, such as the microcanonical one, whose members are systems restricted to possess one particular value of energy. A case in point is a system maintained at constant temperature by a heat reservoir, with which it can therefore exchange energy. Such a system—analysis predicts and experiment confirms—must be described by a distribution in phase none other than Eq. (15). Gibbs (1902), who postulated the distribution (15), called it a *canonical distribution* "on account of its unique importance in the theory of statistical equilibrium." The corresponding ensemble is known as a *canonical ensemble.*

So far we have nowhere invoked any special hypotheses regarding the laws of interaction between atomic particles. The results obtained are therefore valid whatever the nature of the particles, as long as they obey the classical laws of motion. But the situation changes when one proceeds from a recognition of the meaning of phase averages to the task of actually evaluating them. It becomes then imperative to know the particular Hamiltonian $H(q,p)$, and the ensuing formulas will differ with the kind of system.

In the historical development of our subject, the computation of phase averages emerged, next to the ergodic problem, as the major difficulty confronting theorists. Still, we do not wish to pursue this topic any further, if only for the following reason. Since the beginning of this century a profound revolution has taken place in our conception of matter, which invalidates the notion of the phase of a system itself, and creates a set of novel ideas, whose inclusion in a correct theory of statistical thermodynamics is obligatory. We therefore terminate the classical mode of reasoning practised so far, and propose to launch a fresh attack on the statistical-mechanical problem, after having equipped ourselves with the appropriate modern tools in the next two sections.

Despite these remarks the reader should not conclude that the advent of the notions alluded to has destroyed the relevancy of our classical reflections. On the contrary: not only can the new concepts best be explained if they are compared with the old ones, but the superseded theory will be shown to remain important as a special, limiting case of the more comprehensive formalism.

2–5. The Invalidation of Classical Concepts

The revolution in scientific thought, mentioned in the previous section, was the outcome of a realization growing among investigators, since the beginning of the twentieth century, that the Newtonian equations of motion were incapable of accounting for the experimental data on the radiation emitted by atomic particles. Physicists started to grope—though almost reluctantly at first—for a profounder theory that would unravel the anomalous behavior of atoms, and, on extrapolation to objects of ordinary size, could recover the findings of classical laws.

The first step in this direction was taken when Planck (1900) formulated the *quantum theory*, which proved successful in explaining the empirical distribution of energy in the radiation emitted by a blackbody (see Chapter 3). In the next quarter century quantum theory underwent repeated extensions and modifications. It culminated in the postulation of *quantum mechanics*; by Heisenberg (1925), Born and Jordan (1925) in its *matrix-mechanical* formulation, and by de Broglie (1924) and Schrödinger (1926) in its *wave-mechanical* version. For a systematic discussion of quantum mechanics, the reader should consult a textbook on the subject. Here we shall be content to illuminate only a few aspects of wave mechanics that are deemed indispensable to his understanding of our subsequent development of statistical theory.

Nowhere is the breakdown of classical mechanics more strikingly conspicuous than in the inadequacy of its concepts to provide us with a description of atomic events. The formation of classical notions rests upon the premiss that the corresponding measurements can be executed with arbitrarily great precision. It has always been recognized that absolute precision, or zero error, is technically out of man's reach. But classical reasoning maintained that one could minimize the error in measurement to any extent by improving one's observation techniques, so that in principle at least absolute accuracy would still be achievable. Contrariwise, quantum mechanics denies the possibility of such indefinite refinement. It says: not only is there no absolute precision, but in general there is a finite limit to the attainable accuracy! This restriction is inherent in nature, not imposed by the crudeness of our instruments. It stems from the fact that interference is concomitant with observation, so that the act of observation itself disturbs the state of the system under investigation.

To illustrate, one may attempt to "see" an electron—whose dimensions are of the order of 10^{-13} cm—by collecting hard X-rays or gamma rays reflected from it into a photographic emulsion. (Longer waves would be ineffectual as they simply curve around the object.) The process in question can be pictured as involving collisions between the electron and high-energy radiation photons which are scattered into the photographic detector. Because in each collision linear momentum is transferred from a photon to the electron, a position measurement as here conceived necessarily generates a change in the electron's velocity.

The maximum accuracy that can be attained depends upon the quantity measured and the experimental situation. Let us consider the position and velocity of a particle. Either quantity may, in principle if not in practice, be determined with any degree of exactitude, so long as it is realized that mutually exclusive experimental conditions are called for. Any experiment that aims at assigning values of unlimited precision to both these properties at the same moment must end in failure. The reason for this is suggested by the thought experiment outlined in the previous paragraph. A position measurement affects the momentum of the particle; conversely, a measurement of momentum interferes with the object's position. It may be thought that the disturbance experienced by a particle during an observation could be calculated and hence allowed for. This is regrettably not so, as the interaction between object and measuring device cannot be surveyed in such detail. Thus—and this is a crucial point—not only is the disturbance unavoidable, but it is not possible to correct measurements for it either!

Quantum mechanics does however provide a quantitative estimate for the interference between position and momentum determinations of a particle, in the form of the celebrated *uncertainty principle* enunciated by Heisenberg (1927). In symbols, this principle reads

$$\Delta q_j \Delta p_j \geqslant \tfrac{1}{2}\hbar; \qquad (j = 1, 2, 3) \tag{16}$$

in words, it asserts that at any given time the product of the uncertainty in the value of a position coordinate q_j and that of its conjugate momentum p_j is at least $\tfrac{1}{2}\hbar$. The quantity $\hbar = 1.054 \times 10^{-27}$ erg sec is the universal constant $h = 6.626 \times 10^{-27}$ erg sec, divided by 2π, discovered by Planck (1900).

The relations (16) reveal that increased information on any one of the quantities q_j and p_j can be gained only at the expense of a diminished knowledge of the other. They show, in particular, that when q_j has been ascertained with high precision, i.e., Δq_j tends to zero, the latitude in the momentum p_j must be very large, i.e., Δp_j tends to infinity, and in effect p_j cannot be known; conversely, extreme accuracy in the measurement of p_j implies that q_j is practically undefined.

An illustration of the working of Eqs. (16) is furnished by our attempt to "see" an electron, discussed earlier on. To locate the electron with greater sharpness, one has to bombard it with photons of shorter wavelength. But such photons would impart more momentum to the target and therefore cause the electron's momentum to change by a larger amount.

Equations (16) are not restricted to a single particle. They remain valid if q_j stands for any generalized coordinate, and p_j for the momentum conjugate to it, of a mechanical system possessing an arbitrary number of degrees of freedom. It is also important to know that an uncertainty relation exists between the time and the energy of a conservative system:

$$\Delta t \Delta E \geqslant \tfrac{1}{2}\hbar. \tag{17}$$

On the other hand, it should be noticed that $\Delta q_j \Delta p_k \geqslant 0$ replaces Eqs. (16) when $j \neq k$. This means that observations of q_j and p_k do not interfere, or are *compatible*, so that both quantities are capable of exhibiting sharp values simultaneously.

In order to gauge the consequences which the finite value of Planck's constant h has for objects of different sizes, we substitute mv_x for p_x in the uncertainty relation for the x-coordinate, to obtain $\Delta x \Delta v_x \geqslant \tfrac{1}{2}\hbar/m$. Thus the product of the uncertainties in position and velocity is seen to be inversely proportional to the mass m. This circumstance explains why the extreme smallness of h precludes the uncertainty principle from having any noticeable effect on the motion of macroscopic bodies. As a typical example, consider a body of mass 1 gm. Since $\frac{1}{2}\hbar \approx 5 \times 10^{-28}$ erg sec, one can specify its position within 2×10^{-14} cm, and its velocity within 2×10^{-14} cm sec^{-1}, or less than a thousandth of a millimeter per century! Hence, the impression is created that the attainable accuracy in measurement is without limit. For an atomic body such as an electron, whose mass is 9.109×10^{-28} gm, the situation is however altogether different: if its position is fixed within 10^{-10} cm (which is poor for a body of diameter 10^{-13} cm), then the indeterminacy in its velocity will be 50,000 km sec^{-1}. Consequently it would be absurd to ignore the effect of the uncertainty principle on the behavior of atomic particles.

From the uncertainty principle one infers immediately that most of our classical concepts fail, on the atomic level, to correspond to measurable properties. As a result, we might be compelled to ban them from the scientific terminology of the microscopic domain. For it is a widely held dictum of physics that one should employ only concepts associated with quantities which, at least in principle, can be measured.

In view of this criterion, the phase, or the mechanical state, of a system becomes an inadmissible term. Indeed, the phase is described by the values of all the q_j and p_j; and these quantities, as our discussion has shown, cannot all be known simultaneously. Closely allied with the idea of phase is that of a particle's orbit in physical space. In classical theory one could presumably follow the progress of any object continuously and hence determine its orbit. Quantum theory declares such an operation to be impossible. At best one can hope to perform a series of measurements minimizing each of the products $\Delta q_j \Delta p_j$ to the value of $\frac{1}{2}\hbar$. By virtue of the vagueness that remains, and our ignorance of what happens between one observation and the next, these determinations cannot be combined uniquely to define an orbit. The notion of an object's orbit has therefore to be relinquished together with that of its phase. The situation is actually worse than it seems: there is no way of telling even whether or not one is dealing with the same particle in two different observations. In fact, it might be meaningless to raise the question of "sameness" or individuality, especially with respect to similar particles sharing a common region of space.

The breakdown of the cited concepts in connection with the motions of sufficiently small particles explains why classical mechanics, founded upon these ideas, is destined to fail when it attempts to account for phenomena originating in the atomic domain. Quantum mechanics is successful because it avoids the offending notions and operates with a different set of concepts, which do admit interpretations not in conflict with the uncertainty principle.

2–6. Some Further Quantum-Mechanical Aspects

Classical physics is indubitably dominated by the ubiquitous *principle of causality*. This postulate alleges that the evolution of every physical system is controlled by rigorous laws; these, together with the initial state, determine uniquely all the future (and past) states of an isolated system. If in this context one equates—as is customary in classical theory—the state of a mechanical system to its phase, the principle of causality obviously cannot be upheld from the modern viewpoint. Even with any other definition of a state, one could still not hope to detect a causal connection between the results of measurements at different times, as one cannot observe a system without disturbing it by an unknown amount. No contradiction arises however if it is assumed that causality applies unmitigated to a system that is left undisturbed, given a suitable definition of state. Such a definition, whatever its form, must evidently not involve both generalized coordinates and their conjugate momenta.

Quantum mechanics asserts that the *state* of a system comprising N point particles should properly be *described* or *represented* by a continuous, finite, and single-valued function of the generalized coordinates and the time, the so-called *wave function* or *state function* $\psi(q_1, q_2, \ldots, q_{3N}, t) = \psi(q,t)$. The function ψ obeys the famous (time-dependent) *Schrödinger wave equation*, which prominently features in any textbook on quantum mechanics. For our present purposes it will simply be noted that the wave equation is a partial differential equation expressing a causal connection between the conditions of an undisturbed system at different times. It thus plays a role analogous to that of Newton's equation of motion in classical mechanics.

Schrödinger's equation leaves the wave function undetermined to the extent of an arbitrary numerical factor. It is convenient to choose this factor such that ψ becomes *normalized*. This means that the $3N$-fold integral of $\psi\psi^*$ with respect to all the q_j over their complete ranges is unity. (We write $\psi\psi^* = |\psi|^2$, as ψ is inherently a complex function.) After normalization, ψ acquires a simple physical interpretation due to Born (1926): $\psi\psi^*$ is the *position probability density*, or $\psi\psi^* \, dq_1 dq_2 \ldots dq_{3N}$ represents the probability that, at the time t, the coordinate q_1 lies in the interval dq_1, q_2 lies in the interval dq_2, and so on. In order that the normalization of ψ be possible, it is necessary for ψ to vanish at infinity. This implies, in agreement with the foregoing interpretation of ψ, that the system is restrained to a finite part of space—a condition which is indeed satisfied for thermophysical systems.

The Schrödinger wave equation, considered without any restrictions on ψ, has an infinite number of solutions. From all these mathematically possible solutions, the conditions imposed on ψ in the preceding paragraphs, select those which are physically meaningful. Now, for a conservative system, characterized by $H(q,p) = E$, it turns out remarkably that physically meaningful solutions exist only for some definite and discrete values $E_1, E_2, \ldots, E_j, \ldots$ of the energy E. This represents a radical break with the classical view, according to which E, like every q_k, is a continuous variable throughout its complete range. Once the Hamiltonian $H(q,p)$ of a system is known, the wave equation enables one, at least in theory, to discover the set of values E_j. These are called the *energy eigenvalues* or *energy levels* of the system. The latter appellation refers to the fact that the eigenvalues are frequently represented diagrammatically by horizontal lines, spaced vertically by distances proportional to the energy differences.

A measurable quantity such as E that can assume nothing but discrete values in one or more sections of its range is said to be *quantized*. The appearance of discrete values alone in the above energy spectrum is a direct consequence of the boundary condition stating that ψ vanishes at infinity—a stipulation entailing, as we recall, that the system is confined to a finite volume of physical space. If this volume were allowed to grow indefinitely, the density of levels in some high-energy ranges would increase, and finally give rise to continuous regions in the energy spectrum. We may also add that, on the whole, the energy eigenvalues will not be integral multiples of a definite unit. If they are, the unit is known as a *quantum* of energy. Thus, for example, the quantum of energy of electromagnetic radiation of frequency ν is $h\nu$.

The only possible results of precise energy determinations are the eigenvalues E_j. A finite probability generally exists for obtaining any one E_j. Under favorable circumstances though, the probability will be unity for a particular value of the energy, say E_k, and zero for the remaining values. This signifies that a measurement of energy will with certainty produce the value E_k, so that one is entitled to say that the system has the energy E_k. We then describe the system as being in an *energy eigenstate*, with wave function $\psi_k(q,t) = \phi_k(q) \exp(-iE_k/\hbar)t$, and call the time-independent factor ϕ_k of ψ_k the *energy eigenfunction* belonging to the eigenvalue E_k. Any state ψ that is not an energy eigenstate can always be written as a linear combination of energy eigenstates containing a finite or infinite number of terms. And the coefficient c of the eigenstate ψ_j in this expansion or, more precisely, $c_j c_j^*$ is a measure of the probability that the state ψ_j will be realized in an energy determination.

For the sake of simplicity, we have imagined that a single eigenstate is associated with each given value of the energy. But this assumption will hardly ever be true. Mostly, a large number of *independent* eigenfunctions, say g_k, will belong to the same energy E_k; a set of functions is independent if no linear combination (other than the sum with zero coefficients) can be constructed from them to yield zero. The energy level in question is then said to be g_k-*fold degenerate*. In the case of degeneracy, it is impossible to characterize a state of a system uniquely by the value E_k of the energy to which the state belongs, for this value still leaves g_k possibilities open. We may rectify the indicated deficiency in the following manner.

Let F be a measurable property of the system other than its energy E, such as a component of its total angular momentum. As for E, eigenstates necessarily exist for F, and they belong to definite eigenvalues $F_1, F_2, \ldots, F_r, \ldots$ of F, taken here to be discrete. We assume further that observations of F are compatible with those of E, so that both E and F can be measured simultaneously with any degree of precision. Suppose $\phi_1, \phi_2, \ldots$ stand for all possible independent energy eigenfunctions obtained by any method whichsoever. Then one may always construct a new set of functions $\phi_1', \phi_2', \ldots$, which are eigenstates of F as well as of E, by linearly combining among themselves the unprimed functions belonging respectively to the eigenvalues $E_1, E_2, \ldots$.

On inspection of the newly gained set, it will be found that a great many eigenfunctions are in general associated with any particular pair of eigenvalues E_j and F_r. We therefore once again combine, or superimpose, eigenfunctions. And one may reason that the superposition coefficients are so chosen that the set of functions now generated are eigenfunctions not only of E and F but also of G, where G is any property whose measurement is compatible with that of E and F. The eigenvalues of G are, for argument's sake, $G_1, G_2, \ldots, G_m, \ldots$. The addition of compatible properties can theoretically be continued, until finally the initial set of eigenfunctions ϕ_j has been replaced by a set of simultaneous eigenstates containing a single state for any given selection of eigenvalues of $E, F, G, \ldots$.

To stress the unique characterization of states by eigenvalues alone, we may label each state in question with the eigenvalues $E_j, F_r, G_m, \ldots$ to which it belongs, or simply with the indices $j', r', m', \ldots$ assigned to the relevant eigenvalues. In this way arises the notation $\phi_{j'r'm'\ldots}$ or, if one omits the primes, $\phi_{jrm\ldots}$.

The indices $j, r, m, \ldots$ attached to the symbol ϕ are known as *quantum numbers*. In customary formulation, each quantum number pertaining to a microscopic system is either an integer or a half odd integer. An idea of how many quantum numbers are required, emerges from the observation that four quantum numbers, for instance, n, l, m_l, m_s (see below), are needed to fix unambiguously the state of an electron in a hydrogen atom. This means that the unique specification of the quantum state of a thermophysical system comprising N atoms demands something in the order of N quantum numbers.

We render the foregoing reflections on quantum numbers more concrete by examining the case of the hydrogen atom more closely. The three quantum numbers n, l, m_l permit interpretations in language familiar from classical theory, and serve to identify uniquely all the independent solutions of Schrödinger's equation for the hydrogen atom. The number n corresponds to the energy E, while l and m_l, respectively, refer to the magnitude and z-component of the angular momentum $\mathbf{L}$ of the electron. To be precise: the energy eigenvalues E_n are proportional to n^{-2}; L^2 exhibits the eigenvalues $l(l + 1)\hbar^2$; and L_z can assume the values $m_l\hbar$. Corresponding to each of the values $n = 1, 2, 3, \ldots$, l can range over the set $0, 1, 2, \ldots, n - 1$; and for each value of l, m_l is allowed to be any one of the $2l + 1$ values $-l, -l + 1, \ldots, l - 1, l$. Summation of $2l + 1$ over $l = 0, 1, 2, \ldots, n - 1$ gives $2 \times \frac{1}{2}n(n - 1) + n = n^2$, so that the energy level E_n is n^2-fold degenerate.

The fourth quantum number, m_s, is of exceptional importance to us, as it introduces the concept of *spin*, a property of the electron that has no classical analogue, and whose existence is not revealed by the Schrödinger theory either. The reality of spin is suggested, for example, by the following experimental datum: in the energy level scheme of alkali atoms, two levels are observed where Schrödinger's equation predicts only one. This anomaly is explained in all its quantitative aspects by a postulate, due to Uhlenbeck and Goudsmit (1925, 1926), asserting that the electron possesses a *spin angular momentum* $\mathbf{S}$. The term "spin" arose historically from the suggestion that the angular momentum $\mathbf{S}$ is attributable to the rotation, or spin, of the electron about its own axis. This view, it should be emphasized, is untenable. For one thing, if we surmise that S^2 has the eigenvalues $l(l + 1)\hbar^2$, then experiment demands that l be capable of assuming only the value $l = \frac{1}{2}$; whereas, if $\mathbf{S}$ were really the integral of $\mathbf{r} \times \mathbf{p}$ over the volume of the electron, zero and all positive integers would be permitted by theory. The single value of l is designated as the electron's *spin* and commonly written as s. The possible values of S_z are $\frac{1}{2}\hbar$ and $-\frac{1}{2}\hbar$, corresponding to $m_s = \frac{1}{2}$ and $m_s = -\frac{1}{2}$, respectively.

Pauli (1927) proposed that the property of spin be incorporated in the wave-function formalism by positing that the state of an electron depends not only upon its classical position coordinates x, y, z with continuous ranges, but also on a nonclassical *spin coordinate* m_s with a range consisting of only two values, viz., $m_s = +\frac{1}{2}, -\frac{1}{2}$. Thus the wave function becomes $\psi = \psi(x,y,z,m_s)$, if one ignores for the moment its dependence upon time. In this notation, the two eigenstates of S_z may be written respectively as $\psi_{1/2}(x,y,z,m_s)$ and $\psi_{-1/2}(x,y,z,m_s)$ or, more explicitly, as $\phi(x,y,z,\frac{1}{2})\delta_{1/2}(m_s)$ and

$\phi(x,y,z,-\tfrac{1}{2})\delta_{-1/2}(m_s)$, where $\delta_k(m_s) = 1$ or 0, depending on whether $m_s = k$ or $m_s \neq k$.

In order to distinguish L, which derives from the electron's orbital motion, from S, which does not admit of an interpretation in spatial terms, it is customary in quantum mechanics to speak of L as the *orbital* angular momentum. The vector sum of L and S is usually denoted by the symbol J, i.e., $\mathbf{J} = \mathbf{L} + \mathbf{S}$, and is known as the *total angular momentum* of the electron.

The property of spin is not peculiar to the electron—experiment shows it to be an attribute of all atomic particles. However, although s equals $\tfrac{1}{2}$ also for protons, neutrons, and many other elementary particles, the spin can be small half-integers different from $\tfrac{1}{2}$, small integers, and zero. Particles with integer spin are named *bosons*, after Bose, and those with half-integer spin, *fermions*, after Fermi. If the spin s is defined by $S^2 = s(s + 1)\hbar^2$, the number of eigenvalues of S_z must be $2s + 1$, one for each of the values $m_s = -s, -s + 1, \ldots, s - 1, s$ of the quantum number m_s appearing in the eigenvalue equation $S_z = m_s\hbar$.

For arbitrary l and s, the total angular momentum J is correlated with the eigenvalue equations $J^2 = j(j + 1)\hbar^2$, where

$$j = l + s, l + s - 1, \ldots, |l - s|,$$

and $J_z = m_j\hbar$, where $m_j = -j, -j + 1, \ldots, j$. The quantity J has a noteworthy property issuing from the following facts. Magnetic moments are associated with L of a charged particle and with S of any particle. As a consequence of the interaction between these moments, the Hamiltonian function of an atom contains magnetic energy terms in the L's and S's of its constituent particles. The presence of these terms, theory shows, generally prevents L and S of the atom separately from being conserved. $\mathbf{J} = \mathbf{L} + \mathbf{S}$, on the other hand, will be constant in time if the Hamiltonian has the appropriate symmetry.

2–7. The Gibbs Ensemble Method in Quantum Mechanics

After the foregoing excursion into quantum mechanics, we are now in a position to pass on to the construction of the special theoretical apparatus for deriving thermophysical facts from a quantum standpoint.

In classical theory one soon realizes that a determination of the positions and velocities, as functions of the time, of trillions of interacting particles is not feasible; such detailed information is, moreover, not needed for thermophysical systems. Consequently one relinquishes a description of their microscopic mechanical states, and replaces it by the computation of averages over a virtual ensemble of systems replicating the real system.

Quantum theory poses a similar problem, whose solution is again found in the Gibbs ensemble method. An exact description of a state in quantum mechanics is rendered by a wave function ψ as a function of the generalized coordinates $q_1, q_2, \ldots$ and the time t. For any given thermophysical system we do not however know the function $\psi(q,t)$. Indeed, an astronomic number of quantum states, or of *microstates*, is usually compatible with a given set of macroscopic parameters defining a *macrostate* of a thermophysical system. One therefore resorts to the use of a virtual quantum-mechanical ensemble of systems, which is *representative of* the real physical system. Each system of the ensemble must replicate the real system with respect to molecular composition, environment, and macroscopic parameters. But here the similarity ends, because the ensemble has to reflect our ignorance as to the quantum state occupied by the experimental system. This condition is fulfilled by allowing the systems of the ensemble to be distributed over all quantum states consistent with the cited replicated traits.

The logical connection between physical system and ensemble is established by the following postulate. The *time average* of a mechanical property F of a physical system in thermodynamic equilibrium equals its *ensemble average* calculated relative to an ensemble containing an infinitely large number N^* of systems and representing the real system. In symbols:

$$\bar{F} = \langle F \rangle. \tag{18}$$

Mechanical properties, it should be explained, are those classically definable in terms of a phase function $F(q,p)$, such as pressure, volume, energy, and number of molecules; each mechanical property has a definite value in any one of its eigenstates. Nonmechanical quantities, such as temperature, entropy, and chemical potential, do not follow immediately from Eq. (18), but can be arrived at only indirectly when statistical results are combined with the findings of phenomenological thermodynamics.

In the context of Eq. (18), $\bar{F}$ is the time average of the measured value of F over a time interval $(t, t + \Delta t)$ sufficiently long to provide an average value independent of the initial time t. Thus, fluctuations are averaged out in the statement of $\bar{F}$; to gain information about them, one has to compute $<F^2>$ in addition to $<F>$ —cf. Eq. (106).

The ensemble average $\langle F \rangle$, finally, is the ordinary mean of the quantity F over all the systems of the ensemble. In other words, if for argument's sake

N_r^* systems are in a state exhibiting the eigenvalue F_r of the property F, one has

$$N^* \langle F \rangle = \sum N_r^* F_r, \tag{19}$$

where the summation is extended over all allowed *states*. It is clear that an ensemble can be representative of a physical system in thermodynamic equilibrium only provided $\langle F \rangle$ is independent of the time.

It is a debatable question how one should make the selection of a basic set of independent quantum states over which the members of an ensemble are to be distributed. We shall adopt as a basic set the states $\phi_{jrm\ldots}$ uniquely identifiable by the quantum numbers $j, r, m, \ldots$ referring to a set of compatible properties. Let us hasten to add that this view is altogether contrary to what quantum mechanics teaches. For, a particular system of the ensemble will not permanently be in one of the states $\phi_{jrm\ldots}$. There exists only a probability to find, on examination, a system to be in any one of these states; on the whole even this assertion is an oversimplification. Fortunately, the consequences of the theory founded upon the actual state of affairs do not differ appreciably from those flowing from our unsophisticated approach.

In spite of the similarity in notation, the basic states $\phi_{jrm\ldots}$, or ϕ_{jr} for short, if we let r stand for the whole set of quantum numbers $r, m, \ldots$, cannot strictly be the eigenstates of the total energy, defined in the previous section. The reason is that a system occupying a particular eigenstate of its total Hamiltonian H at any one moment will remain in this state for ever; while the state of the real system which the ensemble is supposed to represent faithfully, is a superposition of eigenstates belonging to the same value or different values of the energy. To obtain an ensemble where the individual members are subject to change, we posit that the basic set ϕ_{jr} comprises eigenstates, not of the total Hamiltonian H, but rather of H^0 constituting the dominant part of H. This remark asks for further clarification.

Assume that it is possible to write the Hamiltonian function as a sum,

$$H = H^0 + H', \tag{20}$$

where H' is a "small" correction, or *perturbation*, added to the *unperturbed* Hamiltonian H^0. The nature of the quantities H^0 and H' varies with the physical system that is being investigated. Although H^0 ordinarily has a simple meaning, it might not be possible to write down H' explicitly. For the purpose of a general theory this vagueness however presents no serious drawback. As an illustration of the division in Eq. (20), H^0 and H' can be taken to be synonymous with, respectively, the kinetic energy term T and the potential energy term V of the total energy $H = T + V$. Alternatively, one may think of H' as representing the interaction energy between the system proper and either a weak radiation field or a vessel enclosing the system; in this instance, H^0 will include the potential energy associated with the interaction between particles of the system.

To proceed with our argument, let $E_1^0, E_2^0, \ldots, E_j^0, \ldots$ be the eigenvalues of the unperturbed Hamiltonian H^0 and the functions ϕ_{jr}^0 the eigenstates belonging to them, where the symbol r again denotes a set of compatible quantum numbers. The introduction of the perturbation H' now changes the energy eigenvalues and the energy eigenfunctions respectively by the amounts E_{jr}' and ϕ_{jr}', which are very small compared with the unperturbed values E_j^0 and ϕ_{jr}^0. Thus, while the energy levels will on the whole shift slightly, their general arrangement will, by hypothesis, not seriously be affected; this is the meaning that one has to attach to a "small" correction H' in perturbation theory. It is precisely the eigenstates ϕ_{jr}^0 of H^0 rather than the eigenstates of $H = H^0 + H'$ that we envisage as basic states for the construction of our ensemble, and which we designated by ϕ_{jr}, without a superscript, earlier in this section. We shall continue to omit the superscript o in the notation, not only of the energy eigenfunctions ϕ_{jr}, but also of the energy eigenvalues E_j, whenever the context itself indicates that unperturbed quantities are meant.

In the preceding paragraph, we have regarded the perturbation H' as causing the eigenstates and eigenvalues of the perturbed system to differ somewhat from the same quantities for the unperturbed system. This approach, developed by Schrödinger (1926), requires that H' as well as H^0 do not involve the time explicitly. There also exists another perturbation method, due to Dirac (1926, 1927), that remains applicable even if H' varies explicitly with the time. In the latter method one does not examine any possible modification of energy states and energy levels of the unperturbed system, but views instead the perturbation H' as being responsible for a characteristic development of the perturbed system in time. To be specific: a perturbed system finding itself initially in any one of the unperturbed states ϕ_{jr}, does not permanently remain in this state. Instead, it is considered to undergo continually *transitions* to other unperturbed states ϕ_{ks}, owing to the action of the perturbation H'. It is this point of view that we shall exploit with respect to the members of the virtual ensemble.

In classical statistical theory one defines an ensemble by the number of phase points $N^*\rho dqdp$ occupying the volume element $dqdp$ located at the point (q,p) of γ-space. Analogously, a quantum-mechanical ensemble is described by the number of systems N_{jr}^* in each state ϕ_{jr}. The probability P_{jr} of finding a system, selected at random from the ensemble, in the state ϕ_{jr}

is obviously the *occupation number* N_{jr}^* divided by the total number of systems N^*, i.e.,

$$P_{jr} = \frac{N_{jr}^*}{N^*}. \tag{21}$$

The quantities N_{jr}^* must clearly add up to N^*, and consequently the sum of the probabilities P_{jr} is unity; that is,

$$\sum_{jr} N_{jr}^* = N^* \tag{22}$$

and

$$\sum_{jr} P_{jr} = 1. \tag{23}$$

It is implicit in Eq. (19) that an ensemble can be representative of a physical system in thermodynamic equilibrium only provided the occupation numbers N_{jr}^* are constants. We shall however adopt here a more general standpoint, and assume that the occupation numbers are functions of the time, i.e., $N_{jr}^* = N_{jr}^*(t)$, so that the ensemble will correspond to an experimental system removed from the state of equilibrium. The question then arises: how do the numbers N_{jr}^* vary with the passage of time?

To arrive at an answer, we observe that quantum mechanics asserts the existence of quantities A_{ks}^{jr}, such that $A_{ks}^{jr}(t)$ measures the probability of a system, occupying the state ϕ_{jr} at the time zero, to be found in the state ϕ_{ks} at the end of the time interval $(0, t)$; as a special case, the final state ϕ_{ks} can be identical with the initial state ϕ_{jr}. Accordingly, since $N_{jr}^*(0)$ systems are in the state (specified by the quantum numbers) jr at the time zero, $A_{ks}^{jr}(t)N_{jr}^*(0)$ systems will make the transition from the state jr to the state ks during the time interval $(0, t)$. The number of systems in the state ks at the time t will therefore be

$$N_{ks}^*(t) = \sum_j \sum_r A_{ks}^{jr}(t)N_{jr}^*(0). \tag{24}$$

Subtraction of the evident condition

$$\sum_j \sum_r A_{ks}^{jr}(t) = 1, \tag{25}$$

multiplied by $N_{ks}^*(0)$, from Eq. (24), yields

$$N_{ks}^*(t) - N_{ks}^*(0) = \sum_j \sum_r A_{ks}^{jr}(t)[N_{jr}^*(0) - N_{ks}^*(0)] \tag{26}$$

for the increase of the occupation number N_{ks}^* in the interval $(0, t)$. It is seen that this equation, on division by N^*, can also be written as

$$P_{ks}(t) - P_{ks}(0) = \sum_j \sum_r A_{ks}^{jr}(t)[P_{jr}(0) - P_{ks}(0)], \tag{27}$$

by Eq. (21).

From Eq. (26) one infers immediately that a *stationary* ensemble, or an ensemble in *statistical equilibrium*, defined by $N^*_{ks}(t) = N^*_{ks}(0)$ (all k and s), will obtain when $N^*_{jr}(0) = N^*_{ks}(0)$, at least for all pairs of states jr and ks characterized by $A^{jr}_{ks}(t) \neq 0$.

Perturbation theory reveals that, for given ks, A^{jr}_{ks} is appreciably different from zero only for states jr such that $|E_j - E_k| < 2\hbar/t$. (This result is roughly in agreement with the uncertainty relation $\Delta t \Delta E \geq \frac{1}{2}\hbar$, if the perturbation H' is regarded as a device for measuring the unperturbed energy E_k of the system.) Consequently, even for small values of t, the contribution to the right-hand side of Eq. (27) derives in practice solely from an extremely narrow interval $\Delta E = 2\hbar/t$ centered around the value $E_j = E_k$. In this range, we assume, the $P_{jr}(0)$ depend upon the summation index j so weakly that they can be replaced by $P_{kr}(0)$; thus, the expressions in parentheses in Eq. (27) cease to depend on the index j. Since the energy spectrum of a thermophysical body is very nearly continuous, one is furthermore justified to approximate the summation over j by an integration over the energy E; this procedure, as can be shown, gives

$$\sum_j A^{jr}_{ks}(t) = t W^{(k)}_{sr}. \tag{28}$$

The quantities $W^{(k)}_{sr}$, appearing here, are nonnegative and depend only upon the indices attached to them and on the perturbation H'. They will be time-independent constants provided H' does not refer explicitly to the time. Substitution of Eq. (28) and $P_{jr}(0) = P_{kr}(0)$ into Eq. (27), results in

$$\frac{1}{t}[P_{ks}(t) - P_{ks}(0)] = \sum_r W^{(k)}_{sr}[P_{kr}(0) - P_{ks}(0)] \tag{29}$$

or, if t is small and P_{ks} a slowly varying function of the time, approximately:

$$\frac{dP_{ks}}{dt} = \sum_r W^{(k)}_{sr}[P_{kr}(0) - P_{ks}(0)]. \tag{30}$$

This equation for the time rate of change of the probability P_{ks} was first derived by Pauli (1928), and is known in modern literature as the *master equation*.

Equation (30) permits the following interpretation: of the $N^*P_{kr}(0)$ systems occupying the state kr at the time zero, $N^*P_{kr}(0)W^{(k)}_{sr}$ will, per unit of time, go over into the state ks. Accordingly, $W^{(k)}_{sr}$ is the probability per second that a system will undergo a transition from the state kr to the state ks. The *transition probabilities per unit time* $W^{(k)}_{sr}$ satisfy, besides the equations $W^{(k)}_{sr} \geq 0$, the symmetry relations $W^{(k)}_{rs} = W^{(k)}_{sr}$, a fact which is often referred to as the *principle of microscopic reversibility*. Equation (30) asserts that statistical equilibrium, defined by $\dot{P}_{ks} = 0$ (all k and s), will necessarily obtain when $P_{kr}(0) = P_{ks}(0)$ for all pairs of states kr and ks connected by nonzero transition probabilities $W_{sr}^{(k)}$. If the stated condition is fulfilled, then $W_{sr}^{(k)}P_{kr}(0) = W_{rs}^{(k)}P_{ks}(0)$—that is, the frequency of transitions from the state kr to the state ks equals the frequency of transitions in the opposite direction. This statement expresses the *principle of detailed balancing*, encountered before in connection with chemical reactions (Chapter 1). We have so far shown that detailed balancing is a sufficient condition for statistical equilibrium; in the next section it will be demonstrated that it is also a necessary condition, provided microscopic reversibility holds.

The existence of symmetrical and time-independent transition probabilities per unit time has been established above with the aid of perturbation theory, carried out to terms of the first order in H'. The main objection against the perturbation proof is that its application is restricted to short time intervals, whereas we are interested in the behavior of thermophysical systems during the relatively long periods of time required to reach thermostatic equilibrium. It is possible to forgo perturbation theory, and operate with transition probabilities per unit time that are time-independent over any length of time. But in this approach one has to replace the actual system that is being studied by a theoretical model, called a *Markov chain*, and it is arguable to what extent this chosen model represents a physical system. Be it as it may, we shall adhere to the use of time-independent transition probabilities for arbitrary time intervals, and adopt a master equation, constructed with their help, as the basis of our considerations in the next section.

2–8. *H*-Theorem and Quantum-Mechanical Microcanonical Ensemble

As mentioned earlier, the ensemble representing a real physical system is determined by the thermodynamic state and environment of the real system; both these aspects must be faithfully duplicated in each one of the systems constituting the virtual ensemble. We shall confine ourselves to three types of environment which enjoy great practical interest and pertain to (i) isolated systems, (ii) closed isothermal systems, and (iii) open isothermal systems. In the present section, only the first case will be discussed.

An isolated thermophysical system, in the simplest situation, is characterized not only by a fixed value of the energy E, but also by a definite number of particles N and a volume V. Generally, the system will contain more than one molecular species and, if placed into contact with its surroundings, would be capable of performing work other than volume-work. Under such circumstances, N shall stand for the set $N_1, N_2, \ldots$, representing the number of molecules of species $1, 2, \ldots$, and V shall designate the set of extensive variables associated with all possible types of thermodynamic work.*

The systems in the ensemble corresponding to an isolated system must by hypothesis possess the same values of E, N, V as the given isolated system, at least within the accuracy of experimental determination. The duplication of N and V, as specified for the real system, in every member of the virtual ensemble ensures that the energy eigenstates ϕ_{jr} and energy levels E_j of the real system are copied exactly in each system of the ensemble. Now, the energy of the real system will in practice not be known precisely, but only within a margin of error ΔE. In classical theory we suppose that this error can theoretically be reduced to zero. Quantum theory, however, stipulates that there is a residual error determined by the uncertainty relation $\Delta t \Delta E \geqslant \frac{1}{2}\hbar$, Δt being the time taken by the energy measurement. It is therefore unrealistic to imagine that all members of the ensemble occupy eigenstates belonging to the same value E_j of the energy. Instead, one has to assume that the systems are distributed over energy levels lying within a finite range ΔE; the actual size of ΔE is unimportant, as the verifiable consequences of statistical theory vary only weakly with ΔE. We impose accordingly the following restrictions on the occupation numbers of the ensemble selected to represent an isolated system:

$$\left.\begin{array}{ll} N_{jr}^* \neq 0 & \text{for } E - \frac{1}{2}\Delta E < E_j < E + \frac{1}{2}\Delta E; \\ N_{jr}^* = 0 & \text{otherwise.} \end{array}\right\} \tag{31}$$

Our immediate aim is to demonstrate that the ensemble specified by Eqs. (31) will exhibit a one-directional development in time, terminating with the attainment of statistical equilibrium.

The proof of this statement is based upon the master equation, suggested by Eq. (30),

$$\dot{P}_s = \sum_r W_{sr}(P_r - P_s); \tag{32}$$

this equation provides the rate of increase of the occupation number $N_s^* = N^* P_s$ of the state s at any time t, due to transitions between the given state s and the remaining states r. Each of the subscripts appearing in Eq. (32) signifies a set of quantum numbers—including a quantum number for the energy—required to label uniquely the states with energies E_j such that $E - \frac{1}{2}\Delta E < E_j < E + \frac{1}{2}\Delta E$; the summation in Eq. (32) has to be extended over this group of states. Because the interval ΔE may be conceived to be extremely narrow, the summands of Eq. (32) will practically not depend on

---

*See footnote following Eq. (1), Chapter 1.

E, and it is for this reason that no explicit reference is made to the energy in that equation.

The formula (32) is now used to obtain the rate of increase of the quantum-mechanical *H-function* H^* defined as

$$H^* = \sum_s P_s \log P_s, \tag{33}$$

the summation again being extended over the group of states whose energies are approximately equal to E. Since $\sum P_s = 1$, the time-derivative of $H^* = H^*(t)$ is

$$\dot{H}^* = \sum_s \dot{P}_s \log P_s + \sum_s \dot{P}_s = \sum_s \dot{P}_s \log P_s. \tag{34}$$

If one substitutes in Eq. (34) the value (32) of $\dot{P}_s$, one gets

$$\dot{H}^* = \sum_s \sum_r W_{sr}(P_r - P_s) \log P_s, \tag{35}$$

or, on interchanging the indices r and s and then applying the symmetry relations $W_{rs} = W_{sr}$,

$$\dot{H}^* = \sum_r \sum_s W_{rs}(P_s - P_r) \log P_r = -\sum_r \sum_s W_{sr}(P_r - P_s) \log P_r. \tag{36}$$

Addition of Eqs. (35) and (36) finally yields

$$\dot{H}^* = -\frac{1}{2} \sum_r \sum_s W_{sr}(P_r - P_s)(\log P_r - \log P_s). \tag{37}$$

Since $(x - y)(\log x - \log y) \geqslant 0$ and $W_{sr} \geqslant 0$, each term under the summation signs of Eq. (37) is either zero or positive. Consequently, $H^*(t)$ is a monotonically decreasing function of the time t, i.e.,

$$\boxed{\dot{H}^* \leqslant 0}, \tag{38}$$

where the equality sign obtains if, and only if, $P_r = P_s$ for all pairs of states r and s such that $W_{sr} \neq 0$. Thus H^* decreases and statistical equilibrium is realized only when the cited condition is fulfilled. This statement is the quantum-mechanical version of the celebrated *H-theorem*. We shall discuss the H-theorem itself at some length in the next section; here we merely intend to point out some of its implications that are immediately required.

Let Ω independent states of the given isolated system belong to energy values lying inside the interval ΔE. Since the system is confined to a limited space, Ω will always be a finite number. We assume that the perturbation H'—on which the transition probabilities W_{sr} depend—permits any one state of the indicated group to be reached from any other, by means of transitions, either directly or via some intermediate states. If this supposition, which is the quantum analogue of Boltzmann's ergodic hypothesis, is satisfied, the condition for statistical equilibrium becomes $P_r = P_s$ for all states r and s comprised in the energy interval ΔE. Hence, it follows from $\sum P_s = 1$ that, in statistical equilibrium,

$$
\left.\begin{aligned}
P_{jr} &= \Omega^{-1} \quad \text{for } E - \tfrac{1}{2}\Delta E < E_j < E + \tfrac{1}{2}\Delta E; \\
P_{jr} &= 0 \quad \text{otherwise.}
\end{aligned}\right\} \tag{39}
$$

This proposition is sometimes called the *principle of equal a priori probabilities*.

Equations (39) define a quantum-mechanical *microcanonical* ensemble. This ensemble, being stationary, furnishes time-independent ensemble averages, and thus corresponds to an isolated system in thermostatic equilibrium. The value H_0^* taken on by the H-function for a microcanonical ensemble can easily be written down from definition (33) of H^*. Because the sum (33) contains Ω terms, each of which, by Eqs. (39), has the value $\Omega^{-1} \log \Omega^{-1}$ in equilibrium, one obtains

$$
H_0^* = -\log \Omega. \tag{40}
$$

Another interesting observation deserves mention too. Equations (39), read in conjunction with the postulated identity of the long-time average $\bar{F}$ and the ensemble average $\langle F \rangle$, imply that an actual isolated system settled in thermostatic equilibrium, spends equal time intervals in each one of its possible quantum states over a great period of time. This claim is frequently referred to as the *quantum ergodic hypothesis*.

The parameters E, V, N prescribed for a microcanonical ensemble, the reader will not fail to notice, are none other than the characteristic variables peculiar to the thermostatic entropy S^0. It is to this circumstance that the microcanonical ensemble owes much of its fundamental significance. Entropy enters our statistical considerations in the following manner.

According to the second law, the thermostatic entropy S^0 of an isolated system can never decrease. And this is precisely the salient feature of the function $-H^*$, too. A linear relation therefore suggests itself between the entropy and $-H^*$. One should, however, not lose sight of the fact that the increase of $-H^*$ takes place under conditions largely different from those to which the second law applies. The quantity $-H^*$ increases continuously and monotonically in time with respect to a system that we first isolate and then leave to attain thermostatic equilibrium on its own. The increase of S^0, on the other hand, refers to the property $S_1^0 \leqslant S_2^0 \leqslant S_3^0 \leqslant \cdots$, valid for a sequence of equilibrium states $1, 2, 3, \ldots$; these are realized if one lifts successively the constraints acting on an isolated system and awaits the return of equilibrium after each removal. Indeed, whereas H^* has a definite value for every situation, the entropy S^0 has been defined for thermostatic equilibrium alone. One has therefore to distinguish between equilibrium and nonequilibrium states.

We posit accordingly:

$$S^0 = -kH_0^* = k \log \Omega \qquad \text{in equilibrium;} \tag{41}$$

$$S = -kH^* = -k \sum_s P_s \log P_s \qquad \text{in general,} \tag{42}$$

where k stands for Boltzmann's constant. Equation (41) thus postulates a relation between two quantities defined separately before, while Eq. (42) extends the concept of entropy per definition to the nonequilibrium domain. The generalized entropy Eq. (42) is associated with the name of Gibbs, who advanced (1902) its classical analogue.

Equation (41) for the thermostatic entropy S^0 is deduced with the aid of the H-theorem. It is possible to arrive at an alternative expression for S^0, without appeal to the H-theorem, by a procedure which we shall now explain.

Suppose that the energy eigenvalues pertaining to all independent energy eigenstates have been arranged from low to high values, to provide the sequence

$$E_1, E_2, \ldots, E_j, \ldots, \qquad \text{with } E_{j+1} \geqslant E_j. \tag{43}$$

If the energy level E is g-fold degenerate, the value E will appear g times in the row (43), so that the index j now labels states rather than energy levels. Since the Hamiltonian H of the system depends upon the parameter V, any energy value E_j will likewise be a function of V. Thus, $H = H(V)$ and $E_j = E_j(V)$. We introduce next the symbol $\Phi = \Phi(E,V)$ to denote the number of eigenvalues E_j in the set (43) that are smaller than the value E, and let $\rho = \rho(E,V)$ stand for the density of eigenvalues in the energy spectrum; that is,

$$\rho(E,V)dE = \left(\frac{\partial \Phi}{\partial E}\right)_V dE \tag{44}$$

represents the number of eigenvalues lying in the range between E and $E + dE$.

After these preliminaries, we ask: what is the rate of change of Φ with V, when E is kept constant, i.e., $(\partial\Phi/\partial V)_E$? In answering, we imagine that the energy levels (see Figure 2–1) are divided into groups $a, b, c, \ldots$, such that dE_j/dV inside each group is approximately constant. Thus, dE_j/dV has the value A, say, in the group a, the value B in the group b, and so on. It is worth noting that a group need not consist of neighboring levels; in fact, adjacent levels might have widely different values of dE_j/dV. We now inquire into the shift of the various energy levels in relation to the level, or line, $E = U$, representing an arbitrary but fixed value of the energy, when V is increased by the amount dV.

FIGURE 2–1. Diagrammatic representation of the energy levels in the neighborhood of the line $E = U$.

We consider first the levels belonging to the group a. If $A > 0$, then each level of the group a obeying the inequality $0 < U - E_j < AdV$ will be raised to a position above the line $E = U$, thereby diminishing $\Phi(U,V)$ by the amount $+1$. If, on the other hand, $A < 0$, each level of the group a for which $0 < E_j - U < -AdV$ will be lowered to a position underneath the line $E = U$, thus causing $\Phi(U,V)$ to increase by $+1$. Consequently, with $\rho_a(E,V)$ designating the density of levels in the group a, the contribution to the increase of $\Phi(U,V)$, due to levels of the group a, is $-\rho_a(U,V)AdV$, whatever the sign of A. Similarly, the contribution owing to levels of the group b is $-\rho_b(U,V)BdV$, and so on. When we add the contributions made by the groups $a, b, c, \ldots$, we find that the total increase of $\Phi(U,V)$ as V grows by dV is given by

$$\left(\frac{\partial \Phi}{\partial V}\right)_{E=U} dV = -\rho_a(U,V)AdV - \rho_b(U,V)BdV - \cdots. \qquad (45)$$

Now, ρ_a/ρ is the relative frequency with which a level of the group a occurs, so that the microcanonical ensemble average of dE_j/dV, corresponding to the energy U, is

$$\left\langle \frac{dE_j}{dV} \right\rangle = \rho^{-1}(U,V)[\rho_a(U,V)A + \rho_b(U,V)B + \cdots]. \qquad (46)$$

The right-hand side of Eq. (46) yields, on multiplication by $-\rho dV$, the right-hand side of Eq. (45); hence

$$\left(\frac{\partial \Phi}{\partial V}\right)_{E=U} dV = -\rho(U,V) \left\langle \frac{dE_j}{dV} \right\rangle dV. \tag{47}$$

As a result of Eqs. (44) and (47), the total differential $d\Phi = (\partial \Phi/\partial V)_E dV + (\partial \Phi/\partial E)_V dE$ becomes

$$d\Phi = \rho\left(dE - \left\langle \frac{dE_j}{dV} \right\rangle dV\right). \tag{48}$$

This equation is an assertion purely about the functional dependence of Φ on the variables E and V. It can be transformed into a statement about a physical process if dV is stipulated to be a real change in V taking place with extreme slowness during a time dt. Then, as quantum mechanics shows, the work $-dW_j = (dE_j/dV)dV$ is done on a system occupying a state of energy E_j. Moreover, if dV is sufficiently large, the time interval dt will be long, so that one is justified to identify the ensemble average of dW_j with the work dW done by the actual system of physical interest. Thus, we are able to write $-dW$ for $\langle dE_j/dV \rangle dV$ in Eq. (48) to obtain

$$d\Phi = \rho(dE + dW). \tag{49}$$

By the first and second laws of thermodynamics, $dE + dW = dQ = TdS$, so that Eq. (49) maintains $d\Phi = \rho TdS$, i.e.,

$$dS = \frac{d\Phi}{\rho T} = \frac{d\Phi}{T(\partial \Phi/\partial E)_V}. \tag{50}$$

Since $(\partial S/\partial E)_V = 1/T$, by thermodynamic reasoning, one may be inclined to conclude from Eq. (50) that $S = \Phi$. This conjecture is however wrong, as the following argument will show. Consider two isolated systems with parameters E', V', S', $\Phi'(E',V')$ and E'', V'', S'', $\Phi''(E'',V'')$, respectively. The corresponding quantities for the two systems regarded as one shall be E, V, S, $\Phi(E,V)$, where obviously $E = E' + E''$ and $V = V' + V''$. Then, whereas thermodynamics asserts that $S = S' + S''$, the simple process of counting requires that the number of quantum states of the combined system, with energy less than E, be given by $\Phi(E,V) = \Phi'(E',V')\Phi''(E'',V'')$. Consequently, $\Phi \neq S$. One gains, however, complete agreement with phenomenological theory if one puts:

$$\boxed{S(E,V,N) = k \log \Phi(E,V,N) + C}, \tag{51}$$

where the number of particles N has been explicitly mentioned; the quantity C is independent of E and V and may be omitted in most arguments. For, by hypothesis (51), $S = k \log \Phi + C = k \log \Phi'\Phi'' + C = k \log \Phi' + C' + k \log \Phi'' + C'' = S' + S''$, as demanded above; and $1/T = (\partial S/\partial E)_V = k(\partial \Phi/\partial E)_V/\Phi$, while $dS = k\, d\Phi/\Phi$, so that $TdS = d\Phi/(\partial\Phi/\partial E)_V$, in accord with Eq. (50).

At first sight, the postulate $S^0 = k \log \Phi$ seems to contradict Eq. (41), submitted on the basis of the H-theorem. After all, since $\Omega(E,V) = \rho(E,V)\Delta E$, Eq. (41) claims that $S^0 = k \log \rho + k \log \Delta E$, or, if one neglects the inessential additive constant, $S^0 = k \log \rho$. The apparent conflict, created by the occurrence of ρ instead of Φ, becomes resolved if one notes (see Chapter 3) that in practice $\Phi \sim E^{3N/2}$; consequently, $\rho = (\partial\Phi/\partial E)_{V,N} \sim NE^{3N/2-1}$, so that $\log \Phi \sim N \log E$, as compared with $\log \rho \sim N \log E + \log N$. Since N is something of the order 10^{20} or more, this means that $\log \Phi$ equals $\log \rho$ for practical purposes.

Equation (51) derives its importance from the fact that it provides an expression for the thermostatic entropy in terms of its characteristic variables E, V, N. Once $\Phi(E,V,N)$ is known as a function of the indicated variables, all the remaining parameters can be computed. Indeed, as $dS = (1/T)dE + (p/T)dV - (\mu/T)dN$, where μ stands for the chemical potential per particle, we have:

$$\frac{1}{T} = \left(\frac{\partial S}{\partial E}\right)_{V,N} = \frac{k}{\Phi}\left(\frac{\partial \Phi}{\partial E}\right)_{V,N}, \tag{52}$$

$$\frac{p}{T} = \left(\frac{\partial S}{\partial V}\right)_{N,E} = \frac{k}{\Phi}\left(\frac{\partial \Phi}{\partial V}\right)_{N,E}, \tag{53}$$

$$\frac{\mu}{T} = -\left(\frac{\partial S}{\partial N}\right)_{E,V} = -\frac{k}{\Phi}\left(\frac{\partial \Phi}{\partial N}\right)_{E,V}; \tag{54}$$

and from these equations, T, p, μ can be found by substitution.

2–9. Classical *H*-Theorem, Entropy, and Thermodynamic Probability

One could hardly overrate the significance of the H-theorem in the chronological as well as in the logical development of statistical thermodynamics. In the present section we intend to examine the H-theorem and its implications for thermophysics in greater detail than before. It is unfortunate that the analysis of the H-theorem (38) is hampered by the fact that one has to cope with the abstract concept of an ensemble *and* the novel ideas of quantum mechanics. To separate these aspects from those we seek to emphasize, it is apposite to propound also the original version of the H-theorem, which was formulated by Boltzmann in classical terms and without appeal to the notion of an ensemble. Our discussion will then be based on his ideas rather than on the quantum-mechanical theorem (38). The classical derivation of the H-theorem, forthwith to be given, has the advantage that its assumptions are physically perspicuous and permit of easy visualization.

We consider a gas of sufficiently low density, comprising N similar monatomic molecules with position vectors $\mathbf{r}$ and velocities $\mathbf{v}$. In geometrical language, the dynamical state of the gaseous system may then be represented by an assembly of N image points filling a position-velocity space spanned by six mutually perpendicular axes. This conceptual space is identical with Boltzmann's μ-space, except that the cartesian velocity components v_x, v_y, v_z replace the cartesian momentum components p_x, p_y, p_z. Let the distribution function $f(\mathbf{r},\mathbf{v},t)$ be defined so that $f(\mathbf{r},\mathbf{v},t)\,d\mathbf{r}d\mathbf{v}$ furnishes the number of image points occupying the volume element $d\mathbf{r}d\mathbf{v} = dxdydz\,dv_xdv_ydv_z$ of position-velocity space at time t. We shall, however, initially not operate with this continuous function, but with its discrete analogue, which is mathematically more tractable. For this purpose, we divide position-velocity space into finite *cells*, numbered $1, 2, 3, \ldots$, of equal volumes $\omega_1 = \omega_2 = \omega_3 = \cdots = \omega$, and denote by $N_j(t) = f_j(t)\omega_j$ the number of molecules whose image points lie inside the cell j. Obviously, the sum of the occupation numbers N_j over all available cells equals N, i.e., $\sum N_j = N$. Furthermore, supposing that no long-range forces act between molecules, one is entitled to assign a definite energy ε_j to each cell j, so that $\sum N_j\varepsilon_j = E$, where E is the energy of the gas.

To simplify our discussion, we assume, for the time being, that no external forces are present, and that the molecules are distributed uniformly over configuration space, that is, the space of x, y, z alone. The distribution function will then depend only upon the velocity $\mathbf{v}$ and the time t. Under these conditions, we regard $f = f(\mathbf{v},t)$ as specifying the distribution of image points in velocity space, or the space of v_x, v_y, v_z, and the N_j as the associated occupation numbers.

As a result of collisions between molecules, all these N_j change continually. With Clausius (1857) we postulate that the number of collisions per unit time between molecules whose image points lie initially in the cells i and j, and finally in the cells k and l, is equal to $B_{ij}^{kl}N_iN_j$, where the coefficients $B_{ij}^{kl} = B_{ji}^{kl} = B_{ij}^{lk}$ are independent of the occupation numbers, and determined by the geometry of the collision $(i,j) \rightarrow (k,l)$ and the forces operative during collisions. For the dilute system here investigated one is moreover justified to ignore collisions involving more than two molecules at a time. On these assumptions, the rate of change of N_i is evidently given by

$$\frac{dN_i}{dt} = \sum_j \sum_k \sum_l (B_{kl}^{ij} N_k N_l - B_{ij}^{kl} N_i N_j). \tag{55}$$

This equation is known in literature as the *Stosszahlansatz* or the *collision number hypothesis*. It is ordinarily considered as true that the coefficient B_{ij}^{kl} characterizing the collision $(i,j) \to (k,l)$ is equal to the coefficient for the inverse collision $(k,l) \to (i,j)$, i.e., $B_{ij}^{kl} = B_{kl}^{ij}$. This statement, called the *principle of microscopic reversibility*, can be proved at least for the simple case of spherically symmetric interaction between molecules. If this principle is invoked, Eq. (55) may be simplified to read:

$$\dot{N}_i = \sum_j \sum_k \sum_l B_{ij}^{kl}(N_k N_l - N_i N_j). \tag{56}$$

Furthermore, since in elastic collisions kinetic energy as well as linear momentum must be conserved,

$$B_{ij}^{kl} = 0 \quad \text{unless} \quad \mathbf{v}_i + \mathbf{v}_j = \mathbf{v}_k + \mathbf{v}_l \quad \text{and} \quad \mathbf{v}_i^2 + \mathbf{v}_j^2 = \mathbf{v}_k^2 + \mathbf{v}_l^2. \tag{57}$$

From Eq. (56) it is plain that a sufficient condition for equilibrium, that is, for $\dot{N}_i = 0$ (all i), is given by: either $N_i N_j = N_k N_l$ or $B_{ij}^{kl} = 0$ for each set of values of i, j, k, l. Thus, by Eq. (57), one need only suppose that $\log N_i + \log N_j = \text{const.}$, or $\log f(\mathbf{v}_i) + \log f(\mathbf{v}_j) = \text{const.}$, whenever $\mathbf{v}_i + \mathbf{v}_j = \text{const.}$ and $\mathbf{v}_i^2 + \mathbf{v}_j^2 = \text{const.}$ This condition is fulfilled if, and only if, one puts $f(\mathbf{v}) = f^0(\mathbf{v})$, where

$$f^0(\mathbf{v}) = Ce^{-\frac{1}{2}b(\mathbf{v} - \mathbf{v}_0)^2}, \tag{58}$$

C, b, and $\mathbf{v}_0$ being constants. If b is equated to m/kT, Eq. (58) is seen to be none other than the Maxwellian distribution of velocities (see Problem 2); $\mathbf{v}_0$ is the velocity of the center of mass of the gas.

It can further be shown that the Maxwell distribution is the only stationary one, and—what is more important—any initial distribution $f(\mathbf{v},t)$ will approach the Maxwellian distribution monotonically with the passage of time. The proof of this assertion results from a consideration of Boltzmann's *H-function* H_B, defined by

$$H_B = \sum_i N_i \log N_i; \tag{59}$$

with the notation $P_i = N_i/N$, H_B takes on the form $N \sum P_i \log P_i - N \log N$, which is reminiscent of the expression (33) for H^*. From Eq. (56), together with the equation $\sum_i N_i = N$ and the symmetry relations $B_{ij}^{kl} = B_{ji}^{kl}$ and $B_{kl}^{ij} = B_{ij}^{kl}$, it follows that

$$
\begin{aligned}
\dot{H}_B &= \sum_i \dot{N}_i \log N_i + \sum_i \dot{N}_i = \sum_i \dot{N}_i \log N_i \\
&= \sum_i \sum_j \sum_k \sum_l B_{ij}^{kl}(N_k N_l - N_i N_j) \log N_i \\
&= \frac{1}{2} \sum_i \sum_j \sum_k \sum_l B_{ij}^{kl}(N_k N_l - N_i N_j)(\log N_i + \log N_j) \\
&= \frac{1}{4} \sum_i \sum_j \sum_k \sum_l B_{ij}^{kl}(N_k N_l - N_i N_j)(\log N_i N_j - \log N_k N_l) \leqslant 0. \quad (60)
\end{aligned}
$$

Hence, $H_B(t)$ decreases monotonically, and becomes constant solely when $N_i N_j = N_k N_l$ for all values of i, j, k, l associated with nonzero B_{ij}^{kl}, so that equilibrium obtains only when the Maxwell distribution is reached. Equation (60) expresses the H-theorem of Boltzmann (1872). One notices, incidentally, that at equilibrium, $B_{ij}^{kl} N_i N_j = B_{kl}^{ij} N_k N_l$, which means that the frequency of the direct collision $(i,j) \to (k,l)$ is the same as that of the inverse collision $(k,l) \to (i,j)$. Here we have another illustration of the *principle of detailed balancing*.

The H-theorem can be established also for the more general case in which the distribution function depends upon **r** as well as on **v**, and external forces are present, derivable from a potential energy function $V(\mathbf{r})$. Naturally, the N_i in definition (59) of H_B are now required to denote the occupation numbers of cells in the six-dimensional position-velocity space. We do not demonstrate this proposition, but simply cite one of its main consequences. It is found that, while the distribution in velocity space is again Maxwellian, the distribution in configuration space is no longer uniform; instead it turns out to be proportional to $\exp -\beta V$, with $\beta = b/m$. This means that the equilibrium distribution function now becomes

$$
f^0(\mathbf{r},\mathbf{v}) = C e^{-\beta(\frac{1}{2}m)(\mathbf{v} - \mathbf{v}_0)^2 - \beta V} = C e^{-\beta\varepsilon}, \quad (61)
$$

where ε is the energy of the molecule calculated relative to the center of mass of the gas. Equation (61), with $\beta = 1/kT$, constitutes Boltzmann's generalization (1868) of Maxwell's distribution from velocity space to position-velocity space.

Definition (59) of the function H_B is not physically transparent. It is however possible to ascribe a simple meaning to H_B by the following considerations. But first we reinterpret slightly the numbers N_i appearing in Eq. (59): they shall now designate the occupation numbers of cells in the μ-space of a gas molecule. Any set of values of these occupation numbers is said to describe a *macrostate* of the gas. This type of description suffices to determine all thermophysical properties. One can, of course—reasoning along classical lines—conceive of a more detailed specification of the state of a system. In particular, one may attach a label, so to speak, to each molecule, thereby making it possible to talk of molecules 1, 2, 3, etc. If the cell in μ-space occupied by the image point of each numbered molecule is mentioned definitely, a so-called *microstate* of the system is uniquely determined.

In order to proceed with our argument, we advance the hypothesis that all microstates are equally probable. Then the probability that a particular macrostate will occur is proportional to the number of microstates compatible with the given macrostate. This number obviously equals the number of ways in which N similar objects can be divided into groups containing respectively $N_1, N_2, \ldots$ objects—that is,

$$W(N_1, N_2, \ldots) = \frac{N!}{N_1! N_2! \ldots} = \frac{N!}{\prod_j N_j!}. \tag{62}$$

The quantity W, which is a large integer, is called the *thermodynamic probability*, to distinguish it from ordinary probabilities, which are proper fractions. If we apply the *Stirling* formula, viz., $\log n! = n \log n - n$ (valid with an accuracy higher than one per cent for integral $n > 10$), to Eq. (62), then we can write

$$\log W = (N \log N - N) - \sum_j (N_j \log N_j - N_j)$$

$$= N \log N - \sum_j N_j \log N_j, \tag{63}$$

where use has been made of the condition $\sum N_j = N$ in the last step. Therefore, by substituting Eq. (59) into Eq. (63), one finally gets the simple relation between the H-function and probability:

$$H_B = -\log W + N \log N. \tag{64}$$

After this digression, we may continue with our discussion of the H-theorem. By virtue of the fact that $-H_B$, like the thermostatic entropy S^0, increases monotonically in time, and as H_B has meaning also in nonequilibrium states, we are led to postulate that a linear function of $-H_B$ may be regarded as a generalization S of the thermostatic entropy S^0 for dilute systems. Thus, we posit, after Boltzmann (1877), that

$$S = -A H_B + \text{const.}, \tag{65}$$

or, in view of Eq. (64),

$$S = A \log W + D, \tag{66}$$

where A and D are constants. Indeed, if we adopt the assumption (65), it follows from Eqs. (59), (61), $\sum N_i = N$, and $\sum N_i \varepsilon_i = E$ that at equilibrium,

$$S^0 - \text{const.} = -AH_B^0 = -A \sum N_i^0 (\log C - \beta \varepsilon_i) = -A(N \log C - \beta E);$$

hence $(\partial S^0/\partial E)_{V,N} = A\beta = A/kT$, which is exactly the equation $(\partial S/\partial U)_{V,N} = 1/T$, familiar from phenomenological theory, provided one puts $A = k$.

The identification of A with Boltzmann's constant k was proposed by Planck (1900). He also assumed that $D = 0$ in Eq. (66), which implies that $S = 0$ in the hypothetical state corresponding to $W = 1$. On Planck's suppositions, Eq. (66) reduces to the famous formula

$$\boxed{S = k \log W}, \tag{67}$$

commonly referred to as *Boltzmann's equation*. Equation (67), taken in conjunction with the *H*-theorem, interprets the second law $\Delta S \geqslant 0$ simply as the tendency of an isolated system to develop from less probable states (small W) to more probable states (large W); thermostatic equilibrium corresponds to the state in which W attains its maximum value.

Planck's postulates, it is important to note, assigned for the first time in history an absolute value to entropy, whose zero is undetermined in phenomenological theory. The enunciation of Eq. (67) had far-reaching consequences. It led Planck of necessity to his quantum hypothesis, according to which the energy of radiation is quantized, and from there to the third law of thermodynamics. Equation (67) was therefore inextricably connected with the birth of quantum theory. This fact is all too frequently underestimated or completely ignored in textbooks.

Boltzmann's findings had a great impact on the physics of his time—for two fundamental reasons. First, the *H*-theorem provided an explanation in mechanical terms of the irreversible approach of macroscopic systems towards equilibrium. Second, by correlating entropy with the *H*-function and thermodynamic probability, Boltzmann revealed the statistical character of the second law, which in phenomenological theory is endowed with absolute validity.

When Boltzmann enunciated his ideas, and for some time afterwards, two main objections were raised against the *H*-theorem; these are often called by their German names, the *Loschmidtscher Umkehreinwand* (1876) and the *Zermeloscher Wiederkehreinwand* (1896). It is essential to our appraisal of the

H-theorem to understand the nature of these objections and how they can be overcome. The terminology itself is significant: *Umkehr* connotes "reversal in time," and *Wiederkehr* means "recurrence of the same state," while *Einwand* could perhaps best be translated as "objection" or "counter-argument."

One may formulate the *Umkehreinwand* as follows. The classical equations of motion for a conservative system are invariant with respect to a replacement of the time $+t$ by $-t$. As a result, given any one solution of these equations, one can obtain from it, by reversing all particle velocities, another solution in which the system will pass through its previous states in reverse order. If the *H*-function—which depends on the instantaneous dynamical state of the system—decreases in the process described by the first, or *direct*, solution, it must obviously increase in the development pertaining to the second, or *reverse*, solution!

The *Wiederkehreinwand* is based on a theorem of Poincaré (1890), which was proved rigorously by Carathéodory (1919). According to this theorem, every finite isolated mechanical system is very nearly periodic, if not strictly periodic. To render this assertion more precise, let us consider all possible trajectories lying on the energy surface $H(q,p) = E$, assumed to be finite, in γ-space. Poincaré's theorem then demands that, except for a negligible fraction of the given trajectories, any image point, moving along a trajectory, will after a sufficient length of time return arbitrarily close to its initial position. Thus, almost every phase of a system will be recovered to any degree of approximation, provided we wait long enough. The period of time required for a given phase to reappear within specified limits, the *recurrence time* or *Poincaré cycle*, might be admittedly extremely long. All the same—and this is the relevant point—the *H*-function must ultimately start increasing, if it initially decreased.

The reflections of Loschmidt and Zermelo make it clear that the function H_B cannot invariably decrease as maintained by Boltzmann's *H*-theorem. The reconciliation of the opposing views here involved is to be found in the recognition that through the *Stosszahlansatz*, Eq. (55), we have injected a probability element into the proof of the *H*-theorem. In fact, it is erroneous to perform calculations, as we did, on the assumption that $B_{ij}^{kl} N_i N_j \, dt$ collisions of the type $(i,j) \to (k,l)$ will occur during an arbitrary time interval dt. Instead, $B_{ij}^{kl} N_i N_j$ should be interpreted as the number of collisions taking place on the *average* per unit of time, so that the number of collisions in a particular time interval dt might be quite different from $B_{ij}^{kl} N_i N_j \, dt$. Thus, the *H*-theorem is a statement about the average or probable, rather than actual, behavior of the physical system.

The truth is that the function H_B will not decline along a smooth curve $H_B = H_B(t)$, as predicted by the H-theorem, but fluctuate irregularly about this imagined curve. To put it somewhat differently: if a system removed from the state of equilibrium is examined very many times before equilibrium is attained, one will find that the H-function is decreasing in the overwhelming majority of cases. In a small, yet significant minority of instances, H_B will be found to increase. Hence, the reverse solutions required by Loschmidt are actually realized, albeit not so frequently as the direct ones, for nonequilibrium situations. When thermostatic equilibrium is reached, H_B will not remain constant, as the H-theorem asserts, but continue to fluctuate on a microscopic scale. These fluctuations will however occur around a constant mean value, which implies that increases of H_B happen just as frequently as decreases. In other words, at equilibrium the system exhibits the perfectly symmetric behavior that the cited temporal isotropy of the mechanical laws of motion leads one to expect.

The question still remains why increases of H_B should be so uncommon outside the equilibrium state that it seems impossible for a macroscopic deviation from equilibrium to recur, in conflict with Poincaré's theorem. The answer is briefly that the predominance of cases, in which H_B diminishes, over those where H_B grows is an illusion. This is due to the fact that the recurrence time of a sizable, in contrast with a microscopic, deviation from equilibrium is tremendously long. For instance, the recurrence time of the departure $\Delta\rho$ of a gas density from its equilibrium value ρ_0 might increase billionfold when the size of $\Delta\rho$ is doubled; even for a relative departure $\Delta\rho/\rho_0 \sim 10^{-10}$, it could reach a value larger than the age of the universe! Accordingly, whereas sufficiently small deviations—such as those occurring constantly at equilibrium—can appear quite frequently, macroscopic ones will in general not be expected to arise spontaneously in the course of thermophysical observations. We infer that if a macroscopic deviation is observed, we can virtually be sure that it is not ascribable to spontaneous fluctuations, but has been brought about by external interference. And in the moments following our observation, the deviation is bound to display an apparently smooth decline to the value zero—a phenomenon familiar from everyday perception.

Finally, the implications of the foregoing discussion for our conception of the second law ought to be mentioned emphatically. Since $S = -kH_B +$ const., it follows from the alleged real behavior of H_B that the absolute validity attributed to the second law in phenomenological thermodynamics must be relinquished. One is made to appreciate that it is strictly speaking wrong to contend that S will always either increase or remain constant in an isolated system. It would however be correct to say that the entropy $S = k \log W$ will probably increase, that is, a system will probably develop from a state with low (thermodynamic) probability to a state with high probability. True, the probability that S will increase by far exceeds the probability that it will decrease. It is for this reason that, on the whole, the adoption of the strict form of the second law in thermostatics does not lead to any inconsistencies. In exceptional cases, however, it does. We shall return to this question when treating fluctuations in Chapter 3.

2–10. Quantum-Mechanical Canonical Ensemble

After the foregoing excursion into classical theory, we revert to a quantum mode of reasoning. Our immediate aim is to devise an ensemble that will be representative of a closed isothermal system with given volume. The experimental system here contemplated is thus characterized by definite values of the parameters T, V, N. The key to the proper choice of an ensemble is provided by the observation that in practice one maintains a system's temperature at a particular value T by putting it in thermal contact with a heat reservoir of the same temperature. According to a general precept laid down before, each system of the envisaged ensemble must likewise interact thermally with a constant-temperature environment. This requirement is fulfilled hypothetically in the following manner.

Suppose that the N^* members of the ensemble, each possessing the same values of V and N as the real system, are not completely isolated from one another, as they are in the case of a microcanonical ensemble. Instead, each system is surrounded by a wall that arrests the flow of molecules but is permeable to heat, and together the systems are tightly packed to form a three-dimensional lattice. The entire ensemble is first immersed in a large heat reservoir of temperature T, until thermal equilibrium has been established; the ensemble is then removed from the reservoir and enclosed by a wall isolating the ensemble completely from its environment. Under these conditions, the systems of the ensemble are automatically isothermal, as each of them is embedded in a heat reservoir made up of the remaining $N^* - 1$ systems.

Having defined the appropriate representative ensemble, we next pose the basic question: which fraction of the N^* systems occupies any particular eigenstate of the unperturbed Hamiltonian function of the experimental system? In dealing with this question, we take advantage of the fact that the virtual ensemble is, by hypothesis, isolated. As our discussion in Section 2–8 has equipped us to treat of any isolated system, we make the ensemble rather than the real system the primary object of our immediate study. To elucidate this statement: the ensemble of systems is regarded as a large thermophysical system with energy E^* and volume $V^* = N^*V$ and containing N^*N particles. This system has been called a *supersystem* by some authors, lest it be confused with the experimental system.

In order to enumerate the quantum states of the supersystem, belonging to the energy E^*, we note that the energy corresponding to the thermal interaction between systems of the supersystem may be assumed to be so small that a definite energy eigenstate can be assigned to each individual system at any moment. These eigenstates are, of course, the same for each system. Moreover, since energy can be exchanged between systems, the eigenstates accessible to them do not pertain to one particular value of the energy, in contrast to the eigenstates of systems making up a microcanonical ensemble. We again list the energy eigenstates of a system, or system-states for short, according to the scheme of Eq. (43), so that only one system-state j belongs to the energy eigenvalue E_j. By hypothesis, each system is then in some state j or other; and an energy eigenstate of the supersystem, or supersystem-state, is completely defined once we have specified the energy eigenstate occupied by each system. For example, if every system is numbered, a possible supersystem-state will be determined by the information that system No. 1 is in the system-state 5, system No. 2 is in the system-state 9, and so on. Since every system is of macroscopic dimensions, the labeling here assumed is a permissible mental operation, so that the foregoing definition of a supersystem-state is physically meaningful. Thus we have shown how the totality of supersystem-states can be enumerated in terms of the eigenstates of the individual systems constituting the supersystem.

The specification of a supersystem-state represents the maximum possible information about a supersystem; a far less detailed description will satisfy the needs of statistical theory. To be exact, it is not necessary to label the systems, but only to stipulate the number N_j^* of systems occupying every system-state j. Any set of values of the occupation numbers $N_1^*, N_2^*, \ldots$ defines a quantum-mechanical *distribution*. Obviously, W^* supersystem-states, where [cf. Eq. (62)]

$$W^*(N_1^*, N_2^*, \ldots) = \frac{N^*!}{N_1^*!N_2^*!\ldots} = \frac{N^*!}{\prod_j N_j^*!}, \qquad (68)$$

are compatible with the distribution $N_1^*, N_2^*, \ldots$. For the choice of N^* that we have in mind, the integer W^* will in general be astronomic in size. It is also evident that not all sets of occupation numbers are admissible. Only those distributions are physically meaningful which fulfill the conditions

$$\sum_j N_j^* = N^* \tag{69}$$

and

$$\sum_j N_j^* E_j = E^*, \tag{70}$$

corresponding to the facts that the supersystem consists of a fixed, though arbitrary, number of systems N^* and has a constant energy E^*.

A key quantity in our subsequent discussion is the number of physically possible supersystem-states; it is clearly given by

$$\Omega^*(E^*,N^*) = \sum W^*(N_1^*, N_2^*, \ldots), \tag{71}$$

where the summation is to be extended over all values of N_1^*, N_2^*, ... obeying the restrictions of Eqs. (69) and (70). Now, we have postulated earlier that all allowed quantum states of an isolated system are equiprobable; by virtue of this principle, all supersystem-states consistent with Eqs. (69) and (70) must occur equally often. The probability P^* that a particular distribution N_1^*, N_2^*, ... will be realized is consequently the quotient of W^* and Ω^*:

$$P^*(N_1^*, N_2^*, \ldots) = \frac{W^*(N_1^*, N_2^*, \ldots)}{\Omega^*(E^*,N^*)}. \tag{72}$$

With this definition of P^*, the average value of the occupation number N_k^* is given by

$$\overline{N}_k^* = \sum N_k^* P^*(N_1^*, N_2^*, \ldots). \tag{73}$$

More explicitly, this formula becomes, after substitution from Eqs. (68) and (72),

$$\Omega^*(E^*,N^*)\overline{N}_k^* = \sum N_k^* \frac{N^*!}{N_1^*! \, N_2^*! \ldots} \tag{74}$$

or

$$\Omega^*(E^*,N^*)\overline{N}_k^* = N^* \sum \frac{(N^* - 1)!}{N_1^*! \, N_2^*! \ldots (N_k^* - 1)! \ldots}. \tag{75}$$

To obtain a more tractable expression for $\overline{N}_k^*$, we transform the right-hand side of Eq. (75) by introducing the following set of primed integers:

$$N^{*'} = N^* - 1, \qquad N_k^{*'} = N_k^* - 1, \qquad N_j^{*'} = N_j^* \qquad (j \neq k). \tag{76}$$

In terms of the primed quantities, the conditions of Eqs. (69) and (70) can be rewritten respectively as

$$\sum_j N_j^{*'} = N_1^* + N_2^* + \cdots + (N_k^* - 1) + \cdots = N^* - 1 \tag{77}$$

and

$$\sum_j N_j^{*'} E_j = N_1^* E_1 + N_2^* E_2 + \cdots + (N_k^* - 1)E_k + \cdots = E^* - E_k. \tag{78}$$

Consequently, Eq. (75) may be cast in the form

$$\Omega^*(E^*, N^*)\overline{N}_k^* = N^* \sum{}' \frac{N^{*'}!}{N_1^{*'}! \, N_2^{*'}! \dots}, \tag{79}$$

where the prime affixed to the summation sign indicates that one has now to sum over all values of $N_1^{*'}$, $N_2^{*'}$, ... satisfying the restrictions of Eqs. (77) and (78). By definition (71), the right-hand side of Eq. (79) is seen to be precisely equal to $N^*\Omega^*(E^* - E_k, N^* - 1)$, so that, on division by Ω^*, Eq. (79) reduces to

$$\overline{N}_k^* = \frac{N^*\Omega^*(E^* - E_k, N^* - 1)}{\Omega^*(E^*, N^*)}. \tag{80}$$

Equation (80) can be simplified if one writes down its logarithm and expands the result in a Taylor series:

$$\log \overline{N}_k^*/N^* = \log \Omega^*(E^* - E_k, N^* - 1) - \log \Omega^*(E^*, N^*)$$
$$= -\frac{\partial \log \Omega^*}{\partial E^*} E_k - \frac{\partial \log \Omega^*}{\partial N^*}; \tag{81}$$

the series can legitimately be terminated with the first-order terms, since we are at liberty to make the supersystem so large that $N^* \gg 1$ and $E^* \gg E_k$. Employing the symbols

$$a = \left(\frac{\partial \log \Omega^*}{\partial N^*}\right)_{E^*} \tag{82}$$

and

$$\beta = \left(\frac{\partial \log \Omega^*}{\partial E^*}\right)_{N^*}, \tag{83}$$

one may write Eq. (81) briefly as

$$\overline{N}_k^* = N^* e^{-a - \beta E_k}. \tag{84}$$

The quantity a can immediately be eliminated from Eq. (84), because

$N^* = \sum \bar{N}_j^* = N^* e^{-\alpha} \sum e^{-\beta E_j}$, so that $e^{\alpha} = \sum e^{-\beta E_j}$. If this value of e^{α} is inserted into Eq. (84), one obtains finally

$$\frac{\bar{N}_k^*}{N^*} = \frac{e^{-\beta E_k}}{\sum\limits_j e^{-\beta E_j}}. \tag{85}$$

Equation (85) tells us what the average distribution of systems over system-states will be in a supersystem at equilibrium. The instantaneous distribution will fluctuate around the distribution (85). Fortunately however— as we shall show at the end of this section—the relative fluctuations of the occupation numbers for large enough N^* are negligible. Thus, to an accuracy increasing with N^*, $\bar{N}_k^*/N^*$ can be equated to P_k, where

$$P_k = \frac{N_k^*}{N^*} \tag{86}$$

is the instantaneous probability that an arbitrarily chosen system of the supersystem will be encountered in the system-state k. With this understanding, and using the abbreviation

$$\boxed{Z = \sum_j e^{-\beta E_j}}, \tag{87}$$

we can ultimately present Eq. (85) in the succinct form

$$\boxed{P_k = Z^{-1} e^{-\beta E_k}}. \tag{88}$$

The distribution (88) is the quantum analogue of the canonical distribution in phase $\rho = C e^{-\beta H}$, introduced in Section 2–4. We have therefore established that the systems of a huge supersystem at equilibrium constitute a quantum-mechanical *canonical* ensemble. Such an ensemble will be assumed to represent the closed isothermal system that is actually being studied.

According to Eq. (87), the function Z is found if one sums $\exp -\beta E_j$ over all system-states j. For this reason, Planck (1921) called Z the *Zustandssumme* (sum-over-states) of a system. Modern American and English textbooks favor however the designation *partition function*, introduced by Darwin and Fowler (1922). As later analysis will show, the partition functions Z_A and Z_B of two systems A and B in weak thermal contact indeed determine the partitioning of energy between the systems A and B. The function Z is one of the crucial quantities in statistical thermodynamics, and this for the following reason. It turns out that the Helmholtz free energy F is a simple function of Z. And because the characteristic variables of F are T, V, N, one infers that, once Z is known as a function of the same parameters, all thermodynamic properties can be obtained by sheer computation. On this showing, the role of $Z(T,V,N)$ in relation to the canonical ensemble, may be compared with that of the function $\Phi(E,V,N)$ in the theory of the microcanonical ensemble.

We pass on to discover the exact form of the connection between Z and F. A convenient point of departure is provided by Eq. (70), read in conjunction with Eq. (86), stating that the energy $U = E^*/N^*$ of a single system is given by

$$U = \sum_j P_j E_j. \tag{89}$$

This formula is in agreement with the postulate maintaining that the energy U of the physical system must be identified with the ensemble average $\langle E \rangle$ of the energy.

We first investigate the change dU of the energy U when the experimental system remains closed but undergoes an infinitesimal reversible process, in which both heat and work are exchanged between the system and its environment. Equation (89) implies that

$$dU = \sum (E_j \, dP_j + P_j \, dE_j). \tag{90}$$

Now, from Eq. (88), $\log P_j = -\log Z - \beta E_j$, so that $E_j = -\beta^{-1}(\log Z + \log P_j)$. Consequently,

$$-\sum E_j \, dP_j = \beta^{-1} \sum (\log Z + \log P_j)dP_j$$
$$= \beta^{-1} \sum \log P_j \, dP_j = \beta^{-1} d\left(\sum P_j \log P_j\right); \tag{91}$$

the last two steps derive from the fact that $\sum P_j = 1$, and therefore $\sum dP_j = 0$. We know furthermore that

$$\sum P_j \, dE_j = -dW, \tag{92}$$

$-dW$ being the work done on the system during the given process. Combination of Eqs. (91) and (92) finally yields

$$dU = -\beta^{-1} d\left(\sum P_j \log P_j\right) - dW. \tag{93}$$

Equation (93) is seen, on comparison with the first law, $dU = dQ - dW$, to assert that

$$\beta dQ = -d\left(\sum P_j \log P_j\right). \tag{94}$$

Since the right-hand side is an exact differential, we conclude that β is an integrating factor of dQ, which means, by the second law, that β is proportional to T^{-1}. The constant of proportionality—future considerations will confirm—must be put equal to the reciprocal of the Boltzmann constant k.

Thus, our conclusion reads

$$\boxed{\beta = \frac{1}{kT}}. \tag{95}$$

With this value of β, Eq. (94), when considered next to the second law, $dQ = TdS$, issues in $dS = -kd(\sum P_j \log P_j)$, i.e.,

$$S = -k \sum_j P_j \log P_j + C, \tag{96}$$

where the integration constant C is independent of T and V. As the reader may readily verify, the additivity property of entropy* requires that we set $C = 0$.

To strengthen the plausibility of the preceding result, we deduce at this point the formula (96) by an alternative method. We start from the entropy equation (41) for an isolated system, which asserts that the entropy of our supersystem at equilibrium is given by

$$S^* = k \log \Omega^*(E^*, N^*), \tag{97}$$

so that the entropy $S = S^*/N^*$ per system becomes

$$S = \frac{k}{N^*} \log \Omega^*(E^*, N^*). \tag{98}$$

Now, according to definition (71), $\Omega^*(E^*, N^*)$ is the sum of terms of the kind $W^*(N_1^*, N_2^*, \ldots)$. All these summands are however negligible compared with the summand $W^*(\overline{N}_1^*, \overline{N}_2^*, \ldots)$, which furnishes the number of supersystem-states belonging to the average distribution (85). One can therefore simplify Eq. (98), to an approximation improving with the size of N^*, to get

$$S = \frac{k}{N^*} \log W^*(\overline{N}_1^*, \overline{N}_2^*, \ldots). \tag{99}$$

We are then led to Eq. (96) in a few steps, if we invoke Eq. (68), the Stirling formula, and the condition $\sum \overline{N}_j^* = N^*$; with their aid Eq. (99) transforms into

$$\frac{N^*}{k} S = N^* \log N^* - N^* - \sum (\overline{N}_j^* \log \overline{N}_j^* - \overline{N}_j^*)$$

$$= N^* \log N^* - \sum \overline{N}_j^* \log \overline{N}_j^*$$

$$= \sum (\overline{N}_j^* \log N^* - \overline{N}_j^* \log \overline{N}_j^*) = -\sum \overline{N}_j^* \log \frac{\overline{N}_j^*}{N^*},$$

---

*By this we mean that if two thermodynamic systems A and B at the same temperature are combined to form a compound system AB, then $S_{AB} = S_A + S_B$ must hold.

or, since $P_j = \overline{N}_j^*/N^*$, into $S = -k \sum P_j \log P_j$. And this is precisely the formula (96) with $C = 0$.

We return to our main argument concerning the relation between Z and F. The formulation of this connection lies now within easy reach. By Eqs. (88), (89), (95), and (96),

$$TS = -kT \sum P_j \log P_j = -kT \sum P_j(-\log Z - \beta E_j)$$
$$= kT \log Z + \sum P_j E_j = kT \log Z + U.$$

Consequently, as $F = U - TS$, the desired result is:

$$\boxed{F = -kT \log Z}. \tag{100}$$

Equation (100) represents the most fundamental formula for a closed isothermal system. With its aid, all equilibrium thermodynamic properties of such a system can be computed as soon as the function $Z = Z(T,V,N)$ is given. Indeed, it follows from the thermodynamic equation

$$dF = -SdT - pdV + \mu dN, \tag{101}$$

μ being the chemical potential per molecule, that

$$S = -\left(\frac{\partial F}{\partial T}\right)_{V,N} = k \log Z + kT\left(\frac{\partial \log Z}{\partial T}\right)_{V,N}, \tag{102}$$

$$p = -\left(\frac{\partial F}{\partial V}\right)_{N,T} = kT\left(\frac{\partial \log Z}{\partial V}\right)_{N,T}, \tag{103}$$

$$\mu = \left(\frac{\partial F}{\partial N}\right)_{T,V} = -kT\left(\frac{\partial \log Z}{\partial N}\right)_{T,V}, \tag{104}$$

$$U = F + TS = kT^2\left(\frac{\partial \log Z}{\partial T}\right)_{V,N}. \tag{105}$$

It remains lastly to be proved that the distributions differing from the average distribution (88) can be neglected, as we have supposed all along. For this purpose, we calculate the mean square deviation σ_k^2 of the variable N_k^*. The mean square deviation σ_x^2 of any variable x, with average value $\bar{x}$, is defined by

$$\sigma_x^2 = \overline{(x - \bar{x})^2} = \overline{(x^2 - 2x\bar{x} + \bar{x}^2)} = \overline{x^2} - 2\bar{x}\bar{x} + \bar{x}^2 = \overline{x^2} - \bar{x}^2. \tag{106}$$

To compute

$$\sigma_k^2 = \overline{N_k^{*2}} - \overline{N_k^*}^2, \tag{107}$$

one then needs to know, not only $\overline{N_k^*}$, but also $\overline{N_k^{*2}}$. The latter quantity is, per definition, in the notation of Eq. (73),

$$\overline{N_k^{*2}} = \sum N_k^{*2} P^*(N_1^*, N_2^*, \ldots). \tag{108}$$

Hence, by analogy with Eq. (79),

$$\Omega^*(E^*,N^*)\overline{N_k^{*2}} = N^* \sum{}' (N_k^{*'} + 1) \frac{N^{*'}!}{N_1^{*'}! N_2^{*'}! \ldots}$$

$$= N^* \sum{}' N_k^{*'} \frac{N^{*'}!}{N_1^{*'}! N_2^{*'}! \ldots} + N^*\Omega^*(E^* - E_k, N^* - 1). \tag{109}$$

We may transform the first term on the far right-hand side of Eq. (109) by introducing a set of twice primed numbers:

$$N^{*''} = N^{*'} - 1, \qquad N_k^{*''} = N_k^{*'} - 1, \qquad N_j^{*''} = N_j^{*'} \qquad (j \neq k). \tag{110}$$

Using these quantities, one can write the term in question as

$$N^* N^{*'} \sum{}'' \frac{N^{*''}!}{N_1^{*''}! N_2^{*''}! \ldots} = N^*(N^* - 1)\Omega^*(E^* - 2E_k, N^* - 2),$$

where the double prime affixed to the summation sign indicates that the summation is to be extended over all values of $N_1^{*''}, N_2^{*''}, \ldots$ fulfilling the conditions

$$\sum N_j^{*''} = N^* - 2 \tag{111}$$

and

$$\sum N_j^{*''}E_j = E^* - 2E_k. \tag{112}$$

Eq. (109) thus reduces to

$$\Omega^*(E^*,N^*)\overline{N_k^{*2}} = N^*\Omega^*(E^* - E_k, N^* - 1)$$
$$+ N^*(N^* - 1)\Omega^*(E^* - 2E_k, N^* - 2). \tag{113}$$

The first term appearing on the right-hand side of Eq. (113) equals $\overline{N_k^*}\Omega^*(E^*,N^*)$, by Eq. (80). To discover the meaning of the second term, we put down the Taylor expansion

$$\log \Omega^*(E^* - 2E_k, N^* - 2) = \log \Omega^*(E^*,N^*) - 2\beta E_k - 2a. \tag{114}$$

The quantities a and β employed here are defined as in Eqs. (82) and (83), and the series has been broken off after the first-order terms, since $E^* \gg E_k$ and $N^* \gg 1$. Equation (114) implies that the second term on the right-hand side of Eq. (113) is identical with

$$N^*(N^* - 1)\Omega^*(E^*,N^*)e^{-(2\beta E_k + 2a)} \approx \Omega^*(E^*,N^*)N^{*2}e^{-2(\beta E_k + a)},$$

or, by Eq. (84), with $\Omega^*(E^*,N^*)\overline{N}_k^{*2}$. Substitution of the last result into Eq. (113), divided by $\Omega^*(E^*,N^*)$, gives $\overline{N_k^{*2}} = \overline{N}_k^* + \overline{N}_k^{*2}$ or, by Eq. (107),

$$\sigma_k^2 = \overline{N}_k^*; \tag{115}$$

accordingly, the so-called relative deviation of N_k^* becomes

$$\frac{\sigma_k}{\overline{N}_k^*} = \overline{N}_k^{*-1/2}. \tag{116}$$

The right-hand side of Eq. (116) tends to zero when N^* tends to infinity, as the number of available system-states is finite. It is in this sense that N_k^* can be assumed nearly always to have the value $\overline{N}_k^*$ for all system-states k. To appreciate more clearly the implications of Eq. (116), we scrutinize the behavior of the function $P^*(N_1^*, N_2^*, \ldots)$, providing the relative frequency of the distribution stated by its arguments, in the neighborhood of the point $(\overline{N}_1^*, \overline{N}_2^*, \ldots)$ in the space of the N_j^*.

We first establish that P^* has an extremum, denoted briefly by $\overline{P}^*$, at the point $(\overline{N}_1^*, \overline{N}_2^*, \ldots)$. Since

$$\log P^* = N^* \log N^* - \sum N_j^* \log N_j^* - \log \Omega^*, \tag{117}$$

by Eqs. (68) and (72), and as $\sum dN_j^* = 0$, the first differential of $\log P^*$ becomes $d \log P^* = - \sum dN_j^* \log N_j^*$. If one substitutes for N_j^* from (85) and observes the conditions $\sum dN_j^* = 0$ and $\sum E_j dN_j^* = 0$, the foregoing result reduces to

$$d \log P^* = - \sum dN_j^*(\log N^* - \log Z - \beta E_j) = 0. \tag{118}$$

Hence, an extremum of P^* indeed occurs at the mentioned point.

That this extremum is a maximum, is seen from the negative value of the second differential of $\log P^*$ defined by Eq. (117):

$$d^2 \log P^* = \sum_j \sum_k \frac{\partial^2 \log P^*}{\partial N_j^* \partial N_k^*} dN_j^* dN_k^*$$

$$= - \sum_j \frac{\partial}{\partial N_j^*} (\log N_j^* + 1) dN_j^* dN_j^* = - \sum_j \frac{(dN_j^*)^2}{N_j^*} \tag{119}$$

It follows from Eqs. (118) and (119) that, in the neighborhood of the point $(\overline{N}_1^*, \overline{N}_2^*, \ldots)$,

$$\log \frac{P^*}{\overline{P}^*} = \log P^* - \log \overline{P}^* \approx d \log P^* + \tfrac{1}{2} d^2 \log P^*$$

$$= -\frac{1}{2} \sum_j \frac{(dN_j^*)^2}{\overline{N}_j^*}, \tag{120}$$

that is,

$$P^* = \bar{P}^* \exp -\frac{1}{2} \sum_j \left[d\left(\frac{N_j^*}{\bar{N}_j^*}\right) \right]^2 \bar{N}_j^*. \tag{121}$$

This means that, even for very small values of $d(N_j^*/\bar{N}_j^*)$, P^* will be virtually zero, provided N^* is sufficiently large. We infer that P^* displays an extremely sharp maximum at the point $(1, 1, \ldots)$ in the space of the $N_j^*/\bar{N}_j^*$, corresponding to the point $(\bar{N}_1^*, \bar{N}_2^*, \ldots)$ in the space of the N_j^*; the sharpness of this maximum increases indefinitely when N^* tends to infinity.

2–11. Quantum-Mechanical Grand Canonical Ensemble

The present chapter, treating the general principles of statistical thermodynamics, is brought to a conclusion with an analytical examination of the third kind of thermophysical system mentioned at the beginning of Section 2–8. We have in mind an open isothermal system of unvarying temperature T, volume V, and chemical potential μ; it is assumed for simplicity that the system contains only one chemical component.

In practice one can easily keep V at a fixed value by enclosing the system in a container with immovable walls. If these walls are permeable to molecules as well as to heat, one may furthermore ensure the constancy of T and μ by immersing the confined system in a reservoir of heat and matter, constituted of the same type of molecules as the given system and exhibiting the prescribed values of T and μ. Under these conditions, the system exchanges energy and matter with the reservoir, so that both the energy E and the number of molecules N of the system will be subject to fluctuations about their average values $\bar{E}$ and $\bar{N}$. For contrast, we recall that a closed system shows a constant value of N, and that E and N remain fixed in time for an isolated system.

The virtual systems, composing the ensemble representative of our open isothermal system, should each contain the same molecular species as the actual system and duplicate it with respect to its thermodynamic state (T, V, μ) and environment. These requirements are theoretically met in the following manner. We suppose that the members of the ensemble, again joined to form a lattice, are individually enclosed within walls similar to those of the experimental system. Thus each system has a volume V, and is surrounded by walls across which migration of molecules as well as heat can take place. The ensemble so constructed is first embedded in a huge reservoir of heat and matter, characterized by the temperature T and the chemical potential μ, and left undisturbed until equilibrium has been established. Subsequently, the ensemble is removed from the reservoir and completely isolated from its environment. Any system belonging to an ensemble of N^* members will then be permanently maintained at constant T and μ by the heat and matter reservoir made up of the remaining $N^* - 1$ systems. We have, moreover, with aid of the above imaginary procedure, converted our ensemble into a huge isolated system, named a supersystem as before. It is to this supersystem that we shall devote our immediate attention.

Because of the similarity between the supersystem here defined and that dealt with in the previous section, our reasoning will closely resemble our earlier arguments. The distinctive feature of the supersystem under consideration is that the walls between its systems are penetrable to matter. This fact somewhat complicates the required mathematical analysis as compared with the computations in Section 2–10. The main complication stems from the following circumstance: the Hamiltonian function and consequently the energy eigenstates of a system depend upon the number of molecules N involved. This means that we have to consider, instead of the single row (43) of energy eigenvalues E_j, the two-dimensional array

$$\left.\begin{array}{l} E_1(0),\ E_2(0),\ \ldots \\ E_1(1),\ E_2(1),\ \ldots \\ \cdot\quad\cdot\quad\cdot\quad\cdot\quad\cdot\quad\cdot \\ E_1(n^*),\ E_2(n^*),\ \ldots \end{array}\right\} \tag{122}$$

of nondegenerate energy eigenvalues. The rows of scheme (122) with the general element $E_j(N)$ correspond to $N = 0, 1, 2, \ldots, n^*$, respectively, where n^* signifies the total number of molecules in the supersystem.

The set of energy eigenstates accessible to a single system can be put into one-to-one correspondence with the eigenvalues in (122). Accordingly, for the sake of brevity we shall refer simply to the "state $E_j(N)$." The occupation number of the state $E_j(N)$ will be denoted by $N_j^*(N)$. In other words, $N_j^*(N)$ systems contain N molecules and are in the state $E_j(N)$. We define lastly a quantum-mechanical distribution, as before, by any set of values of the occupation numbers $N_j^*(N)$ (all j,N).

The average distribution is calculated by a method analogous to the one pursued in Section 2–10. We observe once more that the quantum states of the isolated supersystem are equiprobable. However, it should be noticed that the acceptable states of the supersystem must now satisfy a condition over and above Eqs. (69) and (70). This restriction asserts that, independent of the variations of N for individual systems, the sum of the N's extended over all systems of the supersystem must always equal the constant number n^*.

Thus, we obtain in toto the following set of restrictions:

$$\sum_{j} \sum_{N} N_{j}^{*}(N) = N^{*}, \tag{123}$$

$$\sum_{j} \sum_{N} N_{j}^{*}(N)E_{j}(N) = E^{*}, \tag{124}$$

$$\sum_{j} \sum_{N} N_{j}^{*}(N)N = n^{*}, \tag{125}$$

where E^{*} is again the constant energy of the supersystem.

The appearance of the additional restriction (125) causes the number of physically allowed quantum states of the supersystem, Ω^{*}, defined as in Eq. (71), to be a function of n^{*}, as well as of E^{*} and N^{*}; that is, $\Omega^{*} = \Omega^{*}(E^{*},N^{*},n^{*})$. Furthermore, the analogues of Eqs. (77) and (78) have to be supplemented by a third relation, viz.,

$$\sum_{j} \sum_{N} N_{j}^{*\prime}(N)N = N_{1}^{*}(0) + N_{2}^{*}(0) + \cdots + [N_{k}^{*}(N) - 1]N + \cdots$$
$$= n^{*} - N. \tag{126}$$

The analogue of Eq. (81) should consequently be amended by the addition of a term, to read:

$$\log \frac{\overline{N}_{k}^{*}(N)}{N^{*}} = - \frac{\partial \log \Omega^{*}}{\partial E^{*}} E_{k} - \frac{\partial \log \Omega^{*}}{\partial N^{*}} - \frac{\partial \log \Omega^{*}}{\partial n^{*}} N. \tag{127}$$

If we employ the notations

$$a = \left(\frac{\partial \log \Omega^{*}}{\partial N^{*}} \right)_{n^{*},E^{*}}, \tag{128}$$

$$\beta = \left(\frac{\partial \log \Omega^{*}}{\partial E^{*}} \right)_{N^{*},n^{*}}, \tag{129}$$

$$\alpha = \left(\frac{\partial \log \Omega^{*}}{\partial n^{*}} \right)_{E^{*},N^{*}}, \tag{130}$$

the result (127) can briefly be restated as

$$\overline{N}_{k}^{*}(N) = N^{*}e^{-a-\beta E_{k}(N)-\alpha N}. \tag{131}$$

One may immediately eliminate the constant a of the distribution (131) by invoking the condition $\sum \sum \overline{N}_{j}^{*}(N) = N^{*}$, which gives

$$\exp a = \sum \sum \exp \left[-\beta E_{j}(N) - \alpha N \right].$$

On insertion of this value of $\exp a$ into Eq. (131), we obtain

$$\frac{\overline{N}_{k}^{*}(N)}{N^{*}} = \frac{e^{-\beta E_{k}(N)-\alpha N}}{\displaystyle\sum_{j} \sum_{N} e^{-\beta E_{j}(N)-\alpha N}}. \tag{132}$$

Now we could show, as we did for a closed system, that the relative deviations of the occupation numbers $N_k^*(N)$ from their average values (132) tend to zero when N^* grows indefinitely. One is therefore permitted to set $N_k^*(N) = \overline{N}_k^*(N)$ (all k), so that, given the definitions

$$P_k(N) = \frac{N_k^*(N)}{N^*} \tag{133}$$

and

$$\mathfrak{Z} = \sum_j \sum_N e^{-\beta E_j(N) - \alpha N}, \tag{134}$$

Eq. (132) can be written concisely as

$$P_k(N) = \mathfrak{Z}^{-1} e^{-\beta E_k(N) - \alpha N}. \tag{135}$$

By Eq. (133), $P_k(N)$ represents the probability that a system, chosen at random from our ensemble, will contain N molecules and occupy the state $E_k(N)$. An ensemble whose systems are distributed over quantum states in accordance with the law (135) is called a quantum-mechanical *grand canonical ensemble*. Such an ensemble, as our analysis has shown, is representative of an open thermophysical system at equilibrium with prescribed T, V, and μ.

Gibbs (1902)—who, of course, employed only classical ideas—introduced the adjectives *petit* and *grand* to distinguish ensembles, comprised of systems differing in phase alone, from ensembles whose systems differ moreover in the number of particles they contain. Should one make permanent an instantaneous distribution of particles over systems in a grand ensemble by abruptly inhibiting any migration of particles between systems, one would obtain a set of petit ensembles, each having a fixed value of N. A grand ensemble is thus, in a sense, composed of petit ensembles, a fact supplying the rationale for the term "grand ensemble." The intimate connection between the grand canonical and the (petit) canonical ensembles is further demonstrated by an examination of the function $\mathfrak{Z}$, which is defined by Eq. (134) and known as the *grand partition function* of a system. If we anticipate the results $\beta = 1/kT$ and $\alpha = -\mu/kT$ [see Eqs. (142) and (143)], and bear in mind that $E_j = E_j(V,N)$, then it becomes evident that $\mathfrak{Z}$ is a function of T, V, μ—that is, $\mathfrak{Z} = \mathfrak{Z}(T,V,\mu)$. Furthermore, Eq. (134) can be reformulated to read:

$$\mathfrak{Z}(T,V,\mu) = \sum_N e^{-\alpha N} \sum_j e^{-\beta E_j(N)} = \sum_N Z(T,V,N) e^{-\alpha N}, \tag{136}$$

where $Z(T,V,N)$ is the (canonical) partition function appropriate to a physical system with parameters T, V, N.

We next identify the constants β and α of the distribution law (135) and correlate generally statistical with thermodynamic quantities. It is convenient, as in Section 2–10, to start from the formula for the average internal energy of our system, $U = \bar{E}$, which is given by

$$U = \sum_j \sum_N P_j(N)E_j(N); \qquad (137)$$

this equation is true by virtue of both $U = E^*/N^*$ and Eq. (124) read in conjunction with Eq. (133), or it follows from the postulate $\bar{E} = \langle E \rangle$ propounded earlier.

According to Eq. (137), the differential of U is

$$dU = \sum_j \sum_N [E_j(N)dP_j(N) + P_j(N)dE_j(N)]. \qquad (138)$$

By a straightforward extension of the argument connecting Eq. (90) with Eq. (93), to a reversible process in which particles are allowed to leave and enter a system, one is able to proceed from Eq. (138) to

$$dU = \beta^{-1}\left\{-d\left[\sum\sum P_j(N) \log P_j(N)\right] - \alpha d\bar{N}\right\} - p dV; \qquad (139)$$

here $\bar{N}$ stands for the average number of molecules per system, which, owing to both $\bar{N} = n^*/N^*$ and Eq. (125) together with Eq. (133), or from the postulate $\bar{N} = \langle N \rangle$, is given by

$$\bar{N} = \sum_j \sum_N P_j(N)N. \qquad (140)$$

Equation (139) may be compared with the fundamental thermodynamic equation for an open system,

$$dU = TdS - pdV + \mu d\bar{N}. \qquad (141)$$

Agreement between Eqs. (139) and (141) is established if one posits:

$$\beta = \frac{1}{kT}, \qquad (142)$$

$$\boxed{\alpha = -\frac{\mu}{kT}}, \qquad (143)$$

and

$$S = -k \sum_j \sum_N P_j(N) \log P_j(N), \qquad (144)$$

k being Boltzmann's constant in each case. The reader will not fail to note that the expression (144) for S is analogous to the formulas (42) and (96), while Eq. (142) is the same as Eq. (95).

We finally make a vital observation of physical interest, namely, that knowledge of the quantity $\mathfrak{Z}$ as a function of the parameters T, V, μ is equivalent to a complete thermodynamic description of the open isothermal system at equilibrium.

To justify this statement, we should first point out that, by reason of Eqs. (123), (133), (135), (142), (143), and (144),

$$
\begin{aligned}
TS &= -kT \sum \sum P_j(N)[-\log \mathfrak{Z} - \beta E_j(N) - \alpha N] \\
&= kT \log \mathfrak{Z} + U - \mu \bar{N}.
\end{aligned}
$$

From this equation, remembering the definition of the Gibbs free energy, $\mu \bar{N} = U - TS + pV$, one finds that

$$
\boxed{pV = kT \log \mathfrak{Z}}. \tag{145}
$$

It should further be realized that pV is a characteristic function for the parameters T, V, μ. For, it follows from Eq. (141) and the definition preceding Eq. (145) that

$$
\begin{aligned}
\mu d\bar{N} + \bar{N}d\mu &= dU - TdS - SdT + d(pV) \\
&= TdS - pdV + \mu d\bar{N} - TdS - SdT + d(pV),
\end{aligned}
$$

that is,

$$
d(pV) = SdT + pdV + \bar{N}d\mu. \tag{146}
$$

Combination of Eqs. (145) and (146) then yields the results:

$$
S = \left(\frac{\partial pV}{\partial T}\right)_{V,\mu} = k \log \mathfrak{Z} + kT\left(\frac{\partial \log \mathfrak{Z}}{\partial T}\right)_{V,\mu}, \tag{147}
$$

$$
p = \left(\frac{\partial pV}{\partial V}\right)_{\mu,T} = kT\left(\frac{\partial \log \mathfrak{Z}}{\partial V}\right)_{\mu,T} = \frac{kT}{V} \log \mathfrak{Z}, \tag{148}
$$

$$
\bar{N} = \left(\frac{\partial pV}{\partial \mu}\right)_{T,V} = kT\left(\frac{\partial \log \mathfrak{Z}}{\partial \mu}\right)_{T,V}, \tag{149}
$$

where the last step in Eq. (148) derives from Eq. (145).

The foregoing set of equations show that, once $\mathfrak{Z}$ is given as a function of T, V, μ, all the remaining thermostatic properties can be found by differentiation, addition or subtraction. Hence, the role of $\mathfrak{Z}(T,V,\mu)$ in relation to an open isothermal system is similar to that of $Z(T,V,N)$ for a closed isothermal system and $\Phi(E,V,N)$ for an isolated system.

REFERENCES

BECKER, R. *Theorie der Wärme*. Berlin: Springer, 1961.

BIRKHOFF, G. D. *Proc. Nat. Acad. Sci. (U.S.A.)*, **17**, 650, 656 (1931).

BIRKHOFF, G. D., and B. O. KOOPMAN. *Proc. Nat. Acad. Sci. (U.S.A.)*, **18**, 279 (1932).

DE BOER, J., and G. E. UHLENBECK (ed.). *Studies in Statistical Mechanics*. Vol. I. Amsterdam: North-Holland, 1962.

BOLTZMANN, L. *Sitz.-Ber. Akad. Wiss. (Wien)*, **58**, 517 (1868).

BOLTZMANN, L. *Sitz.-Ber. Akad. Wiss. (Wien)*, **63**, 397 (1871).

BOLTZMANN, L. *Sitz.-Ber. Akad. Wiss. (Wien)*, **63**, 712 (1871).

BOLTZMANN, L. *Sitz.-Ber. Akad. Wiss. (Wien)*, **66**, 275 (1872).

BOLTZMANN, L. *Sitz.-Ber. Akad. Wiss. (Wien)*, **76**, 373 (1877).

BOLTZMANN, L. *Lectures on Gas Theory*. Translation of *Vorlesungen über Gastheorie* (1896/1898) by S. G. Brush. Berkeley: U. of California P., 1964.

BORN, M. *Natural Philosophy of Cause and Chance*. London: Oxford U.P., 1949.

CARATHÉODORY, C. *Sitz.-Ber. Akad. Wiss. (Berlin) Math.-phys. Kl.*, 580 (1919).

COHEN, E. G. D. (ed.). *Fundamental Problems in Statistical Mechanics*. Amsterdam: North-Holland, 1961.

DARWIN, C. S., and R. H. FOWLER. *Phil. Mag.*, **44**, 450, 823 (1922).

EHRENFEST, P. and T. EHRENFEST. *The Conceptual Foundations of the Statistical Approach in Mechanics*. Translation of article in *Encykl. Math. Wiss.* (1912) by M. J. Moravcsik. Ithaca: Cornell U.P., 1959.

FOWLER, R., and E. A. GUGGENHEIM. *Statistical Thermodynamics*. New York: Cambridge U.P., 1949.

FRENKEL, J. I. *Statistische Physik*. Translated from the Russian by H. Jancke. Berlin: Akademie-Verlag, 1957.

GIBBS, J. W. *Elementary Principles in Statistical Mechanics*. 1902; New York: Dover, 1960.

TER HAAR, D. *Elements of Statistical Mechanics*. New York: Rinehart, 1954.

KHINCHIN, A. I. *Mathematical Foundations of Statistical Mechanics*. Translated from the Russian by G. Gamow. New York: Dover, 1949.

LANDSBERG, P. T. *Thermodynamics*. New York: Interscience, 1961.

MAXWELL, J. C. *Phil. Mag.*, **19**, 22 (1860).

MAYER, J. E., and M. G. MAYER. *Statistical Mechanics*. New York: Wiley, 1940.

MÜNSTER, A. *Statistische Thermodynamik*. Berlin: Springer, 1956.

MÜNSTER, A. "Prinzipien der statistischen Mechanik," in *Handbuch der Physik*. Vol. III/2. Berlin: Springer, 1959.

VON NEUMANN, J. *Proc. Nat. Acad. Sci. (U.S.A.)*, **18**, 70, 263 (1932).

PAULI, W. *Festschrift zum 60. Geburtstage A. Sommerfelds*. Leipzig: Hirzel, 1928, p. 30.

PLANCK, M. *Verh. Deutsch. Phys. Ges.*, **2**, 237 (1900).

PLANCK, M. *Ann. Phys.*, **66**, 365 (1921).

PLANCK, M. *Vorlesungen über die Theorie der Wärmestrahlung*. Leipzig: Barth, 1923.

POINCARÉ, H. *Acta Math.*, **13**, 67 (1890).

ROSENFELD, L. *Lectures on Statistical Thermodynamics.* Copenhagen: Nordita, 1960.

RUSHBROOKE, G. S. *Introduction to Statistical Mechanics.* London: Oxford U.P., 1962.

SCHRÖDINGER, E. *Statistical Thermodynamics.* New York: Cambridge U.P., 1952.

TOLMAN, R. C. *The Principles of Statistical Mechanics.* London: Oxford U.P., 1950.

UHLENBECK, G. E., and G. W. FORD. *Lectures in Statistical Mechanics.* Providence, R.I.: American Mathematical Society, 1963.

WILSON, A. H. *Thermodynamics and Statistical Mechanics.* New York: Cambridge U.P., 1960.

3

ASSEMBLIES OF NONINTERACTING
STRUCTURELESS PARTICLES

FROM a strictly theoretical point of view, the formulas derived in the previous chapter for a microcanonical ensemble hold only for isolated physical systems. Similarly, the theories of the canonical and grand canonical ensembles should in principle be invoked solely when closed isothermal and open isothermal systems, respectively, are under discussion. However, mathematical analysis shows that essentially the same equilibrium properties of thermodynamic systems can be obtained on the basis of any one of the aforementioned ensembles. This result is in agreement with the empirical observation that the relations between thermostatic parameters are independent of the nature of the constraints accompanying the state of equilibrium. The insensitivity of thermophysical properties to the type of ensemble appealed to has the following explanation.

Although the energy E of a closed system immersed in a heat reservoir deviates continually from its average value $\bar{E}$, and the number of molecules N in an open system varies about its average value $\bar{N}$, fluctuations in E and N of macroscopic proportions are extremely rare. In fact, they occur so seldom that for most thermodynamic purposes E can be assumed always to have the value $\bar{E}$ and N never to depart from the value $\bar{N}$. Correspondingly, the canonical ensemble goes over into a microcanonical ensemble of energy $\bar{E}$, and the grand canonical ensemble approximates a canonical ensemble characterized by a fixed number of molecules $\bar{N}$.

We may mathematically demonstrate the high improbability of sizable fluctuations about $\bar{E}$ and $\bar{N}$ by calculating the standard deviations σ_E and σ_N

of the parameters E and N. To this end we first differentiate the equation defining the canonical ensemble average $\bar{E}$, viz.,

$$\bar{E} \sum_j e^{-\beta E_j} = \sum_j E_j e^{-\beta E_j}, \tag{1}$$

with respect to T, remembering that $\beta = 1/kT$ and $E_j = E_j(N,V)$. The result is

$$\left(\frac{\partial \bar{E}}{\partial T}\right)_{V,N} \sum e^{-\beta E_j} + \frac{\bar{E}}{kT^2} \sum E_j e^{-\beta E_j} = \frac{1}{kT^2} \sum E_j^2 e^{-\beta E_j},$$

or, on division by $Z = \sum \exp -\beta E_j$,

$$\left(\frac{\partial \bar{E}}{\partial T}\right)_{V,N} + \frac{\bar{E}^2}{kT^2} = \frac{\overline{E^2}}{kT^2}.$$

Thus,

$$\sigma_E^2 = \overline{E^2} - \bar{E}^2 = kT^2 \left(\frac{\partial \bar{E}}{\partial T}\right)_{V,N} = kT^2 C_V, \tag{2}$$

where C_V designates the heat capacity at constant volume of the experimental body. Equation (2) asserts that the relative fluctuation of E about its mean value is given by

$$\frac{\sigma_E}{\bar{E}} = \frac{(kT^2 C_V)^{1/2}}{\bar{E}}. \tag{3}$$

To estimate the order of magnitude of the quantity (3), we note that $C_V \sim Nk$ and $\bar{E} \sim NkT$, by virtue of experiment as well as kinetic theory. Consequently, $\sigma_E/\bar{E} \sim N^{-1/2}$, that is, $\sigma_E/\bar{E} \sim 10^{-10}$ for a system containing 10^{20} molecules. This means that for isothermal systems of thermophysical dimensions the occurrence of energy values other than $\bar{E}$ can practically be ignored, as maintained above.

The fluctuations of N in an open isothermal system may be examined in a similar fashion. In this case one differentiates the equation

$$\bar{N} \sum_N Z(T,V,N)e^{-\alpha N} = \sum_N NZ(T,V,N)e^{-\alpha N}, \tag{4}$$

defining the grand canonical average $\bar{N}$, with respect to the chemical potential μ. Bearing in mind that $\alpha = -\mu/kT$, one gets

$$\left(\frac{\partial \bar{N}}{\partial \mu}\right)_{T,V} \sum Z e^{-\alpha N} + \frac{\bar{N}}{kT} \sum NZ e^{-\alpha N} = \frac{1}{kT} \sum N^2 Z e^{-\alpha N}.$$

On division by $\mathfrak{Z} = \sum Z e^{-\alpha N}$ and multiplication by kT, this equation becomes

$$kT\left(\frac{\partial \bar{N}}{\partial \mu}\right)_{T,V} + \bar{N}^2 = \overline{N^2}.$$

This means that the standard deviation of the variable N is given by

$$\sigma_N^2 = \overline{N^2} - \overline{N}^2 = kT\left(\frac{\partial \overline{N}}{\partial \mu}\right)_{T,V}. \tag{5}$$

The derivative on the right-hand side of Eq. (5) can be restated in terms of better known measurable quantities. The familiar equation $dG = -SdT + Vdp + \mu d\overline{N}$ taken together with $dG = d\mu\overline{N} = \mu d\overline{N} + \overline{N}d\mu$, valid for a one-component system, furnishes $\overline{N}d\mu = -SdT + Vdp$. Thus, if both μ and p are regarded to be functions of T and the density $\overline{N}/V$, one gets

$$\left(\frac{\partial \mu}{\partial(\overline{N}/V)}\right)_T = \frac{V}{\overline{N}}\left(\frac{\partial p}{\partial(\overline{N}/V)}\right)_T,$$

or

$$V\left(\frac{\partial \mu}{\partial \overline{N}}\right)_{T,V} = -\frac{V^3}{\overline{N}^2}\left(\frac{\partial p}{\partial V}\right)_{T,N};$$

that is,

$$\left(\frac{\partial \overline{N}}{\partial \mu}\right)_{T,V} = -\frac{\overline{N}^2}{V^2}\left(\frac{\partial V}{\partial p}\right)_{T,N} = \left(\frac{\overline{N}^2}{V}\right)\kappa, \tag{6}$$

where κ is the isothermal compressibility. Substitution of Eq. (6) into Eq. (5) yields

$$\frac{\sigma_N}{\overline{N}} = \left(\frac{\kappa kT}{V}\right)^{1/2}. \tag{7}$$

For an ideal gas, $\kappa = 1/p$ and $pV = \overline{N}kT$, so that $\sigma_N/\overline{N} = \overline{N}^{-1/2}$. The fluctuations in N are therefore completely negligible; and this conclusion holds for other systems as well. Notable exceptions occur when two phases coexist and when a critical point is realized. Then, $1/\kappa = 0$ and $\sigma_N \sim \overline{N}$, so that fluctuations can no longer be neglected. In fact, departures of N from its mean value at a critical point are responsible for the so-called critical opalescence of a fluid. Apart from such special instances, however, one is justified in assuming that $N = \overline{N}$ always obtains and that, as a consequence, the open physical system may be represented by a canonical rather than a grand canonical ensemble.

In summary: for a practical study of thermophysical systems in equilibrium one can, on the whole, employ any one of the microcanonical, canonical, and grand canonical ensembles. One is free to choose between them solely on the grounds of mathematical convenience. Having established this point, we shall devote the present chapter and the next to an examination of various systems warranting attention of physicists and chemists.

3–1. The Quantum-Mechanical Ideal Gas

The results of Chapter 2 are most easily applied to particles which do not interact with one another, that is, to an ideal gas. The convenient tractability of such a system stems from the fact that similar noninteracting particles can be conceived of as occupying the eigenstates of a single particle; and the energy eigenstates of the gas may then be specified in terms of the number of particles present in each single-particle quantum state. To be more explicit, let the energy eigenstates of an individual particle be numbered $1, 2, \ldots,$ $j, \ldots,$ and let $\varepsilon_1, \varepsilon_2, \ldots, \varepsilon_j, \ldots,$ with $\varepsilon_1 = 0$ and $\varepsilon_j \geqslant \varepsilon_{j-1}$, be the corresponding energy eigenvalues, or energy levels, whose occupation numbers are $n_1, n_2, \ldots, n_j, \ldots.$ One eigenstate of the gas is consequently associated with each set of values of the variables $n_1, n_2, \ldots, n_j, \ldots.$ Because of the indistinguishability of like particles, no new physical situation arises when any two particles are interchanged; so that only one quantum state of the gas exists for a given set of values $n_1, n_2, \ldots, n_j, \ldots.$

Now suppose that an ideal gas has an energy E and contains N particles, then it is obvious that

$$N = \sum_j n_j \tag{8}$$

and

$$E = \sum_j n_j \varepsilon_j. \tag{9}$$

If the particles constituting the gas are bosons, Eqs. (8) and (9) represent the sole restrictions on the n_j. For fermions, however, it is found empirically that a further restriction applies: each n_j can have no value other than zero or unity. Hence two fermions are forbidden ever to occupy the same single-particle state; this proposition is the celebrated *Pauli exclusion principle* (1925). We thus have

$$n_j = 0, 1, 2, \ldots \quad \text{for bosons} \tag{10b}$$

and

$$n_j = 0, 1 \quad \text{for fermions.} \tag{10f}$$

Corresponding to this distinction it is necessary to work with two different kinds of statistics, to wit, Bose-Einstein (*BE*) statistics (1924) for a gas consisting of bosons, and Fermi-Dirac (*FD*) statistics (1926) for a fermion gas.

In order to study an ideal gas, one could invoke any one of the ensembles known to us. Since the use of either the microcanonical or the canonical ensemble is complicated by the condition $n_j = N$, a constant, we prefer to employ the grand canonical ensemble, for which N is not a constant.

The starting point of our considerations is the familiar formula

$$P(E,N) = \mathfrak{Z}^{-1}e^{-\beta E - \alpha N}, \tag{11}$$

with

$$\mathfrak{Z} = \sum_E \sum_N e^{-\beta E - \alpha N}, \tag{12}$$

giving the probability that a system will have the energy E and comprise N particles. By virtue of Eqs. (8), (9), and (12), Eq. (11) can be rewritten as

$$P(E,N) = \prod_j z_j^{-1}e^{-(\beta \varepsilon_j + \alpha)n_j}, \tag{13}$$

with

$$z_j = \sum_{n_j} e^{-(\beta \varepsilon_j + \alpha)n_j}. \tag{14}$$

The probability that n_j particles will occupy the single-particle state j therefore becomes

$$p(n_j) = z_j^{-1}e^{-(\beta \varepsilon_j + \alpha)n_j}. \tag{15}$$

The quantity $z_j = z_j(\varepsilon_j, \beta, \alpha)$ can easily be expressed as a function of the indicated parameters; by Eqs. (10b), (10f), and (14) one has

$$z_j = 1 + e^{-(\beta \varepsilon_j + \alpha)} + e^{-2(\beta \varepsilon_j + \alpha)} + \cdots = (1 - e^{-\beta \varepsilon_j - \alpha})^{-1} \tag{16b}$$

and

$$z_j = 1 + e^{-\beta \varepsilon_j - \alpha} \tag{16f}$$

for bosons and fermions, respectively.

In our further arguments the mean value of the occupation number n_j will frequently be utilized. This quantity may forthwith be calculated. From Eq. (15) we obtain:

$$\bar{n}_j = \sum_{n_j} p(n_j)n_j = z_j^{-1}\sum n_j e^{-(\beta \varepsilon_j + \alpha)n_j} = -z_j^{-1}\frac{\partial z_j}{\partial \alpha} = -\frac{\partial \log z_j}{\partial \alpha}, \tag{17}$$

and insertion of Eqs. (16b) and (16f) in Eq. (17) yields, after some simplification,

$$\boxed{\bar{n}_j = (e^{\beta \varepsilon_j + \alpha} \mp 1)^{-1}} \cdot \left(\alpha = -\frac{\mu}{kT}\right) \tag{18b} \tag{18f}$$

These are the *Bose-Einstein* and *Fermi-Dirac distribution laws*, respectively.

The extent to which the occupation number n_j fluctuates about its mean value (18b) or (18f) is found on differentiation of the formula

$$\bar{n}_j \sum e^{-(\beta \varepsilon_j + \alpha)n_j} = \sum n_j e^{-(\beta \varepsilon_j + \alpha)n_j} \tag{19}$$

with respect to α. One gets

$$\frac{\partial \bar{n}_j}{\partial \alpha} z_j - \bar{n}_j \sum n_j e^{-(\beta \varepsilon_j + \alpha) n_j} \overset{.}{=} - \sum n_j^2 e^{-(\beta \varepsilon_j + \alpha) n_j},$$

that is,

$$\frac{\partial \bar{n}_j}{\partial \alpha} - \bar{n}_j^2 = -\overline{n_j^2};$$

this means that the relative fluctuation of n_j is given by

$$\frac{\overline{n_j^2} - \bar{n}_j^2}{\bar{n}_j^2} = -\frac{\partial \bar{n}_j / \partial \alpha}{\bar{n}_j^2}$$

$$= e^{\beta \varepsilon_j + \alpha} = \frac{1}{\bar{n}_j} \pm 1, \qquad (20b) \ (20f)$$

where Eqs. (18b) and (18f) have been invoked in the last two steps.

Equations (18b) and (18f) predict some important differences between boson and fermion gases, which we now briefly study.

Since $\varepsilon_1 = 0$, Eq. (18b) asserts that $\bar{n}_1 = (\exp \alpha - 1)^{-1}$ and, as $\bar{n}_1 > 0$, it follows that $\alpha > 0$. One knows furthermore that $\varepsilon_j \geqslant 0$. Hence Eq. (15) shows that, for a boson gas, the most probable value of the occupation number n_j is given by $\hat{n}_j = 0$.

Equation (18f), on the other hand, maintains that $\bar{n}_1 = (\exp \alpha + 1)^{-1}$. Thus, for fermions α can be negative as well as positive. Let us assume that $\alpha < 0$. Then, by Eq. (15), the value of n_j most likely to occur is zero or unity, depending on whether $\beta \varepsilon_j + \alpha$ is positive or negative. If one recalls that $\alpha / \beta = -\mu$, this means that $\hat{n}_j = 0$ for $\varepsilon_j > \mu$ and $\hat{n}_j = 1$ for $\varepsilon_j < \mu$. Because $\beta \varepsilon_j + \alpha = (1/kT)(\varepsilon_j - \mu)$, one also notices that $\exp(\beta \varepsilon_j + \alpha) \approx 0$ and therefore, by Eq. (18f), that $\bar{n}_j \approx 1$ for all states j whose energies are less than μ by an amount at least of the order $10 \ kT$. And in the limit when T tends to zero, $\bar{n}_j$ becomes unity for all states $\varepsilon_j < \mu$. On substitution of $\bar{n}_j = 1$, the far right-hand side of Eq. (20f) vanishes, so that at $T \approx 0$ fluctuations in the n_j about their mean values can be ignored. This fact explains why, at $T \approx 0$, $\bar{n}_j \approx \hat{n}_j = 1$.

To continue our study of the quantum-mechanical ideal gas, we observe that the grand partition function $\mathfrak{Z}$ of the system in question is, by virtue of Eqs. (12), (14), (16b), and (16f), simply given by

$$\mathfrak{Z} = \prod_j z_j$$

$$= \prod_j (1 \mp e^{-\beta \varepsilon_j - \alpha})^{\mp 1}. \qquad (21b) \ (21f)$$

These are the pivotal equations of our present inquiry. Indeed, from the discussion in Section 2–11, we know that once the right-hand sides of

Eqs. (21b) and (21f) have been expressed as functions of T, V, μ, all the remaining thermodynamic parameters can be obtained from $\mathfrak{Z}$ or, more directly, from its logarithm

$$\log \mathfrak{Z} = \mp \sum_j \log (1 \mp e^{-\beta \varepsilon_j - \alpha}). \qquad \text{(22b) (22f)}$$

3–2. Dilute Bose-Einstein and Fermi-Dirac Gases

The explicit dependence of $\log \mathfrak{Z}$ on T, V, μ may easily be ascertained for an ideal gas having a sufficiently low density. From the formulas

$$\bar{N} = \sum_j \bar{n}_j$$
$$= \sum_j (e^{\beta \varepsilon_j + \alpha} \mp 1)^{-1} \qquad \text{(23b) (23f)}$$

one sees that a small value of the density $\bar{N}/V$ will be realized if $\exp \alpha \gg 1$, that is, if $\exp -\alpha \ll 1$. When this condition is fulfilled, we are permitted to employ the approximation

$$\log (1 \mp e^{-\beta \varepsilon_j - \alpha}) = \mp e^{-\alpha} e^{-\beta \varepsilon_j}, \qquad \text{(24b) (24f)}$$

which, on insertion in Eqs. (22), yields, for bosons and fermions alike,

$$\log \mathfrak{Z} = e^{-\alpha} Z_1, \qquad \text{(25)}$$

where

$$Z_1 = \sum_j e^{-\beta \varepsilon_j}. \qquad \text{(26)}$$

Consequently, in this approximation there exists no difference between the thermophysical properties of a *BE* gas and those of an *FD* gas with the same Z_1.

Our immediate problem is to calculate the partition function Z_1 for a single particle. To this end, we are required to know the energy eigenstates and the associated energy values ε_j. The latter, according to quantum mechanics, are given by

$$\varepsilon_j = \frac{h^2}{8mL^2} (n_x^2 + n_y^2 + n_z^2), \qquad (n_x, n_y, n_z = 1, 2, 3, \ldots) \qquad \text{(27)}$$

for a particle of mass m that is confined to a box of side-length L; the quantum numbers n_x, n_y, n_z completely identify the corresponding eigenstates in the absence of spin. Substitution of Eq. (27) in Eq. (26) gives, for a spinless particle,

$$Z_1^{1/3} = \sum_{n_x = 1}^{\infty} \exp -\frac{\beta h^2}{8mL^2} n_x^2. \qquad \text{(28)}$$

We do not attempt to evaluate the sum (28) as it stands. Instead we note that in any macroscopic container the spacing of energy levels is extremely small compared with kT—i.e., $h^2/mL^2 \ll kT$, even for very low temperatures and the lightest of particles. (The reader can easily verify, for example, that for electrons at $T = 10°K$ contained in a box with $L = 1$ cm, the quantity $h^2/mL^2 \sim 10^{-11}kT$.) Consequently, the summands of Eq. (28) form very nearly a continuum, and it is therefore permissible to replace the summation by an integration over n_x between the limits 0 and ∞. One then gets, using the formula

$$\int_0^\infty \exp -ax^2 \, dx = \frac{1}{2}\left(\frac{\pi}{a}\right)^{1/2},$$

the following relation in lieu of Eq. (28):

$$Z_1^{1/3} = \int_0^\infty \exp -\left(\frac{\beta h^2}{8mL^2}n_x^2\right) dn_x = \frac{1}{2}\left(\frac{8\pi mL^2}{\beta h^2}\right)^{1/2} = \left(\frac{2\pi mkTL^2}{h^2}\right)^{1/2}. \tag{29}$$

Thus, since $V = L^3$ represents the volume of the box, the partition function is

$$Z_1 = \frac{V}{\Lambda^3}, \tag{30}$$

where

$$\boxed{\Lambda = \frac{h}{(2\pi mkT)^{1/2}}}. \tag{31}$$

The quantity Λ possesses a definite physical meaning, as we shall now demonstrate. According to quantum theory, a wavelength $\lambda = h/p$, the so-called *de Broglie wavelength*, is associated with every particle with linear momentum p; thus, $\lambda = h/(2mE_k)^{1/2}$ in terms of the kinetic energy E_k of the particle. As $E_k = \frac{3}{2}kT$ by classical kinetic theory—valid for the high temperatures and low densities here contemplated—we may also write $\lambda = h/(3mkT)^{1/2}$. It follows that λ differs from Λ only by a constant factor of the order unity.

If the value (30) of Z_1 is substituted in Eq. (25), one obtains

$$\log \mathfrak{Z} = e^{-\alpha}\frac{V}{\Lambda^3} = e^{\mu/kT}Vh^{-3}(2\pi mkT)^{3/2}. \tag{32}$$

Since the right-hand side of Eq. (32) is expressed as a function of T, V, μ, the formulas appearing at the end of the previous chapter may now be applied immediately. We have first, by Eq. (148),

$$p = (kT)^{5/2}h^{-3}(2\pi m)^{3/2}e^{\mu/kT}. \tag{33}$$

Next we have, by Eq. (149) (omitting the average sign),

$$N = (kT)^{3/2} V h^{-3} (2\pi m)^{3/2} e^{\mu/kT}. \tag{34}$$

Finally, Eq. (147) reads

$$S = N\left(\frac{5k}{2} - \frac{\mu}{T}\right). \tag{35}$$

Equation (33) in conjunction with Eq. (34) leads to the relation $pV = NkT$, which is the familiar ideal gas law of classical kinetic theory. Linear combinations of the parameters cited above provide the remaining functions of state. For example, it follows from $\mu N = U - TS + pV$ that

$$U = \mu N + TN\left(\frac{5k}{2} - \frac{\mu}{T}\right) - NkT = \tfrac{3}{2}NkT, \tag{36}$$

an equation likewise familiar from classical theory.

Equation (35) represents the entropy of an ideal gas in terms of the variables T, N, μ. One may eliminate μ in favor of V with the aid of Eq. (34) to transform (35) with $N = N_0$ into the following expression:

$$\boxed{s = R\left(\frac{3}{2}\log T + \log \frac{V}{N_0} + \frac{3}{2}\log \frac{2\pi mk}{h^2} + \frac{5}{2}\right).} \tag{37}$$

This result is the renowned *Sackur-Tetrode formula* (1912–13) for the molar entropy of an ideal gas. Equation (37)—it should be stressed—gives the absolute value of the entropy. Herein lies an important advantage of quantum statistical theory over thermodynamics, which determines entropy only up to an additive constant.

It is worthwhile to examine the reason why quantum statistics recovers the findings of classical kinetic theory such as $pV = NkT$ and $U = \tfrac{3}{2}NkT$. In quantum theory it is possible to assign the position of an atomic particle only within a distance of the order λ. One can nevertheless speak of discrete particles, as is customary in kinetic theory, provided λ^3 is much less than V/N, the average volume per particle. This condition is certainly fulfilled in the derivations of the present section, because very low densities N/V are assumed throughout. To summarize: both *BE* and *FD* gases behave like ideal classical gases when the average distance between neighboring particles is large compared with the de Broglie wavelength belonging to the given temperature, that is, if

$$\left(\frac{V}{N}\right)^{1/3} \gg \lambda = \frac{h}{(3mkT)^{1/2}}. \tag{38}$$

At moderate dilution, deviations from ideal-gas behavior take place; these can be surveyed on carrying the expansion of each logarithmic term in Eqs. (22) one step further than in Eqs. (24). We write

$$\log(1 \mp e^{-\beta \varepsilon_j - \alpha}) = \mp e^{-\alpha} e^{-\beta \varepsilon_j} - \tfrac{1}{2} e^{-2\alpha} e^{-2\beta \varepsilon_j}. \qquad \text{(39b) (39f)}$$

Insertion of Eqs. (39) in Eqs. (22) gives

$$\log \mathfrak{Z} = e^{-\alpha} Z_1 \pm \tfrac{1}{2} e^{-2\alpha} \sum_j e^{-2\beta \varepsilon_j}. \qquad \text{(40b) (40f)}$$

Now, $Z_1 = \sum \exp -\beta \varepsilon_j = V(2\pi mkT/h^2)^{3/2}$, by Eqs. (30) and (31); and if one replaces in the foregoing β by 2β, i.e., kT by $\tfrac{1}{2}kT$, one finds that

$$\sum_j e^{-2\beta \varepsilon_j} = V\left(\frac{\pi mkT}{h^2}\right)^{3/2} = V\left(\frac{2\pi mkT}{h^2}\right)^{3/2} 2^{-3/2}. \qquad \text{(41)}$$

Consequently, Eqs. (40) may be stated as

$$\log \mathfrak{Z} = V\left(\frac{2\pi mkT}{h^2}\right)^{3/2} e^{\mu/kT}(1 \pm 2^{-5/2} e^{\mu/kT}). \qquad \text{(42b) (42f)}$$

Equations (42) specify $\mathfrak{Z}$ as a function of T, V, μ, and hence serve to determine the remaining thermodynamic parameters with the aid of Eqs. (147), (148), and (149) of Chapter 2. We obtain, for instance,

$$p = (kT)^{5/2}\left(\frac{2\pi m}{h^2}\right)^{3/2} e^{\mu/kT}(1 \pm 2^{-5/2} e^{\mu/kT}), \qquad \text{(43b) (43f)}$$

by Eq. (148), and

$$N = (kT)^{3/2} V\left(\frac{2\pi m}{h^2}\right)^{3/2} e^{\mu/kT}(1 \pm 2^{-3/2} e^{\mu/kT}), \qquad \text{(44b) (44f)}$$

by Eq. (149).

In order to discover the effect of the second-order term in the expansions (39) on the equation of state of an ideal quantum gas, we eliminate μ between Eqs. (43) and (44). From Eqs. (44) one sees that, to terms of the second order in $\exp -\alpha$,

$$\frac{N}{V} = \Lambda^{-3} e^{-\alpha}(1 \pm 2^{-3/2} e^{-\alpha})$$

and

$$\left(\frac{N}{V}\right)^2 = \Lambda^{-6} e^{-2\alpha},$$

which equations, in conjunction with Eqs. (43), easily produce the equation of state

$$\boxed{\frac{p}{kT} = \frac{N}{V} \mp 2^{-5/2} \Lambda^3 \left(\frac{N}{V}\right)^2.} \qquad \text{(45b) (45f)}$$

The additional term $\mp 2^{-5/2}\Lambda^3(N/V)^2$, that distinguishes the ideal quantum gas from the classical ideal gas, may be compared with the corresponding term in the *van der Waals equation*, which is usually ascribed to the interaction between molecules of a real gas. For this purpose, we cast the van der Waals equation for one mole, viz., $(p + a/v^2)(v - b) = RT$, in the form

$$p = \frac{RT}{v}\left(1 - \frac{b}{v}\right)^{-1} - \frac{a}{v^2} \approx \frac{RT}{v}\left(1 + \frac{b}{v}\right) - \frac{a}{v^2}$$

$$= \left(\frac{RT}{v}\right)\left[1 + v^{-1}\left(b - \frac{a}{RT}\right)\right],$$

and place it next to Eqs. (45) for one mole,

$$p = \frac{RT}{v}\left(1 \mp 2^{-5/2}\Lambda^3\frac{N_0}{v}\right).$$

It is then observed, first, that the quantum correction for a *BE* gas acts like an attraction between particles ($a > 0$) in a classical gas at low temperature; in the case of an *FD* gas its effect is that of a repulsion ($a < 0$) at all temperatures. Second, as an insertion of numerical values for a favorable case (such as helium gas) would show, the quantum correction term is nearly always much less than the van der Waals term for the same gas. This fact explains why one has not been able to verify the existence of the above quantum corrections by experiments on real gases other than He and H_2, in contrast to the effects stemming from intermolecular forces.

So far our discussion has not revealed any significant difference between the predictions of *BE* and *FD* statistics. The reason is that, for large values of α (assumed in this section), $\bar{n}_j$ virtually never exceeds the value unity according to Eqs. (18). If we now relinquish the stipulation $\alpha \gg 1$, the theoretical consequences for a *BE* gas will differ markedly from those for an *FD* gas. In the next few sections we therefore propose to deal with these gases separately.

3-3. Highly Degenerate Fermi-Dirac Gas

A gas whose properties vary from those of a classical gas is said to be *degenerate*. The degeneracy is conveniently measured by the quantity α; $\alpha < 0$ and $\alpha \ll -1$ define *weak* and *strong* degeneracy, respectively. In what follows we shall concern ourselves mainly with a strongly degenerate *FD* gas, so that $\mu \gg kT$.

If Eq. (18f) is written in the form

$$\bar{n}(\varepsilon) = [e^{(\varepsilon - \mu)/kT} + 1]^{-1}, \tag{46}$$

it is seen that $\bar{n}(\mu \pm x) = (\exp \pm x/kT + 1)^{-1}$, whence $\bar{n}(\varepsilon)$ decreases from $\bar{n} \approx 1$ to $\bar{n} \approx 0$ within an interval whose size is a few times kT and which surrounds the point $\varepsilon = \mu$; furthermore, $\bar{n}(\mu) = \frac{1}{2}$. The function $\bar{n}(\varepsilon)$ is therefore graphically represented as in Figure 3–1. This diagram shows that,

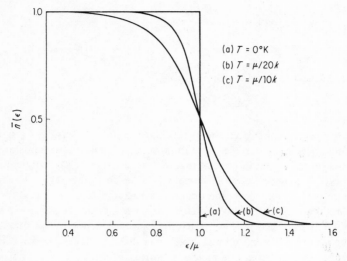

FIGURE 3–1. Representation of the function $\bar{n}(\varepsilon)$, showing that as the temperature T decreases, the particles tend to fill lower-level quantum states.

as the temperature T decreases, the particles increasingly tend to fill quantum states of lower energies. The crowding into the low-energy region does however not continue until the energy of each fermion has been reduced to zero. The reason is that each quantum state can be occupied by one fermion at most. When $T = 0°K$ (complete degeneracy) is realized, Eq. (46) asserts that $\bar{n}(\varepsilon) = 1, 0$ for $\varepsilon \lessgtr \mu_0$, respectively, μ_0 being the value of μ at $T = 0°K$. This means that all levels below $\varepsilon = \mu_0$ are filled, while all levels above μ_0 are empty—a state of affairs represented by the rectangular curve in Figure 3–1.

Ordinary kinetic theory maintains that the energy of an ideal gas vanishes at $T = 0°K$. By contrast, the present theory predicts that an FD gas will exhibit a finite *zero-point energy* U_0. Naturally, U_0 depends upon the maximum energy $\varepsilon_0 = \mu_0$ that a particle can possess at $T = 0°K$. The quantity ε_0, ordinarily called the *Fermi energy*, in turn is a function of the density N/V; this functional relation may be discovered by the following argument.

Because the quantum states of a particle in a macroscopic container are very closely spaced, they can with sufficient approximation be regarded as forming a set characterized by a continuous density function $g(\varepsilon)$; thus, $g(\varepsilon)d\varepsilon$ quantum states have energies lying between ε and $\varepsilon + d\varepsilon$. Accordingly, we replace the condition $N = \sum \bar{n}_j$ by

$$N = \int_0^\infty \bar{n}(\varepsilon)g(\varepsilon)d\varepsilon, \tag{47}$$

which at $T = 0$ °K simplifies to the equation

$$N = \int_0^{\varepsilon_0} g(\varepsilon)d\varepsilon. \tag{48}$$

Eq. (48) expresses the fact that the number of fermions equals the number of states with energy less than the Fermi energy.

To determine the form of the function $g(\varepsilon)$, we examine the energy spectrum (27) of a fermion in a box:

$$\varepsilon_j = \frac{h^2}{8mV^{2/3}} (n_x^2 + n_y^2 + n_z^2) \equiv \frac{h^2}{8mV^{2/3}} n^2. \tag{49}$$

The integral quantum numbers n_x, n_y, n_z, identifying the quantum states except for spin orientation, may formally be treated as the rectangular components of a vector **n** which has the length n and extends from the origin of a coordinate system. Each energy state will then be represented by the end point of such a vector, and the points so found will coincide with the corners of a cubic lattice. Since the smallest cell of this lattice has the volume unity, the number of points in any sufficiently large region of space to a good approximation simply equals the volume of that region. It should also be remembered that the integers n_x, n_y, n_z can assume only positive values, so that the physically significant lattice points are confined to the octant spanned by the positive segments of the coordinate axes. As a result, the number of points whose distance from the origin is more than n but less than $n + dn$, is equal to $\frac{1}{8}4\pi n^2 \, dn$, which is an eighth the volume of a spherical shell with center at the origin and thickness dn. If n is now substituted in terms of ε, one sees, using Eq. (49), that $2\pi(2m/h^2)^{3/2}V\varepsilon^{1/2}d\varepsilon$ energy eigenvalues lie between the values ε and $\varepsilon + d\varepsilon$. But it should be taken into consideration that each one of these levels is twofold degenerate, due to the fact that each fermion can exist in two spin states $m_s = +\frac{1}{2}$ and $m_s = -\frac{1}{2}$. Consequently, the number of quantum states lying in the energy interval $d\varepsilon$ is given by

$$g(\varepsilon)d\varepsilon = 4\pi\left(\frac{2m}{h^2}\right)^{3/2} V\varepsilon^{1/2} \, d\varepsilon. \tag{50}$$

When the formula (50) for the density $g(\varepsilon)$ is invoked, Eq. (48) can easily be integrated and solved to yield the desired expression for the Fermi energy:

$$\varepsilon_0 = \frac{h^2}{8m}\left(\frac{3N}{\pi V}\right)^{2/3}. \tag{51}$$

One may eliminate V between Eqs. (50) and (51) to obtain the brief equation

$$g(\varepsilon) = \frac{3}{2}\frac{N}{\varepsilon_0^{3/2}}\varepsilon^{1/2} \tag{52}$$

for the density of quantum states. The zero-point energy

$$U_0 = \int_0^{\varepsilon_0} \varepsilon g(\varepsilon)d\varepsilon \tag{53}$$

then follows immediately in terms of the Fermi energy. Indeed, utilizing Eq. (52) in Eq. (53), one has:

$$U_0 = \tfrac{3}{5}N\varepsilon_0. \tag{54}$$

Thus, at absolute zero the average energy of a fermion equals $\tfrac{3}{5}\varepsilon_0$.

3–4. Thermodynamic Functions of a Fermi-Dirac Gas

After these preliminaries, we continue our discussion of the highly degenerate *FD* gas by computing the usual thermodynamic quantities as functions of T and the density N/V or of T and ε_0.

Let us, to begin with, consider the chemical potential and the internal energy. An equation implicitly defining μ as $\mu(T,\varepsilon_0)$ is provided by Eq. (47), which with the aid of Eq. (52) reads:

$$1 = \tfrac{3}{2}\varepsilon_0^{-3/2}\int_0^\infty \bar{n}(\varepsilon)\varepsilon^{1/2}\,d\varepsilon; \tag{55}$$

while $U = U(T,\varepsilon_0)$ is determined by the analogue of Eq. (9), viz.,

$$U = \int_0^\infty \varepsilon\bar{n}(\varepsilon)g(\varepsilon)d\varepsilon = \tfrac{3}{2}N\varepsilon_0^{-3/2}\int_0^\infty \bar{n}(\varepsilon)\varepsilon^{3/2}\,d\varepsilon. \tag{56}$$

One observes that in both Eqs. (55) and (56) an integral of the kind

$$J = \int_0^\infty f(\varepsilon)X(\varepsilon)d\varepsilon \tag{57}$$

appears, where $f(\varepsilon) = \bar{n}(\varepsilon)$ and $X(\varepsilon)$ is either $\varepsilon^{1/2}$ or $\varepsilon^{3/2}$. Hence it is appropriate to focus our attention on J. However, as an attempt to calculate J in closed form would fail, one has to resort to an approximation method which we are now going to explain.

First, applying integration by parts, one may transform J into

$$J = f(\infty)\,Y(\infty) - f(0)\,Y(0) - \int_0^\infty f^{(1)}(\varepsilon)\,Y(\varepsilon)d\varepsilon, \tag{58}$$

the function $Y(\varepsilon)$ being defined by

$$Y(\varepsilon) = \int_0^\varepsilon X(\varepsilon')d\varepsilon'. \tag{59}$$

Since $f(\infty) = 0$ and $Y(0) = 0$, the first and second terms on the right side of Eq. (58) vanish, and J reduces to

$$J = -\int_0^\infty f^{(1)}(\varepsilon)\,Y(\varepsilon)d\varepsilon. \tag{60}$$

Next we introduce a new variable x by the definition

$$x = \frac{\varepsilon - \mu}{kT}, \tag{61}$$

and develop Y, here regarded as a function of x rather than of ε, in a Taylor series about the point $x = 0$:

$$Y(x) = \sum_{n=0}^{\infty} Y^{(n)}(0)\,\frac{x^n}{n!}, \tag{62}$$

where

$$Y^{(0)}(0) = Y(0) = \int_0^\mu X(\varepsilon)d\varepsilon, \tag{63}$$

$$Y^{(1)}(x) = \frac{dY}{d\varepsilon}\frac{d\varepsilon}{dx} = kT\frac{dY}{d\varepsilon},$$

and, for $n > 0$,

$$Y^{(n)}(0) = (kT)^n\Big(\frac{d^n Y}{d\varepsilon^n}\Big)_{\varepsilon=\mu} = (kT)^n X^{(n-1)}(\mu). \tag{64}$$

On substitution of Eqs. (62) and (64) in Eq. (60), J is seen to transform into

$$J = J_0 + J_1 + J_2 + \cdots, \tag{65}$$

where

$$J_0 = -Y(0) \int_0^\infty f^{(1)}(\varepsilon)d\varepsilon = Y(0)[f(0) - f(\infty)]$$
$$= Y(0)(e^{-\mu/kT} + 1)^{-1} \tag{66}$$

and

$$J_n = -\frac{1}{n!}(kT)^n X^{(n-1)}(\mu) \int_\alpha^\infty x^n f^{(1)}(x)dx; \quad (n = 1, 2, \ldots) \tag{67}$$

in Eq. (67), $f^{(1)}$ denotes the derivative of f treated as a function of x rather than of ε, and $\alpha = -\mu/kT$ as before. If one defines a quantity K_n by

$$K_n = \int_\alpha^\infty x^n f^{(1)}(x)dx, \tag{68}$$

Eq. (67) can be written more briefly as

$$J_n = -\frac{1}{n!}(kT)^n X^{(n-1)}(\mu)K_n. \tag{69}$$

In order to compute K_n, we note that

$$f^{(1)}(x) = \frac{d}{dx}(e^x + 1)^{-1} = -e^x(e^x + 1)^{-2}$$
$$= -(e^{x/2} + e^{-x/2})^{-2}, \tag{70}$$

from which we recognize that $f^{(1)}(x)$ is an even function of x. Moreover, the far right side of Eq. (70) shows that, as x tends to minus infinity, $f^{(1)}$ tends to zero like $-e^x$ and hence the integrand of K_n like $-x^n e^x$. It follows that, if $\alpha \ll -1$ and n is small or only moderately large, the integrand is negligible compared with unity at values of x less than the lower limit of the integral (68). For example, suppose $\alpha = -100$, then $x^n e^x \propto 100^n e^{-100} \sim 10^{-44+2n}$ at the lower limit, while $-f^{(1)}(x)x^n \sim 10^{-1}$ at $x = 1$. One can therefore displace the lower limit of integration in Eq. (68) from α to $-\infty$, without introducing an appreciable error, and obtains

$$K_n = \int_{-\infty}^\infty x^n f^{(1)}(x)dx. \tag{71}$$

By reason of the fact that $f^{(1)}(x)$ is an even function of x, and x^n is an odd function for odd n and an even function for even n, Eq. (71) gives

$$K_1 = K_3 = K_5 = \cdots = 0 \tag{72}$$

and

$$K_{2n} = 2\int_0^\infty x^{2n} f^{(1)}(x)dx. \quad (n = 1, 2, 3, \ldots) \tag{73}$$

To proceed with the calculation of K_{2n}, we expand $f^{(1)}(x)$ as a power series in e^{-x}, starting from the far right side of Eq. (70):

$$f^{(1)}(x) = -e^{-x}(1 + e^{-x})^{-2} = -e^{-x}(1 - 2e^{-x} + 3e^{-2x} - \cdots)$$
$$= -e^{-x} + 2e^{-2x} - 3e^{-3x} + \cdots. \qquad (74)$$

Substitution of this result in Eq. (73) yields

$$K_{2n} = 2 \sum_{j=1}^{\infty} (-1)^j j \int_0^{\infty} x^{2n} e^{-jx} \, dx$$
$$= 2 \sum_{j=1}^{\infty} (-1)^j j^{-2n} \int_0^{\infty} (jx)^{2n} e^{-jx} \, djx. \qquad (75)$$

The integrals appearing after the second step in Eq. (75) are, per definition, the gamma functions $\Gamma(2n + 1) = (2n)!$. Consequently, Eq. (75) becomes

$$K_{2n} = 2(2n)! \sum_{j=1}^{\infty} (-1)^j j^{-2n}. \qquad (76)$$

On the assumption that $\alpha \ll -1$, i.e., $\mu \gg kT$, Eq. (66) reads, if one recalls Eq. (63),

$$J_0 = Y(0) = \int_0^{\mu} X(\varepsilon) d\varepsilon; \qquad (77)$$

while Eqs. (72) and (76) assert that Eqs. (69) reduce to

$$J_1 = J_3 = J_5 = \cdots = 0 \qquad (78)$$

and

$$J_{2n} = -2(kT)^{2n} X^{(2n-1)}(\mu) \sum_{j=1}^{\infty} (-1)^j j^{-2n}. \qquad (79)$$

Insertion of these equations in Eq. (65) leads finally to

$$J = \int_0^{\mu} X(\varepsilon) d\varepsilon - 2 \sum_{n=1}^{\infty} (kT)^{2n} X^{(2n-1)}(\mu) \sum_{j=1}^{\infty} (-1)^j j^{-2n}. \qquad (80)$$

Equation (80) is rendered more tractable if we employ the well-known mathematical formulas

$$-\sum_{j=1}^{\infty} (-1)^j j^{-2} = \frac{\pi^2}{12} \quad \text{and} \quad -\sum_{j=1}^{\infty} (-1)^j j^{-4} = \frac{7\pi^4}{720},$$

according to which

$$J = \int_0^{\mu} X(\varepsilon) d\varepsilon + \frac{\pi^2}{6} (kT)^2 X^{(1)}(\mu) + \frac{7\pi^4}{360} (kT)^4 X^{(3)}(\mu) + \cdots. \qquad (81)$$

This general result will now be applied to compute μ and U as functions of T and ε_0.

To this end let us first consider Eq. (55). The integral on its right-hand side is given by Eq. (81), provided one substitutes $X(\varepsilon) = \varepsilon^{1/2}$ and therefore puts

$$\int_0^\mu X(\varepsilon)d\varepsilon = \tfrac{2}{3}\mu^{3/2}, \qquad X^{(1)}(\mu) = \tfrac{1}{2}\mu^{-1/2}, \qquad X^{(3)}(\mu) = \tfrac{3}{8}\mu^{-5/2}.$$

With these values, Eq. (55) reads

$$1 = \left(\frac{\mu}{\varepsilon_0}\right)^{3/2}\left[1 + \frac{\pi^2}{8}\left(\frac{kT}{\mu}\right)^2 + \frac{7\pi^4}{640}\left(\frac{kT}{\mu}\right)^4 + \cdots\right]. \tag{82}$$

If one raises Eq. (82) to the power $-\tfrac{2}{3}$ and uses the binomial expansion

$$(1 + y)^{-2/3} = 1 - \tfrac{2}{3}y + \tfrac{5}{9}y^2 - \cdots,$$

Eq. (82) can be rewritten as

$$\begin{aligned}
\mu &= \varepsilon_0\left\{1 - \frac{2}{3}\left[\frac{\pi^2}{8}\left(\frac{kT}{\mu}\right)^2 + \frac{7\pi^4}{640}\left(\frac{kT}{\mu}\right)^4\right] + \frac{5}{9}\frac{\pi^4}{64}\left(\frac{kT}{\mu}\right)^4 + \cdots\right\} \\
&= \varepsilon_0\left[1 - \frac{\pi^2}{12}\left(\frac{kT}{\mu}\right)^2 + \frac{\pi^4}{720}\left(\frac{kT}{\mu}\right)^4 + \cdots\right].
\end{aligned} \tag{83}$$

To eliminate μ from the right-hand side of Eq. (83), we note that

$$\left(\frac{kT}{\mu}\right)^2 = \left(\frac{kT}{\varepsilon_0}\right)^2\left[1 + \frac{\pi^2}{6}\left(\frac{kT}{\varepsilon_0}\right)^2 + \cdots\right] \quad \text{and} \quad \left(\frac{kT}{\mu}\right)^4 = \left(\frac{kT}{\varepsilon_0}\right)^4 + \cdots,$$

so that Eq. (83) may be transformed into

$$\boxed{\mu = \varepsilon_0\left[1 - \frac{\pi^2}{12}\left(\frac{kT}{\varepsilon_0}\right)^2 - \frac{\pi^4}{80}\left(\frac{kT}{\varepsilon_0}\right)^4 + \cdots\right]}, \tag{84}$$

which represents μ as a power series in (kT/ε_0) for a strongly degenerate *FD* gas.

Equation (56), determining the internal energy, permits a similar treatment. In the present case, $X(\varepsilon) = \varepsilon^{3/2}$, so that

$$\int_0^\mu X(\varepsilon)d\varepsilon = \tfrac{2}{5}\mu^{5/2}, \qquad X^{(1)}(\mu) = \tfrac{3}{2}\mu^{1/2}, \qquad X^{(3)}(\mu) = -\tfrac{3}{8}\mu^{-3/2}.$$

On utilizing these values in Eq. (81), Eq. (56) becomes

$$U = \tfrac{3}{5}N\left(\frac{\mu}{\varepsilon_0}\right)^{3/2}\mu\left[1 + \frac{5\pi^2}{8}\left(\frac{kT}{\mu}\right)^2 - \frac{7\pi^4}{384}\left(\frac{kT}{\mu}\right)^4 + \cdots\right]. \tag{85}$$

We may here replace μ with the aid of Eq. (84), according to which

$$\mu^{5/2} = \varepsilon_0^{5/2}\left[1 - \frac{5}{2}\frac{\pi^2}{12}\left(\frac{kT}{\varepsilon_0}\right)^2 - \frac{5}{2}\frac{\pi^4}{80}\left(\frac{kT}{\varepsilon_0}\right)^4 + \frac{15}{8}\left(\frac{\pi^2}{12}\right)^2\left(\frac{kT}{\varepsilon_0}\right)^4 + \cdots\right],$$

$$\mu^{1/2} = \varepsilon_0^{1/2}\left[1 - \frac{\pi^2}{24}\left(\frac{kT}{\varepsilon_0}\right)^2 + \cdots\right],$$

$$\mu^{-3/2} = \varepsilon_0^{-3/2} + \cdots.$$

The outcome of these substitutions in Eq. (85) is easily seen to be

$$U = \tfrac{3}{5}N\varepsilon_0\left[1 + \frac{5\pi^2}{12}\left(\frac{kT}{\varepsilon_0}\right)^2 - \frac{\pi^4}{16}\left(\frac{kT}{\varepsilon_0}\right)^4 + \cdots\right], \tag{86}$$

which furnishes the internal energy of a highly degenerate FD gas in the form of a power series expansion.

Equation (86) may be differentiated to yield immediately the heat capacity at constant volume, that is,

$$\boxed{C_V = \left(\frac{\partial U}{\partial T}\right)_V = Nk\,\frac{\pi^2}{2}\frac{kT}{\varepsilon_0}\left[1 - \frac{3\pi^2}{10}\left(\frac{kT}{\varepsilon_0}\right)^2 + \cdots\right]}\;; \tag{87}$$

while the entropy is obtained on integrating C_V/T with respect to T:

$$S = \int_0^T \frac{C_V}{T}\,dT = Nk\,\frac{\pi^2}{2}\frac{kT}{\varepsilon_0}\left[1 - \frac{\pi^2}{10}\left(\frac{kT}{\varepsilon_0}\right)^2 + \cdots\right],$$

i.e.,

$$S = \frac{N\varepsilon_0}{T}\left[\frac{\pi^2}{2}\left(\frac{kT}{\varepsilon_0}\right)^2 - \frac{\pi^4}{20}\left(\frac{kT}{\varepsilon_0}\right)^4 + \cdots\right]. \tag{88}$$

Equation (88) shows that $S \to 0$ as $T \to 0$, in agreement with the third law.

Finally, combining Eqs. (86) and (88), one gets for the Helmholtz free energy $U - TS$, the value

$$F = \tfrac{3}{5}N\varepsilon_0\left[1 - \frac{5\pi^2}{12}\left(\frac{kT}{\varepsilon_0}\right)^2 + \frac{\pi^4}{48}\left(\frac{kT}{\varepsilon_0}\right)^4 - \cdots\right]. \tag{89}$$

From this formula, determining the dependence of F on its characteristic variables T, V, N, all the remaining thermodynamic parameters can be found. For instance, the pressure is specified by

$$p = -\left(\frac{\partial F}{\partial V}\right)_{N,T} = -\left(\frac{\partial F}{\partial \varepsilon_0}\right)_T\left(\frac{\partial \varepsilon_0}{\partial V}\right)_N = \frac{2}{3}\frac{\varepsilon_0}{V}\left(\frac{\partial F}{\partial \varepsilon_0}\right)_T,$$

where Eq. (51) has been appealed to in the last step. Thus

$$p = \frac{2}{5}\frac{N}{V}\varepsilon_0\left[1 + \frac{5\pi^2}{12}\left(\frac{kT}{\varepsilon_0}\right)^2 - \frac{\pi^4}{16}\left(\frac{kT}{\varepsilon_0}\right)^4 + \cdots\right]. \tag{90}$$

Comparison of Eq. (86) with Eq. (90) reveals the interesting fact that the relation

$$p = \frac{2}{3} \frac{U}{V},$$ (91)

which is traditionally derived on the basis of classical kinetic theory, remains valid even for an *FD* gas exhibiting a high degree of degeneracy.

3–5. Application of Fermi-Dirac Statistics to Electrons in Metals

In the preceding two sections, the theory of an *FD* gas has been developed specially with the view to its relevancy in treating the behavior of electrons in metals. To account for the characteristic properties of metals, in particular their electrical and thermal conductivities, one must indeed suppose that some of the electrons in a metal are not bound to the ions, but are free to move through the ion lattice in a constant potential field like the particles of an ideal gas.

This hypothesis was first advanced by Drude (1900) who succeeded in deriving on the basis of it the Wiedemann-Franz law, which in Lorenz's version (1882) states that the ratio of the thermal to the electrical conductivity of a metal is proportional to its absolute temperature. Against Drude's hypothesis, however, the following serious objection was soon raised. On the assumption that atoms of a solid perform simple harmonic vibrations about their equilibrium positions—the corners of a three-dimensional lattice—the classical theorem of equipartition (see Section 4–1) predicts that the vibrations will contribute an amount $3R$ to the molar heat capacity of a monatomic solid. If the solid happens to be a metal and one treats, as Drude proposes, its conduction electrons as the particles of a classical ideal gas, then the equipartition theorem demands moreover that each conduction electron contributes on the average $3k/2$ to the heat capacity of the solid. The difficulty now arises that this conclusion is not borne out by experience. Instead, the empirical law of Dulong and Petit (1818) asserts that the molar heat capacity of metallic as well as nonmetallic monatomic solids at ordinary temperatures is very nearly given simply by the lattice contribution $3R$. Thus it seemed at first as if the hypothesis claiming the existence of free electrons had to be abandoned, unless one was prepared to make the unlikely assumption that it takes very many atoms to produce a single conduction electron.

However, Sommerfeld (1928) was able to demonstrate that Drude's assumptions can be retained, because a reconcilement between theory and experiment is brought about once it is realized that the postulated system of conduction electrons will constitute a highly degenerate *FD* gas. To elaborate on this point, let us refer to our discussion in Section 3-2. According to Eqs. (36) and (38) of that section, equipartition obtains for an ideal gas when $\Lambda^3 \ll V/N$—that is, when $D \ll 1$, where by Eq. (31) the so-called *degree of degeneration D* is defined

$$D = \frac{N}{V}\left(\frac{h^2}{2\pi mkT}\right)^{3/2} = \frac{N}{V}\Lambda^3 . \tag{92}$$

The inequality $D \ll 1$ will clearly be fulfilled if the density N/V is low enough and the temperature T sufficiently high. Furthermore, the required value of the density will drop and that of the temperature rise as the mass m of the particles becomes less.

In the case of hydrogen atoms, $m = 1.67 \times 10^{-24}$ gm, so that, assuming $T \sim 10°K$ and $N/V \sim 3 \times 10^{19}$ cm^{-3}, one gets $D \sim 0.005$. The condition $D \ll 1$ is therefore satisfied for a gas consisting of hydrogen atoms at not too high densities and down to quite low temperatures. For heavier molecules, $D \ll 1$ is valid within an even wider range of thermodynamic parameters. In short, D is negligible for molecular gases, and consequently classical equipartition prevails, even at very low temperatures.

Electrons in metals, on the other hand, provide a contrasting system due to the small mass and large density of the particles involved. Indeed, for an electron, $m \approx 9 \times 10^{-28}$ gm, which is about one 1800th the mass of a hydrogen atom. And $N/V \sim 10^{23}$ for a metal such as copper, on the assumption that approximately one electron per atom is a conduction electron. As a result, D for copper is roughly 3×10^8 times the value of D for a gas of hydrogen atoms at the same temperature. The inequality $D \gg 1$ is thus realized with respect to the free electrons in copper, and in other metals as well. This means that the kinetic energy of conduction electrons is quantized, and to determine their heat capacity one has to invoke the theory appropriate to a degenerate *FD* gas rather than the law of equipartition.

For most metals, the Fermi energy $\varepsilon_0 \sim 5 \times 10^4 k$, so that $\mu \gg kT$ and we can apply Eq. (87), which was derived for strong degeneration. Thus the heat capacity per conduction electron, originally found by Sommerfeld, is

$$C_{el} = k\frac{\pi^2}{2}\frac{kT}{\varepsilon_0} + \text{terms of the third and higher orders in } \frac{kT}{\varepsilon_0}. \tag{93}$$

C_{el} may be compared with the classical value $3k$ of C_{lat}, the heat capacity per atom due to the lattice vibrations. If one considers that at moderate values of T the ratio of C_{el} to $3k$ is of the order 10^{-2} or so, it becomes clear why at ordinary temperatures the contribution of the conduction electrons to the heat capacity of a metal is negligible.

The situation changes however at sufficiently low temperatures. For, as we shall prove later (see Section 4–6), C_{lat} adopts the classical value $3k$ only at high temperatures; as the temperature drops, C_{lat} approaches the value zero. In fact, one has to write approximately

$$C_{\text{lat}} = 3k \frac{4\pi^4}{5} \left(\frac{T}{\Theta}\right)^3 \tag{94}$$

for all temperatures $T \ll \Theta$, where Θ is a characteristic constant whose value for most metals lies between $100°\text{K}$ and $500°\text{K}$. Combination of Eqs. (93) and (94) gives

$$\frac{C_{\text{el}}}{C_{\text{lat}}} = \frac{5}{24\pi^2} \frac{kT}{\varepsilon_0} \left(\frac{\Theta}{T}\right)^3 ; \tag{95}$$

and this ratio assumes the value unity for temperatures of the order $10°\text{K}$ or lower. Hence at very low temperatures the conduction electrons should make a significant contribution to the heat capacity of a metal, provided one posits that the number of free electrons per ion is of the order unity.

Eqs. (93) and (94) lead one to expect that at low enough temperatures the molar heat capacity of a metal is described by the formula

$$c_v = aT + bT^3. \tag{96}$$

Experiments, notably those of Keesom and Kok (1932–37), have indeed confirmed, for a number of metals, the existence of an equation such as Eq. (96) at very low temperatures. One can compare the empirical values of the constant a in Eq. (96) with its theoretical values computed from the coefficient of T in Eq. (93). Provided one carries out this computation by supposing that every valency electron partakes in the conduction process, it is found that the empirical values of the constant agree with its theoretical values to within a factor lying between 0.8 and 2.0 for metals such as aluminum, copper, and zinc.

As another example of metal electrons behaving like an *FD* gas, let us treat the phenomenon of *thermionic emission*—that is, the emission of electrons from incandescent metal surfaces. Once again we start with the hypothesis that the free metal electrons do not interact with one another and move in a constant potential field. On the other hand, since ordinarily the great majority of electrons remains confined to the metal, a strong retarding force must act upon any electron approaching the metal surface from the inside. Accordingly, we postulate that at the boundary separating the metal from its environment the potential rises abruptly from the value zero inside the metal to a value X, say, immediately outside. This state of affairs is frequently expressed by the assertion that there exists at the surface of the metal a potential barrier of height X. To surmount this barrier and escape from the metal, an electron must possess a kinetic energy at least of the size X.

For the purpose of examining the emission of electrons by a hot metal quantitatively, we stipulate that we are confronted with a closed system made up entirely of a metal and the electrons evaporated from its surface. At equilibrium, the electrons in both the condensed and the vapor phases exhibit the same temperature T and the same chemical potential μ.

One may then inquire what the number n_{vap} of electrons per unit volume in the vapor phase at equilibrium will be. As an electron with a kinetic energy ε possesses a total energy $\varepsilon + X$ in the vapor space, one can write, by Eqs. (46), (47), and (50):

$$n_{\text{vap}} = 4\pi \left(\frac{2m}{h^2}\right)^{3/2} \int_0^\infty \varepsilon^{1/2} [\exp \beta(\varepsilon + \chi - \mu) + 1]^{-1} \, d\varepsilon; \tag{97}$$

the density of electrons confined to the metal space is also given by the right side of Eq. (97), except that one has to omit X. Since electrons—whose average energy is of the order $\frac{3}{5}\mu$ by Eq. (86)—do not spontaneously emigrate from metals at room temperature, one infers that X is considerably greater than μ. Thus, not only is $\beta\mu \gg 1$ (as shown earlier), but also $\beta(\chi - \mu) \gg 1$. It is therefore legitimate to disregard the term $+1$ in the integrand of Eq. (97), so that one obtains

$$n_{\text{vap}} = 4\pi \left(\frac{2m}{h^2}\right)^{3/2} \int_0^\infty \varepsilon^{1/2} \exp -\beta(\varepsilon + \chi - \mu) d\varepsilon$$
$$= 4\pi \left(\frac{2m}{h^2}\right)^{3/2} e^{-\beta(\chi - \mu)} I,$$

where $I = \int_0^\infty \varepsilon^{1/2} \exp -\beta\varepsilon \, d\varepsilon = \beta^{-3/2} \Gamma(\frac{3}{2}) = \beta^{-3/2} \frac{1}{2}\pi^{1/2}$ (cf. Problem 1); this finally yields the vapor density

$$n_{\text{vap}} = 2\left(\frac{2\pi mkT}{h^2}\right)^{3/2} \exp -\frac{\chi - \mu}{kT}. \tag{98}$$

With the aid of Eq. (98) the current density J of electrons emitted by an incandescent conductor can be calculated as follows. At equilibrium, the number of electrons emitted by a unit area of the conductor per unit time equals the number of vapor electrons hitting the same area in the same time.

The latter number, as kinetic theory arguments would show, is given by $\frac{1}{4}\bar{v}n_{vap}$, where $\bar{v}$ is the average speed of an electron (cf. Problem 8). If one denotes by e the charge carried by an electron, this means that

$$J = \tfrac{1}{4}\bar{v}en_{vap}. \tag{99}$$

Since the density of electrons in the vapor is very low, it is permissible to put $\bar{v}$ equal to $(8kT/\pi m)^{1/2}$—a value calculable with the aid of a Maxwellian distribution of velocities (see Problem 2, Chapter 2). Employing this result, we obtain the famous *Richardson-Dushman formula* (1921, 1930):

$$\boxed{J = AT^2 \exp -\frac{\phi}{kT}}, \tag{100}$$

where $A = 4\pi mek^2/h^3$ and $\phi = \chi - \mu$, the so-called *work function*. Equation (100) is widely employed in studies of thermionic emission.

The experimental significance of J deserves to be mentioned briefly. Let an electrical potential difference be applied between two electrodes in a vacuum tube and the (negative) cathode be kept aglow at a constant temperature. The electrons given off by the glowing cathode will then be drawn to the (positive) anode and thus generate a current through the tube. If the applied potential difference is sufficiently large, all the electrons emitted by the cathode will reach the anode, and hence the current density will attain a maximum value. It is this so-called *saturation* current that is referred to as J in Eq. (100).

3–6. Arbitrarily Degenerate Bose-Einstein Ideal Gas

In this section we shall be concerned with a general discussion of an ideal *BE* gas. The *BE* distribution law (18b) differs from the *FD* distribution law (18f) only in that -1 replaces $+1$ in its denominator. None the less, degenerate *FD* and *BE* gases exhibit greatly divergent properties. To begin with, let us point out those characteristic features of a *BE* gas that follow immediately from an inspection of (18b). In this process we shall find it useful to regard the occupation number of a quantum state as a function of its energy, so that (18b) may be cast in the form

$$\bar{n}(\varepsilon) = [e^{(\varepsilon-\mu)/kT} - 1]^{-1}; \tag{101}$$

this is the analogue of the *FD* equation (46).

For $\varepsilon - \mu < 0$, Eq. (101) leads to the nonsensical result $\bar{n}(\varepsilon) < 0$. One infers that $\varepsilon - \mu$ for a *BE* gas, in contrast with an *FD* gas, can never become negative. When applied to the energy $\varepsilon_1 = 0$, this conclusion entails that $\mu \leqslant 0$, i.e., $0 \leqslant \exp -\alpha \leqslant 1$. Equation (101) shows furthermore that as $\varepsilon - \mu$ tends to zero from above, $\bar{n}(\varepsilon)$ tends to plus infinity. These facts are pictorially brought out in Figure 3–2. For the purpose of comparison, we

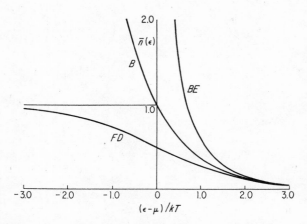

FIGURE 3–2. Bose-Einstein (*BE*), Boltzmann (*B*), and Fermi-Dirac (*FD*) distributions.

have combined in Figure 3–2 a plot of the distribution (101) with plots of the *FD* distribution (46) and the function

$$\bar{n}(\varepsilon) = e^{(\mu - \varepsilon)/kT}, \tag{102}$$

which represents the well-known *Boltzmann distribution law*. Figure 3–2 shows clearly that for given $\mu \leqslant 0$, $\bar{n}(\varepsilon)$ is largest for a *BE* and smallest for an *FD* gas, while it has an intermediary value in the case of a Boltzmann gas.

The distribution (102) is, we note, the form assumed by both the *BE* and *FD* distributions in the limit when $\exp -\alpha$ tends to zero, that is, for vanishing degeneration. A system of particles obeying the Boltzmann distribution, accurately or to a sufficient approximation, is said to be subject to *classical statistics*. The implications of this statistics were examined by us for an ideal gas in Section 3–2, where it was postulated that $\exp -\alpha \ll 1$.

After these preliminary remarks, we proceed with the formal computation of the thermostatic parameters of a *BE* gas. The variables T, V, μ are specified in advance, as has been supposed all along. Any other parameter is obtainable in terms of T, V, μ or, if one prefers, in terms of β, V, α, once the logarithm of the grand partition function $\mathfrak{Z}$ has been determined as a function of β, V, α. For, with the help of Eqs. (22b), (8), and (9), one has

$$\frac{pV}{kT} = \log \mathfrak{Z} = -\sum_j \log (1 - e^{-\beta \varepsilon_j - \alpha}), \tag{103}$$

$$\bar{N} = \sum_j (e^{\beta \varepsilon_j + \alpha} - 1)^{-1} = -\left(\frac{\partial \log \mathfrak{Z}}{\partial \alpha}\right)_{\beta, V}, \tag{104}$$

and

$$U = \sum_j \varepsilon_j (e^{\beta \varepsilon_j + \alpha} - 1)^{-1} = -\left(\frac{\partial \log \mathfrak{Z}}{\partial \beta}\right)_{V, \alpha}. \tag{105}$$

Since $0 \leqslant \exp -\alpha \leqslant 1$, the logarithm appearing in Eq. (103) may be expanded in accordance with the formula

$$\log (1 - x) = -x - \frac{x^2}{2} - \frac{x^3}{3} - \cdots$$

to yield

$$\log \mathfrak{Z} = \sum_j \sum_{r=1}^{\infty} r^{-1} e^{-r(\beta \varepsilon_j + \alpha)} = \sum_{r=1}^{\infty} r^{-1} e^{-r\alpha} Z_1(T/r), \tag{106}$$

where

$$Z_1(T/r) = \sum_j e^{-r\beta \varepsilon_j} \tag{107}$$

is the partition function of a single particle at the temperature T/r. To calculate Z_1, we replace the closely spaced energy eigenstates of a (spin-zero) boson by a continuous set containing, with appeal to Eq. (50),

$$g(\varepsilon) = 2\pi \left(\frac{2m}{h^2}\right)^{3/2} V \varepsilon^{1/2} \tag{108}$$

quantum states per unit energy interval. The sum (107) then goes over into the integral

$$Z_1(T/r, V) = 2\pi \left(\frac{2m}{h^2}\right)^{3/2} V \int_0^{\infty} \varepsilon^{1/2} e^{-r\beta \varepsilon} \, d\varepsilon. \tag{109}$$

Since the integral appearing as a factor on the right equals

$$(r\beta)^{-3/2} \Gamma(\tfrac{3}{2}) = (r\beta)^{-3/2} \frac{\pi^{1/2}}{2},$$

Eq. (109) gives, if one recalls the definition $\Lambda = (\beta h^2 / 2\pi m)^{1/2}$,

$$Z_1(T/r, V) = \left(\frac{2\pi mkT}{h^2}\right)^{3/2} V r^{-3/2} = \Lambda^{-3} V r^{-3/2}. \tag{110}$$

Substitution of Eq. (110) in Eq. (106) leads finally to

$$\log \mathfrak{Z} = \Lambda^{-3} V \sum_{r=1}^{\infty} r^{-5/2} e^{-r\alpha}. \tag{111}$$

With the value (111) of $\log \mathfrak{Z}$, Eqs. (103), (104), and (105) immediately furnish

$$\frac{p}{kT} = \Lambda^{-3} \sum_{r=1}^{\infty} r^{-5/2} e^{-r\alpha}, \tag{112}$$

$$\overline{N} = \Lambda^{-3} V \sum_{r=1}^{\infty} r^{-3/2} e^{-r\alpha}, \tag{113}$$

and

$$\frac{U}{kT} = \tfrac{3}{2} \Lambda^{-3} V \sum_{r=1}^{\infty} r^{-5/2} e^{-r\alpha}. \tag{114}$$

For the sake of brevity, we shall introduce here the general function

$$F_s(\alpha) = \sum_{r=1}^{\infty} r^{-s} e^{-r\alpha}. \tag{115}$$

The series on the right, which converges only for $\alpha > 0$, tends to 0 as α tends to $+\infty$ and reduces at $\alpha = 0$ to

$$F_s(0) = \sum_{r=1}^{\infty} r^{-s} = \zeta(s), \tag{116}$$

the so-called *Riemann zeta function*. With the aid of Eq. (115), the equations preceding it can be written tersely as

$$\frac{p}{kT} = \Lambda^{-3} F_{5/2}(\alpha), \tag{117}$$

$$\overline{N} = \Lambda^{-3} V F_{3/2}(\alpha), \tag{118}$$

$$\frac{U}{kT} = \tfrac{3}{2} \Lambda^{-3} V F_{5/2}(\alpha). \tag{119}$$

Mere inspection of the formulas specifying p, $\overline{N}$, and U gives rise to two observations. First, when $\exp -\alpha \ll 1$, we may approximate in Eqs. (112), (113), and (114) each sum by its first term, to wit, $\exp -\alpha$, with the result that they reduce to their classical counterparts, Eqs. (33), (34), and (36). Second, the equation

$$pV = \tfrac{2}{3} U, \tag{120}$$

found previously to hold for both a classical ideal gas and a highly degenerate *FD* ideal gas, is seen to be valid for a degenerate *BE* ideal gas as well.

Combination of Eqs. (117) and (119) in turn with Eq. (118) demonstrates moreover that

$$\frac{pV}{NkT} = \frac{\frac{2}{3}U}{NkT} = \frac{F_{5/2}(\alpha)}{F_{3/2}(\alpha)}. \tag{121}$$

It is worth digressing at this point in order to advance a concise proof that Eq. (120) obtains quite generally for an ideal gas—that is, independent of the statistics (*BE* or *FD*) employed and the extent of degeneration assumed. Replacing the discrete set of energy eigenstates for a confined particle by a continuum, it is possible to rewrite Eq. (22) as

$$\log \mathfrak{Z} = C\sigma \int_0^\infty \varepsilon^{1/2} \log (1 + \sigma e^{-\beta\varepsilon - \alpha}) \, d\varepsilon, \tag{122}$$

where C is a constant having different values for bosons and fermions, and $\sigma = \mp 1$ for bosons and fermions respectively. The validity of our claim then follows on integration by parts of Eq. (122):

$$\begin{aligned}
\frac{pV}{kT} = \log \mathfrak{Z} &= C\frac{2}{3}\beta \int_0^\infty \varepsilon^{3/2} e^{-\beta\varepsilon - \alpha}(1 + \sigma e^{-\beta\varepsilon - \alpha})^{-1} \, d\varepsilon \\
&= \frac{2}{3}\beta C \int_0^\infty \varepsilon^{3/2}(e^{\beta\varepsilon + \alpha} + \sigma)^{-1} \, d\varepsilon = \frac{2}{3}\frac{U}{kT}.
\end{aligned}$$

We now propose to study the behavior of a *BE* gas when $\exp -\alpha$ is not small compared with unity. In the process special reference will be made to Eq. (118), which may be formulated in terms of the degree of degeneration D as

$$D \equiv \Lambda^3 \frac{\bar{N}}{V} = F_{3/2}(\alpha). \tag{123}$$

As $\exp -\alpha$ increases from 0 to 1 (that is, α decreases from $+\infty$ to 0), $F_{3/2}(\alpha)$, and thus D, increases monotonically from 0 to $\zeta(\frac{3}{2}) = 2.612$—a finite value! This is a rather unexpected result, since it means that

$$N_0 = \zeta(\tfrac{3}{2})V\Lambda^{-3} \tag{124}$$

represents a limiting value that $\bar{N}$ can apparently not exceed. Such a restriction is indeed inconsistent with the equation for the occupation number of the *ground* state ($\varepsilon_1 = 0$), viz.,

$$\bar{n}_1 = (e^\alpha - 1)^{-1}, \tag{125}$$

which implies that one is able to make $\bar{n}_1$, and hence $\bar{N} \geqslant \bar{n}_1$, as large as one pleases by choosing $\exp -\alpha$ close enough to unity.

The contradiction encountered here stems from an inadvertent omission in our computation of $\log \mathfrak{Z}$, whose definition (22b), written out in full, reads

$$\log \mathfrak{Z} = -\log(1 - e^{-\alpha}) - \log(1 - e^{-\beta \varepsilon_2 - \alpha}) - \cdots. \tag{126}$$

The point is that when we converted the sum on the right into an integral to obtain the result (111), we tacitly neglected the first summand by assigning a weight $g(\varepsilon) = C\varepsilon^{1/2} = 0$ to the ground state. This oversight has no serious consequences provided $\exp -\alpha$ is significantly less than unity, for then the first term on the right of Eq. (126) will be negligible compared with the sum of the remaining terms as given by Eq. (111). On the other hand, if $\exp -\alpha$ is increased and allowed to approach unity, the first summand will grow and finally outweigh by any amount all the other terms taken together. The first summand in Eq. (126) must therefore be added to the expression obtained for $\log \mathfrak{Z}$ in Eq. (111) to yield

$$\log \mathfrak{Z} = -\log(1 - e^{-\alpha}) + \Lambda^{-3} V F_{5/2}(\alpha). \tag{127}$$

Equation (127) causes Eq. (118) to be superseded by

$$\bar{N} = -\left(\frac{\partial \log \mathfrak{Z}}{\partial \alpha}\right)_{V,\beta} = (e^{\alpha} - 1)^{-1} + \Lambda^{-3} V F_{3/2}(\alpha), \tag{128}$$

or, on transposition to the left of the first term on the right,

$$N' = \Lambda^{-3} V F_{3/2}(\alpha), \tag{129}$$

where

$$N' = \bar{N} - \bar{n}_1 \tag{130}$$

by Eq. (125); N' denotes the number of particles occupying the *excited* states $(\varepsilon_j, j > 1)$. With the adoption of the modified expression (128) for $\bar{N}$, we have thus replaced $\bar{N}$ by N' in Eq. (118) and thereby resolved the seeming contradiction between Eqs. (124) and (125).

Incidentally, the fact that $\bar{n}_1$ becomes infinite when $e^{\alpha} \to 1$ must not deter us. After all, our statistical distributions have been established on the supposition that $\bar{N}$ is extremely large; we may even let it tend to infinity, provided V is treated similarly and in such a manner that $\bar{N}/V$ remains finite. The quantum states then form a continuum, and the consequences

$$\bar{n}_1 \to +\infty, \qquad \bar{N} \to +\infty, \qquad \text{and} \qquad N' \to N_0 \tag{131}$$

flowing from Eqs. (125), (128), and (129) in this limit ($\alpha \to 0$), simply assert that the fraction $\bar{n}_1/\bar{N}$ stays finite, whereas the fractions $\bar{n}_j/\bar{N}$ ($j > 1$) tend to zero.

The presence of the term associated with the ground state in the expression (127) for $\log \mathfrak{Z}$ has no effect on the internal energy U or the pressure p. In summary, a *BE* gas is described in the region $\exp -\alpha = 1$ (i.e., $\alpha = 0$) as well as in the region $\exp -\alpha < 1$ (i.e., $\alpha > 0$) by Eqs. (117), (129), and (119). We infer that the quantities p, N', U exhibit a continuous behavior at the boundary between the given two regions.

3–7. Properties of a Bose-Einstein Gas as Functions of T, V, N

The discussion of the preceding section furnishes the properties of a *BE* ideal gas in terms of the parameters T, V, μ or, if one so prefers, β, V, α. Although this approach is mathematically the simplest one, it is not the most useful in all cases. In the present section, we accordingly change our point of view and adopt N, instead of μ, as a variable whose value is at our disposal. Thus, T, V, N, rather than T, V, μ, are to be regarded as independent variables, and it is our task to discover how the thermophysical properties vary with the values assigned to the new variables. One may, of course, eliminate the volume V in favor of the density $\rho = N/V$ (in particles per unit volume) and subsequently operate with the parameters T, ρ, N. This choice is especially commendable when one deals, as we shall do, with intensive properties. Such properties do not depend on N, and our immediate object becomes to examine the manner in which they behave when T is varied while ρ is kept fixed, and conversely.

After these remarks, it is clear that we should begin our investigation by determining the functional dependence of μ or α on T and ρ. For this purpose, let us attempt to solve Eq. (113) or Eq. (118), with $\overline{N} = N$, for the parameter α.

The series on the right of Eq. (113) is seen to converge for all $\alpha \geqslant 0$. The solution $\alpha = 0$ evidently obtains when

$$\zeta(\tfrac{3}{2}) = \frac{N}{V}\left(\frac{h^2}{2\pi mkT}\right)^{3/2} \equiv \rho \Lambda^3. \tag{132}$$

This equation defines a temperature $T_0 = T_0(\rho) \propto \rho^{-2/3}$ or a density $\rho_0 = \rho_0(T) \propto T^{3/2}$—depending on one's point of view—at which $\alpha = 0$. So, for example, T_0 satisfies the equation

$$\left(\frac{h^2}{2\pi mkT_0}\right)^{3/2} = \frac{\zeta(\tfrac{3}{2})}{\rho}. \tag{133}$$

Substitution of ρ from Eq. (118) in Eq. (133) yields

$$\frac{\zeta(\tfrac{3}{2})}{F_{3/2}(\alpha)} = \left(\frac{\Lambda_0}{\Lambda}\right)^3 = \left(\frac{T}{T_0}\right)^{3/2}, \tag{134}$$

where $\Lambda_0 = \Lambda(T_0)$. Eq. (134) shows that, as T approaches T_0 from above, α decreases monotonically toward zero and thus exp $-\alpha$ tends monotonically toward unity from below.

Equation (118) and therefore Eq. (134) cease to hold at extremely low values of α where Eq. (118) should be replaced by Eq. (128), which takes account of the $\bar{n}_1$ particles occupying the ground state. Nevertheless, Eq. (134) is valid down to values of α as low as $N^{-2/3}(10^{-16}$ for $N = 10^{24})$, since $\alpha = N^{-2/3}$ implies that $\bar{n}_1 = (e^\alpha - 1)^{-1} \approx N^{2/3}$, which is negligible in comparison with N. It is consequently permissible to employ Eq. (134) to determine α as a function of T and ρ in the range $T > T_0(\rho)$. This we shall now proceed to do.

Our manipulations are facilitated by the usage of D as an auxiliary variable; D is related to α through Eq. (123), which asserts that $D = F_{3/2}(\alpha)$, or, by the definition Eq. (115) of $F_{3/2}$,

$$D = e^{-\alpha}(1 + 2^{-3/2}e^{-\alpha} + 3^{-3/2}e^{-2\alpha} + 4^{-3/2}e^{-3\alpha} + \cdots). \tag{135}$$

On solving Eq. (135) for exp $-\alpha$, one gets

$$e^{-\alpha} = D(1 - a_1 D - a_2 D^2 - a_3 D^3 - \cdots), \tag{136}$$

where

$$a_1 = 2^{-3/2}, \qquad a_2 = 3^{-3/2} - 2^{-2},$$
$$a_3 = 2^{-3} - 5 \times 6^{-3/2} + 5 \times 2^{-9/2}, \quad \text{etc.} \tag{137}$$

If we substitute D inside the parentheses in accordance with the relation

$$D = \left(\frac{T_0}{T}\right)^{3/2} \zeta(\tfrac{3}{2}), \tag{138}$$

given by Eq. (134), the power series in D transforms into a power series in $(T_0/T)^{3/2}$:

$$e^{-\alpha} = D\left[1 - b_1\left(\frac{T_0}{T}\right)^{3/2} - b_2\left(\frac{T_0}{T}\right)^3 - b_3\left(\frac{T_0}{T}\right)^{9/2} - \cdots\right], \tag{139}$$

such that

$$b_1 = a_1\zeta(\tfrac{3}{2}), \qquad b_2 = a_2\zeta^2(\tfrac{3}{2}), \qquad b_3 = a_3\zeta^3(\tfrac{3}{2}), \quad \text{etc.} \tag{140}$$

Finally, taking the logarithm of Eq. (139) and invoking the Taylor expansion of log $(1 - x)$, we are in a position to express α as a function of T and N/V:

$$-\alpha = \log D - e_1\left(\frac{T_0}{T}\right)^{3/2} - e_2\left(\frac{T_0}{T}\right)^3 - e_3\left(\frac{T_0}{T}\right)^{9/2} - \cdots, \tag{141}$$

where

$$e_1 = b_1, \qquad e_2 = b_2 + \tfrac{1}{2}b_1^2, \qquad e_3 = b_3 + b_1 b_2 + \tfrac{1}{3}b_1^3, \quad \text{etc.} \tag{142}$$

The series (141) converges for all values of $T > T_0$, and represents in this range the corrections—of any order in $(T_0/T)^{3/2}$—to the classical value log D of $-\alpha$. Since $-\alpha = \mu/kT = G/NkT$, Eq. (141) may be stated alternatively as

$$\frac{G}{NkT} = \frac{3}{2}\log\frac{h^2}{2\pi mkT} + \log\frac{N}{V} - e_1\left(\frac{T_0}{T}\right)^{3/2}$$
$$-e_2\left(\frac{T_0}{T}\right)^3 - e_3\left(\frac{T_0}{T}\right)^{9/2} - \cdots. \tag{143}$$

It is now possible to eliminate the variable α between Eq. (141) and Eq. (117) or (119) to obtain the pressure and the molar energy as functions of T and N/V:

$$\frac{pV}{NkT} = \frac{U}{\frac{3}{2}NkT} \tag{144}$$

$$= 1 - \tfrac{1}{2}e_1\left(\frac{T_0}{T}\right)^{3/2} - \tfrac{2}{3}e_2\left(\frac{T_0}{T}\right)^3 - \tfrac{3}{4}e_3\left(\frac{T_0}{T}\right)^{9/2} - \cdots. \tag{145}$$

The last three equations obviously suffice to determine also the parameters other than G, p, U as functions of N, the temperature, and the density. For future use we single out the heat capacity at constant volume, which follows on differentiation of Eq. (145), viz.,

$$\frac{C_V}{\frac{3}{2}Nk} = \frac{1}{\frac{3}{2}Nk}\left(\frac{\partial U}{\partial T}\right)_{V,N}$$
$$= 1 + \tfrac{1}{4}e_1\left(\frac{T_0}{T}\right)^{3/2} + \tfrac{4}{3}e_2\left(\frac{T_0}{T}\right)^3 + \tfrac{21}{8}e_3\left(\frac{T_0}{T}\right)^{9/2} + \cdots. \tag{146}$$

This brings us to the close of our examination of the properties of a *BE* ideal gas for $T > T_0(\rho)$, or when $D < \zeta(\tfrac{3}{2})$.

We next focus our attention on the properties of an ideal *BE* gas as functions of T, V, N at temperatures $T < T_0(\rho)$, that is, at values of $D > \zeta(\tfrac{3}{2})$. In the region $T < T_0$, Eq. (113) is not satisfied by any value of α. On the other hand, Eq. (129)—which takes into account also the bosons populating the ground state—does possess a solution α for all values of T. We have seen earlier that as $T \to T_0$ from above, α becomes practically zero. One knows furthermore that α can never be negative. On attempting the solution of Eq. (129), it is therefore not unreasonable to surmise that α remains virtually zero even when T is decreased below the value T_0.

For the sake of definiteness, let it be assumed that α is negligible compared with $N^{-2/3}$ but not compared with N^{-1}. For such small values of α,

$$\bar{n}_1 = (e^\alpha - 1)^{-1} \approx \alpha^{-1} \tag{147}$$

particles occupy the ground state. To discover the occupation numbers of the excited states, we reason as follows. Let

$$n_j^0 = (e^{\beta \varepsilon_j} - 1)^{-1} \qquad (j \neq 1) \tag{148}$$

denote the occupation number of any excited state when $\alpha = 0$. Evidently, one may with sufficient accuracy replace the actual occupation number $\bar{n}_j$ by n_j^0 provided the relative deviation

$$\frac{n_j^0 - \bar{n}_j}{\bar{n}_j} = \frac{(e^\alpha - 1)e^{\beta \varepsilon_j}}{e^{\beta \varepsilon_j} - 1} \approx \frac{\alpha e^{\beta \varepsilon_j}}{e^{\beta \varepsilon_j} - 1} \tag{149}$$

is much smaller than unity. This condition is clearly fulfilled when $\beta \varepsilon_j \sim 1$ or larger.

But one may also allow $\beta \varepsilon_j \ll 1$, if at the same time $\beta \varepsilon_j$ for the first excited state—and consequently for all other excited states—is much larger than α, i.e., if $\beta \varepsilon_2 \gg \alpha$. For, under these circumstances, the deviation (149) becomes $\alpha/\beta \varepsilon_j \leqslant \alpha/\beta \varepsilon_2 \ll 1$. Hence we are led to inquire into the likelihood that $\beta \varepsilon_2 \gg \alpha$. By virtue of Eq. (27), the energy of the lowest excited state $(n_x = 2, n_y = 1, n_z = 1)$ relative to the ground state $(n_x = n_y = n_z = 1)$ is

$$\varepsilon_2 = \frac{3h^2}{8mV^{2/3}}. \tag{150}$$

Equation (150), with the aid of the definition (133), gives

$$\beta \varepsilon_2 = \frac{3\pi}{4} \frac{h^2}{2\pi mkT_0 V^{2/3}} \frac{T_0}{T} \sim \frac{T_0}{T} N^{-2/3}, \tag{151}$$

which means, as $\alpha \ll N^{-2/3}$, that indeed $\beta \varepsilon_2 \gg \alpha$ for all $T \leqslant T_0$. The deviation (149) is therefore much less than unity and the distribution law for excited states becomes indistinguishable from Eq. (148)—that is, the *BE* distribution with $\alpha = 0$.

Let us apply these results to Eq. (128). For the first term on its far right-hand side we substitute the approximate value (147), while in the second term, representing the sum of the n_j's for the excited states, we put $\alpha = 0$. The outcome is

$$N = \alpha^{-1} + \Lambda^{-3} V \zeta(\tfrac{3}{2}) = \alpha^{-1} + N \left(\frac{T}{T_0} \right)^{3/2}, \tag{152}$$

if one recalls, in making the last step, the definition (133) of T_0 in the form

$$\Lambda^3 = \left(\frac{T_0}{T} \right)^{3/2} \frac{V}{N} \zeta(\tfrac{3}{2}). \tag{153}$$

On transposition of terms, Eq. (152) reads

$$\alpha^{-1} = N\left[1 - \left(\frac{T}{T_0}\right)^{3/2}\right].$$ (154)

Equation (154) demonstrates that $\alpha \sim N^{-1}$, i.e., zero for most purposes, throughout the range $0 < T < T_0$.

The result $\alpha = 0$ implies, since $\alpha = -G/NkT$, that

$$\frac{G}{kT} = 0.$$ (155)

In addition, substitution of $\alpha = 0$ in Eqs. (117), (129), and (119) causes them to reduce to

$$\frac{p}{kT} = \Lambda^{-3}\zeta(\tfrac{5}{2}),$$ (156)

$$N' = \Lambda^{-3}V\zeta(\tfrac{3}{2}),$$ (157)

and

$$\frac{U}{kT} = \tfrac{3}{2}\Lambda^{-3}V\zeta(\tfrac{5}{2}).$$ (158)

If Eq. (153) is invoked, the foregoing equations may be rewritten as

$$\frac{pV}{NkT} = \frac{U}{\tfrac{3}{2}NkT}$$ (159)

$$= \frac{\zeta(\tfrac{5}{2})}{\zeta(\tfrac{3}{2})}\left(\frac{T}{T_0}\right)^{3/2}$$ (160)

and

$$\frac{N'}{N} = \left(\frac{T}{T_0}\right)^{3/2}.$$ (161)

Once T, V, N have been specified, Eqs. (155), (159), and (160) enable us to compute, for all temperatures $T < T_0$, the values not only of G, p, U, but of the remaining thermodynamic parameters as well. One finds, for example, that

$$C_V = \left(\frac{\partial U}{\partial T}\right)_{V,N} = \frac{15}{4} Nk \frac{\zeta(\tfrac{5}{2})}{\zeta(\tfrac{3}{2})}\left(\frac{T}{T_0}\right)^{3/2}$$ (162)

and

$$S = \frac{1}{T}(U + pV - G) = \frac{5}{2}\frac{pV}{T} = \frac{5}{2}Nk\frac{\zeta(\tfrac{5}{2})}{\zeta(\tfrac{3}{2})}\left(\frac{T}{T_0}\right)^{3/2}.$$ (163)

The reader will have noticed that the heat capacity C_V and the entropy S are both proportional to $T^{3/2}$, while p and U are proportional to $T^{5/2}$. S is thus seen to become zero as T approaches the absolute zero, in agreement with the third law of thermodynamics.

3–8. Behavior of a Bose-Einstein Gas near the Condensation Temperature

An examination of the formulas appearing in the last two paragraphs reveals the existence of a rather unusual phenomenon. It is a well-known experimental fact that the pressure and energy of an ordinary gas depend on N, the number of particles, no less than on T and V. By contrast, we observe that, according to Eqs. (156) and (158), p and U of a *BE* ideal gas at $T < T_0$ are independent of N. From a classical point of view, this is a surprising result. It implies that, if one introduces bosons into a container of fixed volume filled with a boson gas at constant temperature $T < T_0$, the pressure and internal energy will not be affected. Equation (157) affords the reason: all the additional particles settle down in the ground state ($\varepsilon_1 = 0$), where they do not make any contribution to either p or U.

This behavior calls to mind the state of affairs that prevails in a system consisting of a liquid in equilibrium with its saturated vapor. In such a system, the injection of a particular number of molecules at constant V and T is occasioned by the condensation of an equal amount of molecules, thereby leaving the pressure of the vapor unchanged. The existence of this analogy, first remarked on by Kahn and Uhlenbeck (1938), explains why the word *condensation* is frequently used to describe the sudden crowding of bosons into the ground state when the temperature of a *BE* gas falls below T_0. The temperature T_0 is accordingly referred to as the *condensation temperature*. It should not be forgotten though that the resemblance to the condensation of a real gas is very limited: while the latter is due to intermolecular forces and occurs in coordinate space, the condensation of a *BE* ideal gas is a pure quantum phenomenon taking place in momentum space in the absence of any interaction between particles.

The condensation of a *BE* ideal gas was first discussed by Einstein (1925), and is usually called after him. It may be stressed that this condensation at $T \leqslant T_0$ is in marked contrast with the behavior of an *FD* ideal gas. Indeed, as we have already pointed out, the exclusion principle forbids the occupation of any quantum state by more than one fermion. As a consequence, the addition of new fermions at low temperature results in an increase in the population of the more excited states, rather than in a condensation into the lower states.

Now that we have familiarized ourselves with the properties of a *BE* gas at temperatures $T < T_0$ and $T > T_0$, respectively, we shall compare the approach from higher values of T to the point of division $T = T_0$ with the approach from lower values of T. To be more exact: while V and N are kept constant, we vary T and inquire how the properties of a BE gas behave when the temperature T_0 is traversed.

One then notes immediately that the parameters G, p, U, as well as the variables obtained from these by ordinary arithmetic operations, are continuous at $T = T_0$ with values G_0, p_0, U_0 given by

$$G_0 = 0, \tag{164}$$

$$\frac{p_0 V}{NkT_0} = \frac{U_0}{\frac{3}{2}NkT_0} \tag{165}$$

$$= \frac{\zeta(\frac{5}{2})}{\zeta(\frac{3}{2})}. \tag{166}$$

It happens that the heat capacity $C_V = (\partial U/\partial T)_{V,N}$ likewise behaves smoothly at T_0. However, the second derivative of U, or $(\partial C_V/\partial T)_{V,N}$, exhibits a discontinuity. The proofs of the last two assertions follow at once.

For the sake of brevity, we define the quantity

$$\lambda = e^{-\alpha} = e^{\mu/kT} \tag{167}$$

(not to be confused with the de Broglie wavelength), and regard all properties as functions solely of T and λ. Obviously, λ is continuous and equal to unity at $T = T_0$:

$$\lambda \to 1 \quad \text{as} \quad T \to T_0 \pm 0. \tag{168}$$

Moreover, $d\lambda/dT$ tends to zero as T_0 is approached from below:

$$\frac{d\lambda}{dT} \to 0 \quad \text{as} \quad T \to T_0 - 0. \tag{169}$$

To discover the limiting value of $d\lambda/dT$ for an approach from above, one appeals to Eq. (123), which in terms of λ reads

$$D = F_{3/2}(\alpha) = \sum_{r=1}^{\infty} r^{-3/2}\lambda^r. \quad (T > T_0) \tag{170}$$

Differentiation of Eq. (170) yields

$$\frac{d\lambda}{dD} = \frac{\lambda}{\sum r^{-1/2}\lambda^r}; \tag{171}$$

and since the denominator diverges when $\lambda \to 1$, Eq. (171) implies that

$$\frac{d\lambda}{dD} \to 0 \quad \text{as} \quad T \to T_0 + 0. \tag{172}$$

Now, $d\lambda/dT = (d\lambda/dD)(dD/dT)$, and it follows from the definition (92) that

$$\frac{dD}{dT} = -\frac{3}{2}\frac{D}{T}, \tag{173}$$

i.e.,

$$\frac{dD}{dT} = -\frac{3}{2}\frac{\zeta(\frac{3}{2})}{T_0} \qquad \text{at } T = T_0. \tag{174}$$

Hence,

$$\frac{d\lambda}{dT} \to 0 \qquad \text{as} \qquad T \to T_0 + 0. \tag{175}$$

We notice further, by reason of Eq. (119), that $(\partial U/\partial T)_\lambda$ is continuous at $T = T_0$:

$$\left(\frac{\partial U}{\partial T}\right)_\lambda \to \left(\frac{\partial U}{\partial T}\right)_{\lambda=1} \qquad \text{as} \qquad T \to T_0 \pm 0, \tag{176}$$

where

$$\left(\frac{\partial U}{\partial T}\right)_{\lambda=1} = \frac{\frac{3}{2}NkT_0\zeta(\frac{5}{2})}{\zeta(\frac{3}{2})}. \tag{177}$$

Substitution of Eqs. (169), (175), and (176) in the formula

$$\frac{dU}{dT} = \left(\frac{\partial U}{\partial T}\right)_\lambda + \left(\frac{\partial U}{\partial \lambda}\right)_T \frac{d\lambda}{dT},$$

produces

$$\frac{dU}{dT} \to \left(\frac{\partial U}{\partial T}\right)_{\lambda=1} \qquad \text{as} \qquad T \to T_0 \pm 0. \tag{178}$$

In other words, C_V is continuous at $T = T_0$, as maintained above.

To investigate the behavior of $(\partial C_V/\partial T)_{V,N}$ when a BE gas passes through $T = T_0$, let us differentiate Eq. (171) with respect to D:

$$\frac{d^2\lambda}{dD^2} = \frac{\lambda}{\left(\sum r^{-1/2}\lambda^r\right)^2} - \frac{\lambda \sum r^{1/2}\lambda^r}{\left(\sum r^{-1/2}\lambda^r\right)^3}. \quad (T > T_0) \tag{179}$$

If one permits λ to approach unity, all three sums appearing here tend to infinity. Hence, it is evident that the first term on the right-hand side becomes zero. The second term, however—mathematical analysis would show—tends to a finite value, viz., $(2\pi)^{-1}$. Consequently,

$$\frac{d^2\lambda}{dD^2} \to -(2\pi)^{-1} \qquad \text{as} \qquad T \to T_0 + 0. \tag{180}$$

From Eq. (180) it can be inferred that the function

$$\frac{d^2\lambda}{dT^2} = \frac{d}{dT}\frac{d\lambda}{dD}\frac{dD}{dT}$$

$$= \frac{d\lambda}{dD}\frac{d^2D}{dT^2} + \frac{dD}{dT}\frac{d^2\lambda}{dD^2}\frac{dD}{dT}$$

behaves discontinuously at the point $T = T_0$. For, by Eqs. (172), (174), and (180),

$$\frac{d^2\lambda}{dT^2} \to \left(\frac{dD}{dT}\right)^2\frac{d^2\lambda}{dD^2} = -\frac{9}{8\pi}\left(\frac{\zeta(\frac{3}{2})}{T_0}\right)^2 \qquad \text{as} \qquad T \to T_0 + 0, \qquad (181)$$

while

$$\frac{d^2\lambda}{dT^2} \to 0 \qquad \text{as} \qquad T \to T_0 - 0. \qquad (182)$$

Consider now, in the light of the foregoing results, the quantity

$$\frac{d^2U}{dT^2} = \left(\frac{\partial^2U}{\partial T^2}\right)_\lambda + \frac{\partial^2U}{\partial\lambda\partial T}\frac{d\lambda}{dT} + \frac{d\lambda}{dT}\frac{d}{dT}\left(\frac{\partial U}{\partial\lambda}\right)_T + \left(\frac{\partial U}{\partial\lambda}\right)_T\frac{d^2\lambda}{dT^2}.$$

The terms on the right-hand side except the last one are continuous according to Eqs. (119), (169), and (175). Thus, d^2U/dT^2 displays a discontinuity at $T = T_0$ whose size, by Eq. (182), is

$$\left(\frac{\partial U}{\partial\lambda}\right)_{T = T_0 + 0}\left(\frac{d^2\lambda}{dT^2}\right)_{T = T_0 + 0}. \qquad (183)$$

The value of the second factor in Eq. (183) is contained in Eq. (181). The first factor is computed with the aid of Eqs. (114) and (166); we get

$$\left(\frac{\partial U}{\partial\lambda}\right)_{T = T_0 + 0} = \frac{\zeta(\frac{3}{2})}{\zeta(\frac{5}{2})}U_0 = \tfrac{3}{2}NkT_0. \qquad (184)$$

The expression (183) therefore reduces to

$$-\frac{27}{16\pi}\frac{Nk}{T_0}[\zeta(\tfrac{3}{2})]^2 = -\frac{3.660Nk}{T_0}, \qquad (185)$$

because $\zeta(\tfrac{3}{2}) = 2.612$. Seeing that d^2U/dT^2 is synonymous with $(\partial^2U/\partial T^2)_{V,N}$, we have established the discontinuous nature of $(\partial C_V/\partial T)_{V,N}$ at $T = T_0$. It has moreover been demonstrated that the said discontinuity has the value of Eq. (185).

The formulas (146) and (162) specify the dependence of C_V on T in the ranges $T > T_0$ and $T < T_0$, respectively. The preceding discussion of the manner in which these solutions join at $T = T_0$, completes our description of C_V as a function of T for a *BE* ideal gas. This variation of C_V with T is pictorially represented in Figure 3–3. For the purpose of comparison, graphs of C_V versus T have been drawn also for an *FD* and a classical ideal gas.

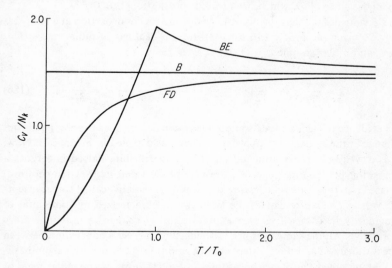

FIGURE 3–3. Heat capacity at constant volume for a Bose-Einstein (*BE*), a Fermi-Dirac (*FD*), and a classical (*B*) ideal gas.

There remains finally this problem: can empirical data be adduced in support of the theoretical predictions put forward in the present section? It is clear that the quantum effects in question are most likely to become manifest in an experimental system of bosons that fulfills the following two requirements. In the first place, the forces acting between the molecules of the system should be negligible. The reason is that the deviations from classical ideal-gas behavior, foretold by our theory even for a system of noninteracting particles, simulate qualitatively the effects produced in a classical gas by intermolecular attractive forces. These forces, as calculations would show, are likely to cause deviations much larger than—and thus bound to obscure—the corrections of purely quantum-mechanical origin. In the second place, to observe quantum phenomena, one must demand that a high degree of degeneracy D can be realized in practice. Since $D \propto m^{-3/2}$, this means that a small molecular mass m is called for.

The two requirements together are best met by helium gas. For although hydrogen gas—whose molecules would also obey *BE* statistics—is lighter, the forces between helium molecules are weaker than those between hydrogen molecules or between any other molecules. Owing to this fact, helium boils at a much lower temperature, $T_b \approx 4.2°$K, than hydrogen ($T_b \approx 20.5°$K), so that helium remains in a gaseous state down to temperatures accompanied by high values of D, which, we recall, is proportional to $T^{-3/2}$.

BE statistics predicts the occurrence of Einstein condensation at a temperature T_0 given [according to Eq. (133)] for an ideal gas of molar mass $M = mN_0$ and molar volume $v = (V/N)N_0 = N_0/\rho$ by

$$T_0 = \frac{h^2}{2\pi mk}\left(\frac{\rho}{2.612}\right)^{2/3} = \frac{h^2 N_0^{5/3}}{2\pi k}\frac{1}{M}\left(\frac{1}{2.612v}\right)^{2/3} = \frac{114.7}{Mv^{2/3}}. \quad (186)$$

As evidence of such a condensation one would accept, for instance, an abrupt change in the slope of the C_V versus T curve, as depicted in Figure 3-3. Now, it is a well-known experimental fact that liquid helium indeed undergoes a transition between its (high-temperature) phase I and its (low-temperature) phase II at $T = 2.19°$K. It is true that this λ-transition—called so because its C_p versus T curve resembles the letter λ—is characterized by some kind of singularity in C_V itself as well as by an abrupt change in its temperature derivative. All the same, it is not far-fetched to suspect a connection between the λ-transition and the Einstein condensation. In support of this hypothesis, it may be noted that if one substitutes in Eq. (186) for M the molar mass of helium, viz., 4 gm, and for v the molar volume of liquid helium, viz., 27.6 cm^3 mole^{-1}, one obtains $T_0 = 3.13°$K. This value is seen to agree remarkably well with the experimental transition temperature 2.19°K provided one allows for the fact that helium is not an ideal gas. Indeed, the forces between helium molecules are strong enough to cause deviations from classical ideal behavior, that are comparable with the deviations introduced by quantum theory.

Suppose the λ-transition in ordinary helium, that is, the naturally occurring isotope He⁴, is actually due to the Einstein condensation of its molecules. One must then expect that a transition of the same kind will be absent in the isotope He³, since this isotope contains an odd number of elementary particles and thus should obey *FD* statistics. Now, experiments have in fact failed to show the existence of a phase transition in artificially produced pure He³, even at temperatures as low as a few tenths of 1°K.

The suggestion that helium II be treated like a highly degenerate *BE* gas was put forward in 1939 by F. London, who demonstrated that at least some of the strange properties exhibited by He II become understandable from such a point of view. It might be mentioned that an equally plausible rival theory of He II was advanced in 1941 by Landau. However, a satisfactory synthesis of the main ideas contained in these two theories was effected by the theoretical researches of Tisza (1947) and Feynman (1953, 1954).

The theory of Tisza, in particular, is based upon his phenomenological *two-fluid model* (1938). According to this model, He II is regarded as a mixture of two hypothetical fluids, one composed of *normal* atoms and another consisting of *superfluid* atoms; the latter component flows without viscous effects and behaves like an ideal gas below its condensation temperature. Admittedly, this model might represent nothing more than a convenient, temporary device for the coordination of experimental data. None the less, it seems almost certain that whatever theory of He II will finally emerge, it is bound to feature the notion of an Einstein condensation.

3-9. Statistics of a Photon Gas

The foregoing discussion of helium makes it clear that a perfect example of an ideal *BE* gas cannot be found among molecular systems, owing to the omnipresence of intermolecular forces. But there does exist a nonmolecular system to which the theory of an ideal *BE* gas can be applied in a fairly straightforward manner. Let us first define this system.

According to quantum theory, electromagnetic radiation—ordinarily treated as waves—behaves on certain occasions as if it were composed of corpuscles; these have become known as *radiation quanta* or *photons*. All photons are propagated with the same velocity $c = 3 \times 10^{10}$ cm sec^{-1} in vacuum and have zero rest mass. The energy and momentum of a photon however depend on the frequency of the radiation involved. To be more specific, one must assume that $\varepsilon = h\nu$ and $p = h\nu/c$ for a photon associated with radiation of frequency ν, as was first suggested by Einstein (1905). In agreement with this picture, it is permissible to treat radiation with an arbitrary frequency spectrum, confined to an evacuated container, as a gas of photons possessing different energies. This approach accords with the prediction of classical electromagnetic theory, confirmed by experiment, that radiation, like the particles of a material gas, exerts a pressure on the walls of the vessel containing it. Since photons do not interact at all, the radiation gas strictly exemplifies an ideal gas. Furthermore, as photons have spin $s = 1$, this gas can be expected to satisfy *BE* statistics.

Before we can apply the theory of an ideal *BE* gas as expounded above to a photon gas in an enclosure, it is incumbent on us to examine if and when such a system is amenable to description in terms of thermodynamic parameters alone. To this end, suppose that the walls of the enclosure are capable of absorbing and emitting radiation of any frequency and are kept at a fixed temperature T. The walls will then continually emit radiation into the cavity formed by them, and at the same time absorb photons from it; and this exchange will continue until the average rates of emission and absorption have become equal. From this point on, the radiation will be in *equilibrium*. This state of the radiation is characterized by the constancy of all its macroscopic properties with respect to time, space, and direction. The equilibrium radiation is said to have the temperature T. In the event that the walls do not absorb any one or more frequencies, equilibrium will not obtain. One can however remedy this defect by introducing into the cavity a speck of soot held at the temperature T. This substance is capable of absorbing and emitting all frequencies, and hence will induce the desired thermal equilibrium.

Classical electromagnetic theory teaches that to each point in a radiation field one may assign an *energy density*, i.e., energy per unit volume; we shall denote the time-average of this quantity by u. Thus, for equilibrium radiation of energy U pervading a cavity of volume V, one has $u = U/V$. The contribution to u that stems from radiation with frequencies lying in the infinitesimal range $(v, v + dv)$ will be written as $u_v dv$, so that u is found on integration of u_v over v between the limits 0 and ∞. At equilibrium, the energy density per unit frequency range, u_v, is of course a function of v and T. It is conceivable though that u_v is dependent on other factors as well, such as the nature of the walls and the shape and size of the cavity. This possibility is, however, ruled out by the following imaginary experiment due to Kirchhoff (1859).

Consider two contiguous radiation-filled enclosures A and B with common temperature T, but which might differ in any other respects. Now suppose, for the sake of argument, that under equilibrium conditions u_v for a particular frequency v is larger in A than in B. If we then perforate the wall separating A from B and cover the opening with a filter of negligible heat capacity that is transparent only to radiation with frequencies in the range $(v, v + dv)$, more radiant energy will flow from cavity A to cavity B than in the opposite direction. In consequence, the temperature of B will rise and that of A fall until u_v has attained the same value in both A and B. This means that heat is transferred from the enclosure A to the warmer enclosure B without work being performed at the same time. Now, as we know, such a process is forbidden by the second law of thermodynamics. It follows that our initial assumption $u_{Av} > u_{Bv}$ is untenable; likewise, the assumption $u_{Av} < u_{Bv}$ could not be upheld. In other words, u_v must be a function solely of v and T, i.e., $u_v = u_v(v, T)$, and therefore $u = u(T)$.

Remembering that a photon of frequency ν contributes the amount $h\nu$ to the energy $u_\nu \, d\nu$, one is able to reformulate the foregoing results: the manner in which the photons in a unit volume of an equilibrium radiation gas are distributed over energy values depends only on its temperature T. From this we infer that all the intensive macroscopic properties of the equilibrium gas are functions of T alone; the extensive properties will depend on the volume V as well. This conclusion justifies our subsequent treatment of a photon gas as a thermodynamic system.

A photon gas differs from simple material thermodynamic systems in that two parameters T and V, instead of three, suffice to determine all its macroscopic properties. We hence deduce that the chemical potential μ appearing in the formulas for a BE gas must cease, in the present case, to play the role of an independent variable. In fact, one has to assume that μ is a constant with value zero; thus, $\mu = 0$ and $\alpha = -\mu/kT = 0$. To justify the assertion $\alpha = 0$, we recall the original definition of α as expressed by Eq. (130), Chapter 2. This equation shows that α entered our discussion through the condition of Eq. (125), Chapter 2, which symbolizes the constancy of the total number of particles n^* constituting the grand canonical supersystem. Now, in spite of the postulated isolation of our supersystem, the number of particles is no longer conserved when one imagines that the supersystem consists of photons rather than molecules. The absorption (emission) of one photon might indeed be accompanied by the emission (absorption) of more than one photon, as long as the frequencies of the photons involved are such that the energy of the supersystem remains constant. We have accordingly to abolish the said restriction (125) or, what amounts to the same thing, put $\alpha = 0$ in the BE distribution law (18b). This means that whereas for a molecular ideal BE gas α becomes negligible only when $T \leqslant T_0$, in the case of a photon gas $\alpha = 0$ at all temperatures.

Another feature distinguishing a photon gas is of course the zero rest mass of its constituents. This fact necessitates that one employs special considerations in computing the density of photon energy eigenstates. We note first that a particle of spin $s = 1$ and non-zero rest mass possesses three independent spin states, namely, $m_s = 1$, $m_s = 0$, $m_s = -1$. For a photon, however, the state $m_s = 0$ is missing; the two remaining states correspond to the two independent directions of polarization characterizing an electromagnetic wave. The energy levels of a photon are therefore only twofold degenerate, so that in this respect a photon simulates a fermion with $s = \frac{1}{2}$. But if we turn to formula (50), which provides the number of quantum states $g(\varepsilon)d\varepsilon$ in the energy range $(\nu, \nu + d\nu)$ for spin-half fermions, we observe that substitution of $m = 0$ in it gives $g(\varepsilon)d\varepsilon = 0$ for all ε. It is clear then that

Eq. (50) cannot be taken over literally. On the other hand, if we eliminate the kinetic energy ε in favor of the linear momentum p, with the aid of the formulas $p^2 = 2m\varepsilon$ and $2p\,dp = 2m\,d\varepsilon$, Eq. (50) transforms into the relation

$$g(p)dp = \frac{8\pi V}{h^3} p^2 \, dp, \tag{187}$$

which no longer contains the mass m and does apply to photons. In Eq. (187), $g(p)dp$ denotes the number of quantum states whose momenta lie between p and $p + dp$ for a photon confined to a volume V. It is convenient for our purpose to rewrite Eq. (187) in terms of the frequency ν by invoking the relation $p = h\nu/c$. One finds easily

$$g(\nu)d\nu = \frac{8\pi V}{c^3} \nu^2 \, d\nu, \tag{188}$$

where $g(\nu)d\nu$ signifies the number of quantum states with frequencies in the range $(\nu, \nu + d\nu)$.

Equation (188) together with the statements $\alpha = 0$ and $\varepsilon = h\nu$ show that, in the special case of a photon gas, Eqs. (103), (104), and (105) should respectively be read as

$$\frac{pV}{kT} = -\frac{8\pi V}{c^3} \int_0^\infty \nu^2 \log (1 - e^{-h\nu/kT})d\nu \equiv \frac{8\pi V}{c^3} I, \tag{189}$$

$$N = \frac{8\pi V}{c^3} \int_0^\infty (e^{h\nu/kT} - 1)^{-1}\nu^2 \, d\nu \equiv \frac{8\pi V}{c^3} J, \tag{190}$$

$$U = \frac{8\pi Vh}{c^3} \int_0^\infty (e^{h\nu/kT} - 1)^{-1}\nu^3 \, d\nu \equiv \frac{8\pi Vh}{c^3} K. \tag{191}$$

To evaluate the integrals I, J, K defined here, let us write their integrands as power series in $\exp -h\nu/kT$; we then get, using an obvious transformation of variables,

$$I = \sum_{r=1}^\infty \int_0^\infty \nu^2 r^{-1}e^{-rh\nu/kT} \, d\nu$$

$$= \left(\frac{kT}{h}\right)^3 \sum r^{-4} \int_0^\infty x^2 e^{-x} \, dx = 2\left(\frac{kT}{h}\right)^3 \zeta(4), \tag{192}$$

$$J = \sum_{r=1}^\infty \int_0^\infty \nu^2 e^{-rh\nu/kT} \, d\nu$$

$$= \left(\frac{kT}{h}\right)^3 \sum r^{-3} \int_0^\infty x^2 e^{-x} \, dx = 2\left(\frac{kT}{h}\right)^3 \zeta(3), \tag{193}$$

$$K = \sum_{r=1}^\infty \int_0^\infty \nu^3 e^{-rh\nu/kT} \, d\nu$$

$$= \left(\frac{kT}{h}\right)^4 \sum r^{-4} \int_0^\infty x^3 e^{-x} \, dx = 6\left(\frac{kT}{h}\right)^4 \zeta(4), \tag{194}$$

where the formula $\Gamma(n) = (n - 1)!$ has been employed, and the Riemann zeta function has the values $\zeta(3) = 1.202$ and $\zeta(4) = \pi^4/90 = 1.082$.

If the foregoing expressions for I, J, K are substituted in Eqs. (189), (190), and (191), these reduce to

$$p = \frac{8\pi^5}{45c^3h^3} (kT)^4, \tag{195}$$

$$N = 16\pi V \left(\frac{kT}{ch}\right)^3 \zeta(3), \tag{196}$$

$$U = \frac{8\pi^5 V}{15c^3h^3} (kT)^4. \tag{197}$$

Comparison of Eqs. (195) and (197) reveals that the radiation pressure equals one third of the energy density U/V, that is,

$$\boxed{p = \frac{u}{3}}. \tag{198}$$

This result differs by a factor $\frac{1}{2}$ from the relation $p = 2u/3$ derived commonly for a molecular ideal gas irrespective of the kind of statistics assumed. The explanation of this disagreement is to be found in the fact that the relation between energy ε and momentum $\mathbf{p}$ is unlike for the two systems in question: $\varepsilon = c|\mathbf{p}|$ for photons, while $\varepsilon = \mathbf{p}^2/2m$ for particles with nonzero rest mass. Accordingly, the reasoning that gives rise in kinetic theory to the equation $p = \frac{1}{3}nm\overline{v^2}$, leads, when applied to photons, to the result

$$p = \frac{1}{3}n\overline{(\varepsilon/c)c} = \frac{1}{3}n\overline{\varepsilon} = \frac{u}{3}. \tag{199}$$

In the derivation of Eq. (199) we supposed of course that the photons, like the molecules of a material gas, undergo perfectly elastic collisions with the walls of the container. However, only a very special type of wall (an ideal reflector) will reflect all the photons incident on it, and those not reflected will most likely be absorbed. Since an absorbed photon surrenders half as much linear momentum to a wall as a reflected one, it would seem that the pressure p should in general be less than $u/3$. Yet this is not the case; $p = u/3$ regardless of the nature of the walls. The reason is: at equilibrium, a wall absorbing radiation at a certain rate, must emit it at an equal rate, so that the photons emitted impart to the wall the same momentum as the absorbed photons would, had they been reflected. We may add that the formula $p = u/3$ could equally well be deduced on the basis of the classical electromagnetic theory of a radiation field.

After this brief digression, let us consider Eq. (196) in conjunction with Eq. (197); we see that

$$U = \frac{\pi^4 NkT}{30\zeta(3)} = 2.701 NkT,$$ (200)

and hence, by Eq. (198),

$$\boxed{pV = 0.900NkT}.$$ (201)

The reader will not fail to recognize the close resemblance between these relations and their counterparts pertaining to a classical ideal gas.

To facilitate comparison of the expressions for the various thermophysical parameters, one may use the abbreviation

$$a = \frac{8\pi^5 k^4}{15c^3 h^3} = 7.561 \times 10^{-15} \quad \text{erg cm}^{-3} \text{ deg}^{-4}.$$ (202)

With the help of this symbol, Eqs. (195) and (197) can be stated concisely as

$$p = \tfrac{1}{3}aT^4$$ (203)

and

$$U = aVT^4.$$ (204)

To these we should add the relation

$$G = 0,$$ (205)

which follows from the proposition $\mu = 0$ advanced at the beginning of this section. These equations, determining p, U, G as functions of T and V, will now furnish readily all the remaining parameters. In particular, entropy, Helmholtz free energy, and heat capacity at constant volume, are given by

$$S = \frac{1}{T}(U + pV) = \frac{4}{3}\frac{U}{T} = \frac{4}{3}aVT^3,$$ (206)

$$F = U - TS = -\tfrac{1}{3}aVT^3,$$ (207)

and

$$\boxed{C_V = \left(\frac{\partial U}{\partial T}\right)_V = 4aVT^3},$$ (208)

respectively. Thus, it is seen that $C_V \propto T^3$ for all T, and that S tends to zero as T approaches zero.

3–10. Blackbody Radiation and the Laws of Planck and Stefan

The theory expounded in the previous section permits an application of crucial importance to the radiation emitted by a body of a very peculiar kind, that we shall define forthwith. When radiant energy is incident on the surface of an arbitrary object, the fractions α, ρ, and τ are absorbed, reflected, and transmitted, respectively, so that

$$\alpha + \rho + \tau = 1. \tag{209}$$

For a body that is perfectly opaque, one obviously has $\tau = 0$. Following Kirchhoff (1860), we speak of a *blackbody* when both $\rho = 0$ and $\tau = 0$, and thence, by Eq. (209), $\alpha = 1$. Such a body therefore absorbs all the radiation falling upon it. The absence of any reflected radiation causes the surface of a blackbody to appear completely black, unless the body is so hot that it becomes self-luminous. A surface like this, which reflects none of the radiation incident on it, is said to be (*ideally*) *black*. If the temperature of a blackbody is to remain constant, it must evidently emit and absorb energy at equal rates. This means, a blackbody is not only a perfect absorber, but a perfect emitter as well. The radiation issuing from a blackbody at constant temperature is known as *blackbody radiation*. It is this radiation that we intend to study presently.

An example of a material blackbody does not exist. And neither is any material surface ideally black; in practice, a surface of lampblack, for which $\alpha = 0.99$, comes closest to it. An ideally black surface can however be realized as nearly as one wishes by a small opening in a hollow enclosure. It can easily be understood why this is so. Radiation entering the cavity through the opening is reflected from wall to wall and reduced in intensity by a factor ρ at each reflection. If the enclosure is properly constructed, reflections will take place so many times that the intensity is effectively reduced to zero before the radiation can escape through the opening. For all practical purposes any incident radiation is thus completely absorbed, as the definition of an ideally black surface requires. The opening, though incapable of reflecting radiation, will naturally radiate of its own, just like any material surface. And if the cavity is filled with equilibrium radiation, we shall refer to the radiation emanating from the small opening as *cavity radiation*.

The *emissive power* or *radiancy R* of a surface is defined as the rate at which it emits energy in all directions per unit area. The radiancy due to radiation whose frequencies lie in the interval $(\nu, \nu + d\nu)$ will be denoted by $R_\nu \, d\nu$. Accordingly, R equals the integral of R_ν with respect to ν between the limits 0 and ∞.

Consider now an arbitrary surface at a fixed temperature T in equilibrium with radiation. In general, R_ν will depend not only upon ν and T, but on the nature of the surface as well. In the special case of a black surface however, the radiancy $R_{b\nu}$ corresponding to the frequency ν is a function merely of ν and T and is identical with the radiancy $R_{c\nu}$ for cavity radiation of the temperature T. This statement is easily verified. We note first that an argument, analogous to the one on which the result $u_\nu = u_\nu(\nu,T)$ was based, would show that the values of $R_{c\nu}$ agree for all cavities having the same temperature. Next, imagine a blackbody in equilibrium with radiation inside a cavity of temperature T. The radiant energy of frequency ν incident upon a unit area of the blackbody per unit time is given by $R_{c\nu}\,d\nu$, and this energy is absorbed entirely; the unit area simultaneously emits $R_{b\nu}\,d\nu$ units of energy. Since the energy density u_ν is independent of time or position, the inference is that $R_{c\nu} = R_{b\nu}$. This completes our verification.

We proceed to ascertain the functional dependence of $R_{b\nu}$ on ν and T. In accordance with the reasoning customary in kinetic theory, the number of photons striking unit area of a surface embedded in a cavity filled with equilibrium radiation is $\frac{1}{4}c\rho_\nu\,d\nu$; here $\rho_\nu\,d\nu$ represents the number of photons per unit volume possessing frequencies in the range $(\nu, \nu + d\nu)$. Because each of these photons has an energy $h\nu$, and as $h\nu\rho_\nu\,d\nu = u_\nu\,d\nu$, the total energy of the incident photons is $R_{c\nu}\,d\nu = \frac{1}{4}cu_\nu\,d\nu$. In other words, since $R_{c\nu} = R_{b\nu}$,

$$R_{b\nu} = \tfrac{1}{4}cu_\nu. \tag{210}$$

The computation of $R_{b\nu}$ is now an easy matter. By virtue of Eq. (191), one gets

$$u_\nu = \frac{8\pi h\nu^3}{c^3}\,(e^{h\nu/kT} - 1)^{-1}, \tag{211}$$

so that, by Eq. (210), the radiancy of a black surface becomes

$$R_{b\nu} = \frac{2\pi h\nu^3}{c^2}\,(e^{h\nu/kT} - 1)^{-1}. \tag{212}$$

Considering that the wavelength λ, rather than the frequency ν, is the more familiar quantity for the experimentalist, we may rewrite Eqs. (211) and (212) in terms of λ with the aid of the relations $\nu = c/\lambda$ and $d\nu = -(c/\lambda^2)d\lambda$. If $-u_\lambda\,d\lambda = u_\nu\,d\nu$ and $-R_{b\lambda}\,d\lambda = R_{b\nu}\,d\nu$ designate the energy density and radiancy, respectively, in the wavelength interval $(\lambda, \lambda + d\lambda)$, one obtains

$$\boxed{u_\lambda = \frac{8\pi ch}{\lambda^5}\,(e^{ch/k\lambda T} - 1)^{-1}} \tag{213}$$

and

$$R_{b\lambda} = \frac{2\pi c^2 h}{\lambda^5} \left(e^{ch/k\lambda T} - 1\right)^{-1}. \qquad (214)$$

Equations (213) and (214)—or Eqs. (211) and (212) if one so prefers—are the celebrated *Planck's energy density* and *radiation laws* (1900) for blackbody radiation.

The radiation law, Eq. (214), furnishes the distribution of energy over the spectrum of a blackbody. One may restate it, using the abbreviations

$$c_1 = 2\pi c^2 h = 3.7405 \times 10^{-5} \quad \text{erg cm}^2 \text{ sec}^{-1} \qquad (215)$$

and

$$c_2 = \frac{ch}{k} = 1.4388 \quad \text{cm deg}, \qquad (216)$$

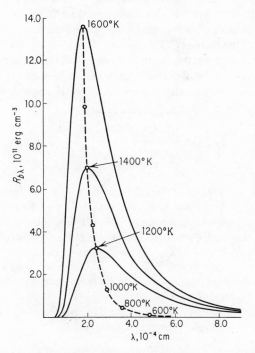

FIGURE 3–4. Spectral energy distribution for blackbody radiation according to Planck's formula.

in the customary form

$$R_{b\lambda} = \frac{c_1}{\lambda^5} (e^{c_2/\lambda T} - 1)^{-1}. \tag{217}$$

This equation is graphically illustrated in Figure 3–4 for three values of T. Theoretical graphs like these fit remarkably well the experimental curves representing measurements that determine the spectral composition of radiation emitted by a blackbody furnace at various temperatures.

Analysis of the law (217) reveals some remarkable features. To begin with, we notice that the right-hand side of Eq. (217) is of the form $T^5 f(\lambda T)$; thus, for all temperatures T' and all wavelengths λ', obeying the relation $\lambda' T' = \lambda T$, one has the equality

$$R_{b\lambda'}(T') = \left(\frac{T'}{T}\right)^5 R_{b\lambda}(T). \tag{218}$$

Verbally expressed, this equation has the following meaning. If one starts with the energy distribution curve pertaining to the temperature T, one can transform it into the curve for a higher temperature T' in two steps: by first decreasing the abscissa of each point by the factor T/T', and then multiplying each ordinate by the factor $(T'/T)^5$.

The foregoing statement implies in particular that, on varying the temperature, the maximum of the distribution curve undergoes a displacement such that its abscissa λ_m and ordinate R_{λ_m} always satisfy the equations

$$\boxed{\lambda_m T = \text{const.}} \tag{219}$$

and

$$R_{\lambda_m} T^{-5} = \text{const.} \tag{220}$$

The relation $R_{b\lambda} = T^5 f(\lambda T)$, where f is an undetermined function, and its consequences, Eqs. (219) and (220), were first derived by Wien (1893) on thermodynamic grounds. Accordingly, Eq. (219) is historically known as *Wien's displacement law*. Combination of Eqs. (219) and (220) yields

$$R_{\lambda_m} \lambda_m^5 = \text{const.} \tag{221}$$

This is the equation for the locus of the radiancy maxima, which has been represented in Figure 3–4 by a broken curve.

The value of *Wien's displacement constant*, which appears on the right-hand side of Eq. (219), follows from the equation $(\partial R_{b\lambda}/\partial \lambda)_T = 0$ defining the wavelength λ_m, i.e., from

$$e^{-c_2/\lambda_m T} + \frac{c_2}{5\lambda_m T} - 1 = 0. \tag{222}$$

The root of this transcendental equation—numerical procedure would show—
is given by

$$\lambda_m T = 0.20140 c_2 = 0.28978 \text{ cm deg} \tag{223}$$

to five significant digits, where the value of c_2 as specified by Eq. (215) has
been used.

The shift of λ_m predicted by Wien's law, Eq. (219), is responsible for the
variation in color exhibited, e.g., by a platinum wire when it is gradually
heated by an electric current. At low temperatures the wire is seen by reflected
light only, because the wavelengths of the emitted radiation lie predominantly
in the invisible infrared region of the radiation spectrum. After sufficient
heating however the emitted radiation becomes visible as a dull red glow. A
further gradual increase in temperature will cause the wire to turn—in succession—red, bright red, orange, yellow, and ultimately white, as λ_m shortens.
The nonappearance of blue in this sequence is due to the fact that when λ_m
corresponds to the blue part of the spectrum, radiation of adjacent wavelengths is also copiously produced; and the resulting mixture of colors creates
the visual sensation that prompts us to describe the wire as being "white
hot."

Closely related to laws (219) and (220) is the functional dependence of the
total radiancy R_b of a blackbody on its temperature. The quantity R_b is found
if one integrates $R_{b\lambda}$ over λ from 0 to ∞ or, alternatively, $R_{b\nu}$ over ν from 0
to ∞:

$$R_b = \int_0^\infty R_{b\lambda}\, d\lambda = \int_0^\infty R_{b\nu}\, d\nu. \tag{224}$$

R_b may thus be visualized geometrically as the area under the energy distribution curve. Since $R_{b\nu} = cu_\nu/4$ by Eq. (210), the second integral in Eq. (224)
is seen to equal $(c/4)u$. But, by virtue of Eq. (204), $u = aT^4$, so that Eq. (224)
immediately furnishes

$$\boxed{R_b = \sigma T^4} , \tag{225}$$

where

$$\sigma = \frac{ac}{4} = \frac{2\pi^5 k^4}{15 c^2 h^3} = 5.670 \times 10^{-5} \quad \text{erg cm}^{-2} \text{ sec}^{-1} \text{ deg}^{-4}. \tag{226}$$

Equation (225) states the famous *Stefan-Boltzmann law*, which was discovered
empirically by Stefan (1879) and confirmed theoretically by Boltzmann (1884)
who relied upon sheer thermodynamical reasoning. The quantity σ is known
as the *Stefan-Boltzmann constant*.

It is worthwhile to digress for a moment in order to reproduce Boltzmann's ingenious thermodynamic proof of law (225). His method consists simply in the application of the first and second laws of thermodynamics to an equilibrium radiation gas contained in a cylinder fitted with a movable piston. For this system, we know, $U = Vu$, $p = u/3$, and $u = u(T)$; therefore the fundamental relation $TdS = dU + pdV$ assumes the special form $TdS = Vdu + \frac{4}{3}udV$, or

$$dS = \frac{V}{T}\frac{du}{dT}dT + \frac{4}{3}\frac{u}{T}dV. \tag{227}$$

As dS is an exact differential, the partial derivative of the coefficient of dT with respect to V must equal the partial derivative of the coefficient of dV with respect to T:

$$\frac{1}{T}\frac{du}{dT} = \frac{4}{3}\frac{d}{dT}\frac{u}{T}, \tag{228}$$

that is,

$$\frac{du}{u} = \frac{4dT}{T}. \tag{229}$$

Integration of this result yields $\log u = 4 \log T +$ constant, i.e., $u = aT^4$, where a is an undetermined constant. If the last equation is multiplied by $c/4$, one finally obtains law (225).

To complete our analysis of Planck's formula (217), we examine its limiting forms for very short and very long wavelengths.

Suppose the wavelength is so short that $\lambda T \ll c_2$, then the term unity in Eq. (217) can be neglected and law (217) reduces to what is known as *Wien's distribution law*:

$$R_{b\lambda} = \frac{c_1}{\lambda^5} e^{-c_2/\lambda T}, \tag{230}$$

which is in excellent agreement with the experimental data at low values of λT. This law, with the constants c_1 and c_2 left undetermined, was first derived by Wien (1896) on the basis of thermodynamic arguments and some rather arbitrary suppositions concerning the role that the molecules play in the emission process.

If, on the other hand, the wavelength is so long that $\lambda T \gg c_2$, the exponential function in Eq. (217) can be approximated by $1 + c_2/\lambda T$, so that one is led to the so-called *Rayleigh-Jeans distribution law*:

$$R_{b\lambda} = \frac{c_1\lambda T}{\lambda^5 c_2} = \frac{2\pi ckT}{\lambda^4}. \tag{231}$$

This formula—it does not contain Planck's constant!—was first established, apart from a wrong numerical factor, by Lord Rayleigh (1900) who availed himself of classical statistics; Jeans subsequently (1905) rederived Eq. (231) in its correct version. Of course, the Rayleigh-Jeans law breaks down at short wavelengths, a fact that is apparent from Eq. (231) itself, since its right-hand side tends to infinity when λ approaches zero. This failure of the nonquantal law at short wavelengths was historically referred to as the "ultraviolet catastrophe."

3-11. Historical Postscript to Planck's Radiation Law

The method whereby Planck originally arrived at his radiation law naturally differs from the approach adopted in this chapter. Because Planck's discovery heralded the birth of quantum theory, a momentous event in the history of science, we may be permitted to review here briefly the manner of reasoning that culminated in the enunciation of his law.

Planck's interest in the problem of spectral energy distribution was aroused by the measurements of Lummer and Pringsheim, which were commenced shortly after the publication of Wien's distribution law. These experimenters, using an instrument known as a bolometer, examined the radiation issuing from a small aperture in an enclosure kept at a fixed temperature. Their empirical results, besides substantiating Wien's displacement law for all λ and T, confirmed Wien's distribution law for small values of λT. The same distribution law was, however, contradicted by the observations pertaining to larger values of λT. In fact, subsequent measurements carried out by Rubens and Kurlbaum, on radiation emitted by fluorspar and rock salt, revealed that the spectral energy depends linearly, rather than exponentially, on T in the infrared part of the spectrum. A similar conclusion was reached about the same time by Lord Rayleigh on the basis of theoretical considerations.

The distribution laws of Wien and Rayleigh were thus seen to describe the spectral energy for the opposite limits $\lambda T \ll 1$ and $\lambda T \gg 1$, respectively. The task Planck set himself was to discover an expression for the radiancy $R_{b\lambda}$ of a blackbody that would comprise the limiting forms of Wien and Rayleigh as special cases, and hold for all intermediate values of λT as well. We may conveniently distinguish three steps in the theoretical researches performed toward this end.

As mentioned earlier, arguments advanced by Kirchhoff demonstrate that the properties of equilibrium radiation inside a cavity in no way depend on the nature of the walls, but exclusively upon its temperature. As a result, one has considerable freedom in choosing a model to represent the processes responsible for the emission and absorption of radiation by the walls. Planck accordingly hypothesized that the walls consist of minute charged linear oscillators characterized by definite but different natural frequencies. Due to damping forces, any one of these oscillators in a state of isolation would progressively lose its energy and thus undergo a decrease in the amplitude of its oscillation. However, since the oscillator always interacts with a surrounding radiation field of external origin, it will also absorb from this field radiation whose frequencies are equal or close to its own frequency. The oscillations will therefore be sustained; and at thermal equilibrium the fluctuations in energy will be symmetric, so that one can assign a definite average U to each oscillator.

One would be inclined to expect that U depends not only upon the temperature and the natural frequency of the oscillator in question, but on its charge and mass as well. It was consequently a great surprise when Planck was led by classical electrodynamics to the relation

$$U = \frac{c^3}{8\pi\nu^2}\, u_\nu, \tag{232}$$

which asserts that the energy of an oscillator is expressible solely in terms of its frequency ν and the energy density u_ν of the surrounding field in the frequency interval $(\nu,\ \nu + d\nu)$. To Planck this result was most gratifying, because it reduced the problem of finding the energy distribution $u_\nu = u_\nu(\nu,T)$ to the much simpler one of ascertaining the function $U = U(\nu,T)$. To find U was his next goal.

Attempts by Planck to determine U on the basis of classical electrodynamics did not meet with any success. He consequently decided to attack the problem from a thermodynamic point of view. The highly original idea then occurred to him to search for a connection between U and the entropy S of an oscillator rather than for the direct correlation of U with the temperature T. In this approach he endowed the oscillator with an entropy S such that

$$dS = \frac{dU}{T}. \tag{233}$$

From this definition of S, it follows that $dS/dU = 1/T$ and thence

$$\frac{d^2S}{dU^2} = -\frac{1/T^2}{dU/dT}. \tag{234}$$

Planck now invokes Wien's distribution law for short wavelengths, viz., $u_\lambda \propto \lambda^{-5} \exp -c_2/\lambda T$, and the empirical formula of Rubens and Kurlbaum for long wavelengths, viz., $u_\lambda \propto \lambda^{-4}T$. These relations, read in conjunction with Eq. (232) in the form $U = (\lambda^4/8\pi)u_\lambda$, lead to

$$U = Ae^{-B/T} \tag{235}$$

and

$$U = CT, \tag{236}$$

respectively, where A and B are both proportional to λ^{-1}, and C is independent of λ.

Equation (235) implies that $dU/dT = BU/T^2$ and Eq. (236) that $dU/dT = C$. On substituting the first expression for dU/dT in Eq. (234), one obtains

$$\frac{d^2S}{dU^2} = -\frac{1}{BU}, \tag{237}$$

while the second expression for dU/dT gives

$$\frac{d^2S}{dU^2} = -\frac{C}{U^2}. \tag{238}$$

Equations (237) and (238) state that d^2S/dU^2 is proportional to U^{-1} and U^{-2} for small and large energies, respectively. In conformity with these results, Planck ventured the guess that in the general case

$$\frac{d^2S}{dU^2} = -\left(BU + \frac{U^2}{C}\right)^{-1} = -\frac{1}{BU} + \frac{1/B}{BC + U}. \tag{239}$$

Integration of this equation yields, as $dS/dU = 1/T$,

$$\frac{1}{T} = \frac{1}{B}\log\left(1 + \frac{BC}{U}\right), \tag{240}$$

provided one chooses the integration constant such that $T \to \infty$ as $U \to \infty$. On inversion, Eq. (240) is seen to furnish the result

$$U = BC(e^{B/T} - 1)^{-1}. \tag{241}$$

Equation (241) represents the form in which Planck originally submitted his radiation law to the Berlin Physical Society at a meeting on October 19, 1900. Recalling that $R_{b\lambda} = (c/4)u_\lambda = (2\pi c/\lambda^4)U$ and that $B \propto \lambda^{-1}$, one easily perceives that Eq. (241) is identical in appearance with the radiation formula (217).

Planck naturally was not content with having discovered the correct radiation law by what he modestly called "a lucky intuition." He embarked without pausing on the task of exploring the law's true physical significance.

This final phase in his researches was brought to a successful conclusion with his proof of the radiation law in the explicit form (214), which he publicly announced on December 14, 1900.

No doubt the derivation of Eq. (214) was in itself an eminently important accomplishment. Of far greater consequence for the development of physics was however the pivotal assumption of the derivation: an oscillator of natural frequency v can emit and absorb energy only in multiples of hv, where h is a universal constant. This postulate—that the energy of an oscillator is quantized—Planck recognized to be indispensable if the entropy, defined by $dS/dU = 1/T$ in conjunction with Wien's law $\lambda T = $ constant, were to be a measure of probability, as posited by Boltzmann's relation $S = k \log W$. The last relation together with the assumption $\Delta U = nhv$ leads to the identifications $C = k$ and $B = hv/k$ in Eq. (241), and from there, with the aid of Eq. (232), to Eq. (214). Using the experimental data of Lummer and Pringsheim, on the one hand, and those of Rubens and Kurlbaum on the other, Planck was able to compute reasonably accurate values of h and k. The constant k, he noticed, is none other than the universal gas constant R divided by Avogadro's number N_0.

REFERENCES

BECKER, R. *Zeitschr. Phys.*, **128**, 120 (1950).

BECKER, R. *Theorie der Wärme*. Berlin: Springer, 1961.

BOLTZMANN, L. *Sitz.-Ber. Akad. Wiss. (Wien)*, **58**, 517 (1868).

BOLTZMANN, L. *Sitz.-Ber. Akad. Wiss. (Wien)*, **63**, 397 (1871).

BOLTZMANN, L. *Ann. Phys.*, **22**, 291 (1884).

BOSE, S. N. *Zeitschr. Phys.*, **26**, 178 (1924).

DAVIDSON, N. *Statistical Mechanics*. New York: McGraw-Hill, 1962.

DIRAC, P. A. M. *Proc. Roy. Soc. (London)*, A112, 661 (1926).

DRUDE, P. *Ann. Phys.*, **1**, 566 (1900).

DUSHMAN, S. *Rev. Mod. Phys.*, **2**, 381 (1930).

EINSTEIN, A. *Ann. Phys.*, **17**, 132 (1905).

EINSTEIN, A. *Sitz.-Ber. Akad. Wiss. (Berlin)*, *Phys.-math. Kl.*, **261** (1924); 3, 18 (1925).

FERMI, E. *Zeitschr. Phys.*, **36**, 902 (1926).

FEYNMAN, R. P. *Phys. Rev.*, **91**, 1301 (1953).

FEYNMAN, R. P. *Phys. Rev.*, **94**, 262 (1954).

FOWLER, R., and E. A. GUGGENHEIM. *Statistical Thermodynamics*. New York: Cambridge U.P., 1960.

GUGGENHEIM, E. A. "Thermodynamics, Classical and Statistical," in *Handbuch der Physik*. Vol. III/2. Berlin: Springer, 1959.

HILL, T. L. *An Introduction to Statistical Thermodynamics*. Reading, Mass.: Addison-Wesley, 1960.

JEANS, J. H. *Phil. Mag.*, **10**, 91 (1905).

KAHN, B., and G. E. UHLENBECK. *Physica*, **5**, 399 (1938).

KEESOM, W. H., and J. A. KOK. *Comm. Kamerlingh Onnes Lab.* (*Leiden*), **219d** (1932); **232d** (1933).

LANDAU, L. D. *J. Phys.* (*Moscow*), **5**, 71 (1941).

LONDON, F. *Phys. Rev.*, **54**, 948 (1938).

LONDON, F. *J. Phys. Chem.*, **43**, 49 (1939).

MAYER, J. E., and M. G. MAYER. *Statistical Mechanics*. New York: Wiley, 1940.

MÜNSTER, A. *Statistische Thermodynamik*. Berlin: Springer, 1956.

PAULI, W. *Zeitschr. Phys.*, **31**, 776 (1925).

PLANCK, M. *Verh. Deutsch. Phys. Ges.*, **2**, 237 (1900).

PLANCK, M. *Ann. Phys.*, **4**, 553 (1901).

PLANCK, M. *Vorlesungen über die Theorie der Wärmestrahlung*. Leipzig: Barth, 1923.

PLANCK, M. *A Scientific Autobiography and Other Papers*. London: Williams & Norgate, 1950.

RAYLEIGH, LORD. *Phil. Mag.*, **49**, 539 (1900).

RICHARDSON, O. W. *Emission of Electricity from Hot Bodies*. London: Longmans, 1921.

ROCARD, Y. *Thermodynamics*. Translated from the French by C. R. S. Manders. London: Pitman, 1961.

RUSHBROOKE, G. S. *Introduction to Statistical Mechanics*. London: Oxford U.P., 1962.

SACKUR, O. *Ann. Phys.*, **40**, 67, 87 (1913).

SCHRÖDINGER, E. *Statistical Thermodynamics*. New York: Cambridge U.P., 1952.

SOMMERFELD, A. *Zeitschr. Phys.*, **47**, 1 (1928).

SOMMERFELD, A. *Thermodynamics and Statistical Mechanics*. Translated from the German by J. Kestin. New York: Academic, 1956.

STEFAN, J. *Sitz.-Ber. Akad. Wiss.* (*Wien*), **79**, 391 (1879).

TETRODE, H. *Ann. Phys.*, **38**, 434 (1912).

TISZA, L. *Nature*, **141**, 913 (1938).

TISZA, L. *J. Phys. et Radium*, **1**, 164, 359 (1940).

TISZA, L. *Phys. Rev.*, **72**, 838 (1947).

WIEN, W. *Sitz.-Ber. Akad. Wiss.* (*Berlin*), *Phys.-math. Kl.*, **55** (1893).

WIEN, W. *Ann. Phys.*, **58**, 662 (1896).

WILSON, A. H. *Thermodynamics and Statistical Mechanics*. New York: Cambridge U.P., 1960.

4

STATISTICAL THEORY AND MORE
COMPLEX PHYSICAL SYSTEMS

4-1. Low-Density Ideal Molecular Gases

UP to the present point we have calculated thermodynamic properties only for (effectively) structureless particles. Our results have consequently enjoyed limited physical application. We now propose to extend the scope of our considerations to include one-component molecular systems as well. Such a system shall exist in its gaseous state, and it will be assumed that the average distance between molecules is so large that one may neglect the intermolecular forces and hence treat the system as a dilute ideal gas. The discussion at the beginning of Section $3-2$ then shows that the molecules will obey Boltzmann's distribution law, $\bar{n}_j = \exp -(\alpha + \beta \varepsilon_j)$ [Eq. (102), Chapter 3], for BE as well as FD molecules. The vanishing of the distinction between BE and FD molecules permits of a simple physical explanation: when the number of molecular (i.e., single-particle) quantum states of energy $\varepsilon_j \gtrsim kT$ far exceeds the total number of molecules, the chances of more than one molecule occupying a given state are anyway so slight that it makes no practical difference whether one supposes that such an event is allowed (BE statistics) or forbidden (FD statistics).

Employing the Boltzmann distribution law, we found earlier that the grand partition function $\mathfrak{Z}$ is related to the *molecular partition function $Z_1 = \sum \exp -\beta \varepsilon_j$* [Eq. (26), Chapter 3] by virtue of the equation $\log \mathfrak{Z} = Z_1 \exp -\alpha$ [Eq. (25), Chapter 3]. It is convenient to eliminate the parameter α appearing here in favor of the parameter N signifying the total number of molecules. This amounts to our operating with the canonical partition function $Z = Z(T,V,N)$ that corresponds to $N = \bar{N}$, the average number of molecules associated with prescribed values for β, V, α.

The partition function Z can be expressed in a more tractable form by the following argument. From Eqs. (100) and (145) of Chapter 2, one has $\beta F = -\log Z$ and $\beta p V = \log \mathfrak{Z}$, respectively. Recalling the definitions $\mu N = G = F + pV$, we thus obtain $\log \mathfrak{Z} = \beta p V = \beta(\mu N - F) = -\alpha N + \log Z$, that is,

$$\log Z = \log \mathfrak{Z} + \alpha N. \tag{1}$$

But for the special case of a low-density ideal gas ($\exp \alpha \gg 1$),

$$N = e^{-\alpha} Z_1 \tag{2}$$

by Eqs. (23), Chapter 3, and

$$\log \mathfrak{Z} = N \tag{3}$$

by Eq. (25), Chapter 3, and Eq. (2) above. Thus, Eq. (1) becomes $\log Z = N + \alpha N$, or, since $\alpha = \log (Z_1/N)$ from (2),

$$\log Z = N + N \log \frac{Z_1}{N} = \log \frac{Z_1^N}{N!}, \tag{4}$$

where Stirling's formula $\log N! = N \log N - N$ has been utilized in the last step. In consequence we find the important approximate result

$$\boxed{Z = \frac{Z_1^N}{N!}.} \tag{5}$$

The striking feature of Eq. (5) is the presence of the divisor $N!$. How can the division by $N!$ be understood physically? By definition, the partition function Z is a sum in which each independent quantum state i of the gas, with energy E_i, contributes a term $\exp -\beta E_i$. The molecular partition function Z_1, on the other hand, is composed of one term $\exp -\beta \varepsilon_j$ for each state j of a single molecule. Hence, in the sum expressing Z_1^N there occurs one term $\exp -\beta E_i$ for each conceivable permutation of any particular set of N molecular states among N molecules. This means that in Z_1^N, in contrast with Z, most quantum states of the gas appear more than once. Indeed, if the molecular states are all different from one another, they give rise, on permutation among the N molecules, to $N!$ terms in Z_1^N. Contrariwise, in Z they correspond to only one term; for, due to the indistinguishability of the molecules in a one-component gas, mere interchange of molecules with respect to their states does not furnish new quantum states of the gas as a whole. If therefore Z_1^N contained only terms corresponding to the occupation by each molecule of a different molecular state, division of Z_1^N by $N!$ would convert it into Z.

We easily recognize though that the foregoing condition is not fulfilled. In reality, Z_1^N also comprises many terms representing quantum states in which two or more molecules occupy the same molecular state. These terms are absent from the expression for Z in case the molecules obey FD statistics; and when they do occur in Z, due to the applicability of BE statistics, the correction factor is obviously no longer simply $(N!)^{-1}$. By reason of this, there does not exist in general a direct relation between Z and Z_1^N. Nevertheless, for the low-density gas under consideration—as we have already pointed out—the multiple occupancy of a molecular state is relatively speaking a very rare event, owing to the preponderance of the number of low-energy states over the number of molecules. It follows that terms relating to multiple occupancy make only a trivial contribution to Z_1^N and can, for practical purposes, be neglected. In this way, no serious error is committed if one applies the same correction factor $(N!)^{-1}$ to all terms of Z_1^N to obtain Z, as in Eq. (5).

Since all the thermodynamic properties of our gaseous system are determinable once the function $Z(T,V,N)$ is known, our problem has been reduced to the computation of the molecular partition function Z_1, by Eq. (5). The explicit determination of Z_1 is rendered complicated in the present instance by the fact that, in addition to the coordinates of its center of mass, a molecule possesses many more coordinates, to wit, those describing the motions of its electrons and nuclear constituents relative to its center of mass. These motions introduce so-called *internal degrees of freedom*. Fortunately, an appropriate choice of coordinates will cause the Hamiltonian function of a molecule to become separable in its individual coordinates or sets of them. This means that if we postulate, for the sake of argument, three such sets of coordinates, representing the sets of degrees of freedom A, B, C, we get

$$H = H_A + H_B + H_C, \tag{6}$$

where, for example, H_A is a function only of the coordinates corresponding to the set A and their conjugate momenta. When Eq. (6) is satisfied, quantum mechanics tells us that the energy eigenvalues of a molecule are given by

$$\varepsilon_{ijk} = \varepsilon_i^A + \varepsilon_j^B + \varepsilon_k^C, \tag{7}$$

with ε_i^A (all i), ε_j^B (all j), ε_k^C (all k) signifying the eigenvalues of H_A, H_B, H_C, respectively. Thus, the molecular partition function

$$Z_1 = \sum_i \sum_j \sum_k e^{-\beta\varepsilon_{ijk}} = \sum_i e^{-\beta\varepsilon_i^A} \sum_j e^{-\beta\varepsilon_j^B} \sum_k e^{-\beta\varepsilon_k^C} = \zeta_A \zeta_B \zeta_C \tag{8}$$

factorizes into the partition functions ζ_A, ζ_B, ζ_C, where

$$\zeta_A = \sum_i e^{-\beta\varepsilon_i^A}, \tag{9}$$

and similarly for ζ_B and ζ_C. Because of the result in Eq. (8), the many-coordinate problem of determining Z_1 is seen to resolve into the relatively simple task of computing a few partition functions which individually involve only one coordinate or at worst a small set of coordinates.

One notices, moreover, that by Eq. (8) these partition functions appear as factors of Z_1. Each set of coordinates is therefore responsible for an additive contribution to $\log Z = N \log Z_1 - \log N!$ and hence to those thermodynamic properties derivable from $\log Z$ in agreement with Eqs. (102) to (105) of Chapter 2. With reference to Eq. (105), for instance, Eqs. (8) and (102), Chapter 3, show that

$$U = -\left(\frac{\partial \log Z}{\partial \beta}\right)_{V,N} = U_A + U_B + U_C, \tag{10}$$

where

$$U_A = -N\left(\frac{\partial \log \zeta_A}{\partial \beta}\right)_V, \tag{11}$$

while U_B and U_C may be defined by analogy.

The method whereby functions of the type Eq. (9) may be computed, depends on the relative position of the energy levels in the energy level scheme associated with a particular set of degrees of freedom such as A. With regard to the spacing of these energy levels, one can distinguish the following three possibilities.

First, let the energy of the first excited state exceed that of the lowest level by an amount $\Delta \varepsilon^A \gg kT$. If one then denotes the degeneracy of the lowest level by g_0^A, the only significant contribution to ζ_A will derive from its first g_0^A terms, so that one finds approximately

$$\zeta_A = g_0^A e^{-\beta \varepsilon_0^A}, \tag{12}$$

where ε_0^A stands for the lowest energy eigenvalue. It is customary to say that the degrees of freedom A are *unexcited*. We might add that if only a few degrees of freedom are involved in A, then g_0^A, which may include degeneracy arising from angular momentum (orbital and spin), generally has a value unity or of the order unity.

A second possibility—the antithesis of the first one—obtains when the distances between energy levels are much smaller than kT, i.e., $\Delta \varepsilon^A \ll kT$, in any case for the low-lying energy levels, which make the major contribution to ζ_A. In this event, one commits no appreciable error if one substitutes for the sum-over-states on the right-hand side of Eq. (9) an integral over ε^A of $g(\varepsilon^A) \exp -\beta \varepsilon^A$, with $g(\varepsilon^A)d\varepsilon^A$ denoting the number of states in the energy interval ε^A to $\varepsilon^A + d\varepsilon^A$. Suppose the set A consists of n degrees of freedom which are described in classical mechanics by the generalized coordinates $q_1, q_2, \ldots, q_n$, then it is true—as the reader may verify for the special examples to be presented later on—that this integral is identical with the $2n$-dimensional integral

$$\zeta_{A\,\text{class}} = \frac{1}{h^n} \int \cdots \int e^{-\beta H_A} dq_1 \ldots dq_n \, dp_1 \ldots dp_n \,. \tag{13}$$

The integration is here extended over all those values of the q's and p's that the molecule, treated as a classical system, can assume. Since the integral (13) may be calculated without an appeal to quantum mechanics, the degrees of freedom A are called *classical* when the conditions $\Delta\varepsilon^A \ll kT$ are fulfilled. Obviously, all degrees of freedom other than those relating to spin will come under this heading provided the temperature T is sufficiently high. *

There remains finally the case for which neither of the two cited possibilities occurs, as in the situation where the spacing $\Delta\varepsilon^A \sim kT$ for many of the low-energy levels. It is then customary to refer to the set A as *quantum degrees of freedom*. For such a set it is no longer legitimate to approximate the sum in Eq. (9) by an integral. Nor will it be possible, on the whole, to express this sum in terms of some simple tabulated function(s); in that case one has to perform a numerical calculation of the sum as it stands, to the degree of accuracy desired.

The formula (13) has a consequence of considerable interest, which we shall often encounter in our further discussions. It may be arrived at in the following manner. On replacing ζ_A in Eq. (11) by its classical value (13), one gets

$$\frac{U_A}{N} = \frac{\iint H_A e^{-\beta H_A} dq\,dp}{\iint e^{-\beta H_A} dq\,dp} = \langle H_A \rangle, \tag{14}$$

the canonical phase average of H_A, where the notation $dq = dq_1 dq_2 \ldots dq_n$ and $dp = dp_1 dp_2 \ldots dp_n$ has been used for brevity. Let now H_A depend on one of the variables q_i, p_i $(i = 1, 2, \ldots, n)$ only through an additive squared term. If this variable is denoted by the symbol z, our assumption reads

$$H_A = az^2 + H_A', \tag{15}$$

where the coefficient a is independent of z, and H_A' stands for a sum of terms not containing z. Substitution of Eq. (15) causes the right-hand side of Eq. (14) to resolve into two terms:

$$\frac{U_A}{N} = \frac{U_z}{N} + \frac{U_A'}{N}, \tag{16}$$

---

*A formal justification of the claim that, in the expression for the canonical partition function belonging to n classical degrees of freedom, a volume h^n in phase space is to be associated with every quantum state, as in Eq. (13), is presented, e.g., in: Kirkwood, J. G. *Phys. Rev.*, **44**, 31 (1933), or Huang, K. *Statistical Mechanics*, Sec. 10.2. New York: Wiley, 1963.

such that $U_z/N = <az^2>$ and $U_A'/N = <H_A'>$. Since

$$az^2 e^{-\beta H_A} = \tfrac{1}{2}z(\partial H_A/\partial z) \, e^{-\beta H_A} = -\frac{z}{2\beta}(\partial e^{-\beta H_A}/\partial z),$$

this means that
$$\frac{U_z}{N} = -\frac{1}{2\beta} \frac{\iint z(\partial e^{-\beta H_A}/\partial z)dz(dqdp)'}{\iint e^{-\beta H_A} \, dqdp}, \tag{17}$$

where $dz(dqdp)' \equiv dqdp$. If on the right-hand side we now integrate by parts over z, while assuming that the boundary contribution vanishes (which will be the case if the integration limits for z are 0 or infinite), then the numerator of (17) is seen to transform to the negative of the integral in its denominator. Thus, Eq.(17) reduces simply to

$$\boxed{\frac{U_z}{N} = \frac{kT}{2}}. \tag{18}$$

Equation (18) is the analytical expression of *Boltzmann's equipartition theorem* (1871) in a rather general form.* It asserts that in a gas in thermostatic equilibrium at a temperature T, each molecule possesses a mean energy $kT/2$ for every separable [in the sense of Eq. (15)] squared term occurring in its Hamiltonian. This theorem, as our discussion has shown, is valid only provided the variables in question relate to classical degrees of freedom.

Equation (13) has another implication, which is of major theoretical significance. On comparison with Eq. (9), formula (13) reveals that in the classical limit any quantum state of a molecule with f degrees of freedom corresponds to a cell of volume $dq_1 \ldots dq_f \, dp_1 \ldots dp_f$ equal to h^f in the molecular phase space, or μ-space. This fact agrees with the uncertainty principle, according to which—the reader will recall—any coordinate q and its canonically conjugate momentum p cannot be measured simultaneously with an accuracy greater than that allowed by the relation $\Delta q \Delta p \sim h$. Division of the volume element in Eq. (13) by h^n incidentally also ensures that the right-hand side of this equation becomes dimensionless. To complete our argument, we substitute Eq. (13) in Eq. (5) to find the classical partition function for a gas consisting of N similar molecules, each having f degrees of freedom; we get

$$\boxed{Z_{\text{class}} = \frac{1}{N!h^{fN}} \int\int e^{-\beta H(q,p)} \, dqdp} \tag{19}$$

on employing the abbreviation $dqdp = dq_1 \ldots dq_{fN} \, dp_1 \ldots dp_{fN}$ and if $H(q,p)$ stands for the Hamiltonian of the gas.

When compared with the definition $Z = \sum \exp -\beta E_j$, Eq. (19) is seen to

---

*See Problem 1(a) for Tolman's (1918) general version of this theorem, which requires restrictions to be placed only on the behavior of the Hamiltonian at the limits of integration.

aver: one effects for a gas the transition from quantum to classical theory by associating with each of its quantum states a cell in its phase space, i.e., γ-space, of volume $N!h^{fN}$. The salient point here is that the volume of the elementary cell is not simply h^{fN}, as a direct generalization of the transition rule for a single molecule would demand.

This $N!$-fold enlargement of the elementary cell in γ-space, just as the division by $N!$ in Eq. (5), has its origin in the indistinguishability of the molecules in a one-component gas, as postulated by quantum mechanics. For the sake of understanding this proposition better, let us label the individual molecules by the numbers $1, 2, \ldots, N$, as one may according to classical views. The most detailed specification of the state of the gas, that is at the same time compatible with the uncertainty principle, will then consist in an assertion of the following kind: the phase points of the molecules 1, 2, etc. lie respectively within fixed cells a, b, etc., with volume of the order h^f in μ-space. The same state is represented in γ-space by a single phase point occupying a cell of volume $\Delta q \Delta p \sim h^{fN}$ centered at a fixed point (q,p).

At high temperatures we may assume that the cells a, b, etc., hardly ever coincide completely, so that the phase points representing the states of the molecules 1, 2, etc., can be permuted in $N!$ ways among the given cells a, b, etc. Since, according to the quantum viewpoint, the molecules cannot be distinguished from one another, these permutations will leave the quantum state of the gas unchanged. The permutations will nevertheless cause the phase point representing the detailed state of the gas as a whole to roam generally over $N!$ different cells in γ-space, each of volume h^{fN}; thus a volume $N!h^{fN}$ is covered in all. We therefore conclude that a single quantum state of the gas should be associated with an element of volume $N!h^{fN}$ in γ-space when one calculates the classical partition function Z_{class}.

4–2. Thermodynamic Properties of Monatomic Ideal Gases

In the present section we propose to study monatomic ideal gases, which provide us with the simplest application of the theory expounded above. Our interest will center mainly on the internal energy and the heat capacity of such a system.

From among the degrees of freedom of a monatomic molecule, three can be chosen to characterize the motion of its center of mass. We shall refer to them as the *translational degrees of freedom*. There remain the internal degrees of freedom, which will in this case describe the motions of the electronic and nucleonic constituents of the molecule relative to its center of mass. These are called the *electronic* and *nucleonic* or *nuclear degrees of freedom*, respectively.

Now, independent of whether a molecule is monatomic or not, one is always allowed to separate its translational from its internal degrees of freedom. In consequence, the Hamiltonian of any molecule has the form

$$H = H_{tr} + H_{int}, \tag{20}$$

where H_{tr} is a function solely of the momenta conjugate to the translational coordinates, while H_{int} involves only the internal degrees of freedom. This statement corresponds to a well-known result of classical mechanics, asserting that the kinetic energy E_{kin} of a system of particles can be written as the sum $m\mathbf{v}^2/2 + E'_{kin}$; here m stands for the mass of the system and $\mathbf{v}$ for the velocity of its center of mass, whereas E'_{kin} denotes the kinetic energy with respect to a nonrotating system of axes whose origin coincides permanently with the center of mass.

Before proceeding with our main argument, we might render more precise the meaning of "separation of coordinates" in quantum mechanics. The symbol H appearing in Eq. (20), and in similar equations later on, is closely related to, but not synonymous with, the Hamiltonian (function) of classical mechanics. It signifies really the so-called *Hamiltonian operator*. One constructs it in the simplest cases from the classical Hamiltonian $H(q,p)$ of a molecule merely by replacing each cartesian momentum p_j by the differential operator $-i\hbar(\partial/\partial q_j)$; but in general it contains additional energy terms stemming from interactions that are unknown in classical theory. An illustration of these purely quantum interactions will be given later on.

Whatever the form of the Hamiltonian operator, the following fact holds. If ϕ represents an energy eigenstate of a molecule, then the associated energy eigenvalue ε obeys the equation

$$H\phi = \varepsilon\phi. \tag{21}$$

This means that an energy eigenfunction distinguishes itself from other functions of the position and spin coordinates of a molecule by this property: when it is acted upon by the Hamiltonian operator, the only effect is its multiplication by a constant ε which is characteristic of the eigenfunction. Corresponding to the splitting of H into the terms H_{tr} and H_{int}, the eigenfunction can be written as the product $\phi = \phi^{tr}\phi^{int}$ such that $H_{tr}\phi^{tr} = \varepsilon^{tr}\phi^{tr}$ and $H_{int}\phi^{int} = \varepsilon^{int}\phi^{int}$.

In spite of the foregoing remarks, we shall continue to refer indiscriminately to H as the Hamiltonian, as it will always be clear from the context whether we have the classical function or the quantum-mechanical operator in mind.

We now resume the thread of our main argument. Analysis of H_{int} with the view of separating the electronic from the nucleonic degrees of freedom would show that $H_{int} = H_{el} + H_{nuc} + H'$, where H' contains electronic as well as nucleonic variables. However, it is commonly supposed that the interaction term H' is very small compared with either H_{el} or H_{nuc}, so that with negligible inaccuracy the separation of electronic from nucleonic degrees of freedom can be realized. Thus, we may rewrite Eq. (20) to read approximately

$$H = H_{tr} + H_{el} + H_{nuc}. \tag{22}$$

By Eq. (8), the molecular partition function accordingly becomes

$$Z_1 = \zeta_{tr}\zeta_{el}\zeta_{nuc}. \tag{23}$$

We intend to examine, one by one, the partition functions appearing on the right-hand side of Eq. (23).

From the observation following Eq. (20), one infers that, for a molecule of mass m,

$$H_{tr} = \frac{1}{2m}(p_x^2 + p_y^2 + p_z^2), \tag{24}$$

in which $(p_x, p_y, p_z) = (mv_x, mv_y, mv_z)$, or $\mathbf{p} = m\mathbf{v}$, if $\mathbf{v}$ denotes the velocity of the molecule's center of mass. Since the function (24) has the same form as the Hamiltonian of a free particle, its eigenvalues ε_i^{tr} are given by the right-hand side of Eq. (27), Chapter 3. By analogy with Eq. (28), Chapter 3, we therefore get

$$\zeta_{tr}^{1/3} = \sum_{n_x=1}^{\infty} \exp{-\frac{\beta h^2}{8mV^{2/3}} n_x^2}. \tag{25}$$

The distance $\Delta\varepsilon^{tr}$ between any two low-lying translational energy levels is, according to Eq. (27), Chapter 3, a small multiple of $h^2/8mV^{2/3}$. This energy unit—the reader may easily verify—is of the order $10^{-14}k$ for a helium molecule ($m \approx 4 \times 1.67 \times 10^{-24}$ gm) when $V = 1$ cm³; for heavier molecules and larger volumes the unit obviously has an even smaller value. Therefore, $\Delta\varepsilon^{tr} \ll kT$ at all attainable temperatures and for all translational quantum states contributing significantly to ζ_{tr}, so that the translational degrees of freedom are classical without any doubt. As a consequence of the inequality just stated, one is entitled to replace the sum in Eq. (25) by an integral with respect to n_x. Such a substitution has already been carried out in Section 3–2, and leads, as Eq. (30), Chapter 3, shows, to the result

$$\zeta_{tr} = V\Lambda^{-3}, \tag{26}$$

with the abbreviation $\Lambda = h/(2\pi mkT)^{1/2}$.

In Section 4–1 we maintained that the partition function for any set of classical degrees of freedom is furnished by Eq. (13). Let us digress here for a moment to demonstrate that this is indeed true for translational motion. If Eq. (13) is combined with Eq. (24), one finds, with $V = L^3$, that

$$\zeta_{tr}^{1/3} = \frac{1}{h} \int_0^L \int_{-\infty}^{\infty} \left(\exp -\frac{\beta p_x^2}{2m} \right) dx \, dp_x = \frac{L}{h} \int_{-\infty}^{\infty} \left(\exp -\frac{\beta p_x^2}{2m} \right) dp_x$$

$$= \left(\frac{2\pi m}{\beta} \right)^{1/2} \frac{L}{h}.$$

That is, $\zeta_{tr} = (2\pi m k T)^{3/2}(V/h^3)$, which agrees with the result Eq. (26).

Of all the possible thermodynamic functions that can be obtained from Eq. (26), we write down only

$$U_{tr} = \tfrac{3}{2} NkT, \tag{27}$$

which follows from Eq. (11), and

$$\boxed{C_V^{tr} = \frac{dU_{tr}}{dT} = \tfrac{3}{2} Nk}. \tag{28}$$

The last equation is, of course, none other than the equipartition theorem applied to H_{tr}.

In order to discuss the partition function ζ_{el} satisfactorily, it will be necessary to examine first the classification of the eigenvalues of H_{el} in some detail.

Naturally, for an isolated atom whose nucleus contains Z protons and is surrounded by n electrons, H_{el} includes the kinetic energy of the electrons as well as the terms

$$- \sum_{i=1}^{n} \frac{Ze^2}{r_i} + \frac{1}{2} \sum_{i \neq j}^{n} \sum_{j}^{n} \frac{e^2}{|\mathbf{r}_i - \mathbf{r}_j|} \tag{29}$$

affording the potential energies that correspond respectively to the electron-nucleus and electron-electron Coulomb interactions. In addition though, H_{el} comprises the nonclassical terms

$$\sum_{i=1}^{n} \xi(\mathbf{r}_i) \mathbf{L}_i \cdot \mathbf{S}_i, \tag{30}$$

in which $\mathbf{L}_i$ denotes the orbital angular momentum and $\mathbf{S}_i$ the spin angular momentum of the ith electron, while the form of the function $\xi(\mathbf{r}_i)$ need not concern us here. The so-called *spin-orbit energy*, Eq. (30), is readily explained: $\xi(\mathbf{r}_i)\mathbf{L}_i \cdot \mathbf{S}_i$ represents the energy that originates from the interaction between the magnetic moments associated with each of the angular momenta L_i and S_i.

Consider next the angular momenta defined by the equations

$$L = \sum_{i=1}^{n} L_i, \tag{31}$$

$$S = \sum_{i=1}^{n} S_i, \tag{32}$$

$$J = L + S. \tag{33}$$

The operator J has a very useful property in that it (i.e., every one of its components J_x, J_y, J_z) *commutes* with the operator H_{el}, or, in symbols, $JH_{el} = H_{el}J$. The commutation of J with H_{el} is attributable to the obvious fact that H_{el} is not altered by any rotation of the system of electrons in physical space. By reason of the commutability of J with H_{el}, quantum-mechanical theory further asserts that the eigenstates of H_{el} may be chosen to be also eigenstates of anyone of the components J_x, J_y, J_z, say J_z; only one component is here singled out because J_x, J_y, J_z do not commute among themselves.

In support of the claim that simultaneous eigenstates of H_{el} and J_z exist, let ϕ represent an eigenstate of H_{el} belonging to the energy ε^{el}. Then, owing to the propositions $H_{el}J_z\phi = J_z H_{el}\phi$ and $H_{el}\phi = \varepsilon^{el}\phi$, one sees that $H_{el}J_z\phi = \varepsilon^{el}J_z\phi$, or that $J_z\phi$ is an eigenstate of H_{el} with the same eigenvalue, ε^{el}, as ϕ. Thus no inconsistency arises from the assumption $J_z\phi \propto \phi$, which implies that ϕ is an eigenstate of J_z too.

From $JH_{el} = H_{el}J$, one infers that $J^2 H_{el} = H_{el}J^2$. It could moreover be shown that $J^2 J_z = J_z J^2$ as well, and hence that suitable linear combinations of electronic energy eigenstates will yield simultaneous eigenstates of H_{el}, J^2, and J_z. Accordingly we shall suppose that the eigenstates of H_{el} are identified partly by the quantum numbers J and M. These numbers are defined so that $J(J + 1)\hbar^2$ provides the eigenvalues of J^2, and $M\hbar$ those of J_z, for particular values of J and M that are specified below.

If the spin-orbit contribution, Eq. (30), to H_{el} is neglected, the angular momenta L and S separately, besides their sum J, commute with H_{el}. In analogy with the treatment of J, the quantum numbers L, M_L, S, M_S can therefore be employed to further characterize the electronic energy eigenstates. However, since M_L and M_S are dependent upon J and M, we need not consider them. We are thus left with L, S, J, M as a set of labels essential to a unique classification of the electronic eigenstates. These quantum numbers are capable of assuming the values $L = 0, 1, 2, \ldots$, $S = 0, \frac{1}{2}, 1, \frac{3}{2}, \ldots$, $J =$

$L + S, L + S - 1, \ldots, |L - S|$, and $M = -J, -J + 1, \ldots, J$. It follows that, for a given L, the number of possible J values is $2S + 1$, if $L > S$, or $2L + 1$, if $L < S$; as a special case, $L = 0$ entails that J can have only one value, viz., $J = S$. It is seen furthermore that M can take on $2J + 1$ different values.

In specifying the electronic energy eigenvalues, the labels L and S should be retained. Indeed, due to the energies $e^2/|\mathbf{r}_i - \mathbf{r}_j|$ in Eq. (29), energy levels with different values of L and S are widely separated; these levels are known as (*spectral*) *terms*. The labels J and M, however, become superfluous, owing to the coincidence, in regard to energy, of eigenstates having different values of J and M. This degeneracy with respect to the "directional" quantum number M must be ascribed to the spherical symmetry of H_{el} for an isolated atom.

Up to this point, the spin-orbit energy, Eq. (30), has been ignored. Inclusion of this energy does not remove the $(2J + 1)$-fold degeneracy with respect to M. But it does lift the degeneracy in J. This means that each spectral term is split into either $2S + 1$ or $2L + 1$ (*spectral*) *components*, depending on whether $L > S$ or $L < S$. Hence it is now required to use the labels L, S, J to identify the (still degenerate) electronic energy levels.

It should be added that L and S are, strictly speaking, no longer legitimate labels, as the operators $\mathbf{L}^2$ and $\mathbf{S}^2$ fail to commute with the spin-orbit energy. However, for most light atoms—and only those interest us—this energy is insignificant compared with the Coulomb interactions among electrons. As a result, the distances between terms are much greater than the spacings of the components within any term. Overlapping of terms is thus avoided, and it remains possible to associate definite values of L and S with each level.

We will finally explain the manner in which the electronic energy levels are customarily designated. The *multiplicity* of a spectral term is, by definition, always taken to be $2S + 1$, despite the fact that there are $2S + 1$ components in a term only when $L > S$. Corresponding to $S = 0, \frac{1}{2}, 1$, etc., one therefore speaks of terms as *singlets, doublets, triplets*, and so on. It is also the practice to employ the code $S, P, D, F, G, \ldots$ when one wishes to indicate that L has one of the values $L = 0, 1, 2, 3, 4, \ldots$, respectively. The reader is cautioned not to confound the latter S with the spin quantum number S; between the two there is no connection whatsoever. In agreement with these remarks, the notation adopted to define the electronic energy levels is $^{2S+1}L_J$, where the superscript stands for the multiplicity and the value of L has to be stipulated according to the code $S, P, D, \ldots$. Thus, for example, a level with $L = 1$, $S = \frac{1}{2}$, $J = \frac{3}{2}$ will be written as $^2P_{3/2}$.

After this rather lengthy digression, we are now equipped to formulate our ideas pertaining to the electronic partition function ζ_{el} with greater precision.

For hydrogen atoms, inert gases (He, Ne, A, Kr, Xe, Rn), as well as the vapors of alkali metals (Na, K, Li) and alkaline earth metals (Ca, Sr, Ba), the ground spectral term is an S-term; it thus consists of a single level $(2L + 1 = 1)$. The spacing $\Delta\varepsilon^{el}$ between this level and the next higher one ranges from about 1 to 20 electron-volts, where 1 ev $= 1.602 \times 10^{-12}$ erg. Since $kT = 8.62 \times 10^{-5}T \deg^{-1}$ev, it follows that $\Delta\varepsilon^{el} \sim kT$ when $T \sim 10^{5}$°K; hence $\Delta\varepsilon^{el} \ll kT$, i.e., the electronic degrees of freedom are unexcited, for all temperatures below at least 2000°K. One consequently has, by virtue of Eq. (12),

$$\zeta_{el} = g_0^{el} \tag{34}$$

if the energy of the lowest electronic level is put equal to zero. The degeneracy g_0^{el} of this level is $2J + 1 = 1$ for the inert gases and $2J + 1 = 2$ for hydrogen atoms and the alkali metals, inasmuch as the terms in question are $^1S_0$ and $^2S_{1/2}$, respectively.

The singleness of the ground term, on which Eq. (34) depends, does in general not obtain. In atoms other than those mentioned above, the lowest term often comprises two or more components endowed with spacings which are of the order kT or less. When this is the case, one obviously has to retain also some excited states in the computation of the function ζ_{el}. A simple illustration is afforded by the halogen atoms F, Cl, Br, I. Here the ground term consists of two levels: $^2P_{3/2}$ with degeneracy 4 and, above it, $^2P_{1/2}$ with degeneracy 2. The separation $\Delta\varepsilon^{el}$ between these levels is, in order of magnitude, 10^{-1} ev for fluorine, chlorine, bromine and 1 ev for iodine, as opposed to the distance 10 ev between the level $^2P_{1/2}$ and the first level of the next higher term. We are consequently obliged, at least when treating F, Cl, Br, to go one step further than in Eq. (34) and get

$$\zeta_{el} = 4 + 2 \exp -\frac{\Delta\varepsilon^{el}}{kT}. \tag{35}$$

We finally consider the nucleonic partition function ζ_{nuc}. The situation here is uncomplicated. At temperatures attainable in practice, the spacing $\Delta\varepsilon^{nuc}$ between the two lowest levels of the energy H_{nuc} always far exceeds kT. In fact, $\Delta\varepsilon^{nuc} \sim 10^6$ ev, so that $\Delta\varepsilon^{nuc} \sim kT$ only for temperatures $T \sim 10^{10}$°K. For purely thermal systems, the nucleonic degrees of freedom can therefore be assumed to be unexcited. We write accordingly

$$\zeta_{nuc} = g_0^{nuc}, \tag{36}$$

choosing ε^{nuc} to be zero when the nucleus occupies its ground state. The degeneracy g_0^{nuc} of the lowest nuclear level equals $2I + 1$, if I denotes the quantum number appropriate to the total angular momentum of the nucleus, that is, to the so-called *nuclear spin*.

On the basis of Eqs. (34) and (36) we infer that neither the electronic nor the nucleonic degrees of freedom make any contribution to the heat capacity. Thus, to recapitulate, the additive contributions to the heat capacity C_V of an atom has been shown to be: $C_V^{tr} = 3k/2$, $C_V^{el} = C_V^{nuc} = 0$. It follows that one has, for a monatomic molecule,

$$C_V = \frac{3k}{2}, \tag{37}$$

$$C_p = \frac{5k}{2}, \tag{38}$$

$$\gamma = \frac{C_p}{C_V} = \frac{5}{3} = 1.667. \tag{39}$$

These formulas are very satisfactorily confirmed by measurements carried out in various temperature and pressure regions. So, for instance, experimental values of the ratio γ do not differ from the theoretical value 1.667 by more than one or two per cent for sufficiently low pressures.

4–3. Separation of Degrees of Freedom in a Diatomic Molecule

We turn now to a discussion of ideal diatomic gases. In this section we shall be concerned with the manner in which the molecular Hamiltonian can be divided or split to simplify our task.

The spatial configuration of a diatomic molecule will be known once we have specified, with respect to some fixed set of axes, the coordinates of its electrons and its nuclei, as well as the position of each of its nucleons (protons and neutrons) inside the nucleus to which the nucleon belongs. These latter nucleonic, or intranuclear, coordinates separate out, as in the case of a monatomic molecule, and hence make an additive contribution H_{nuc} to the molecular Hamiltonian. Consequently, we are permitted to ignore the structure of nuclei and treat them as if they were point particles.

The configuration of a diatomic molecule will then be determined, for example, by the cartesian coordinates

$$x_1, y_1, z_1, x_2, y_2, z_2, \ldots \quad \text{(or } x, \text{ for short)}$$

of its electrons together with the cartesian coordinates

$$X_1, Y_1, Z_1, X_2, Y_2, Z_2 \quad \text{(or } X, \text{ for short)}$$

which fix the positions of its nuclei. Let further m be the mass of an electron and M_1 and M_2 the masses of the nuclei. If one neglects spin-dependent forces, the Hamiltonian H of the molecules is then composed of the terms given by

$$H = H_{\text{nuc}} + H_{\text{el}}^{\text{kin}} + H_{\text{nuclei}}^{\text{kin}} + H_{\text{pot}}. \tag{40}$$

Here

$$H_{\text{el}}^{\text{kin}} = -\frac{\hbar^2}{2m} \sum_i \left(\frac{\partial^2}{\partial x_i^2} + \frac{\partial^2}{\partial y_i^2} + \frac{\partial^2}{\partial z_i^2} \right) \tag{41}$$

is the operator corresponding to the kinetic energy of the electrons,

$$H_{\text{nuclei}}^{\text{kin}} = -\frac{\hbar^2}{2} \left(\frac{1}{M_1} \frac{\partial^2}{\partial X_1^2} + \frac{1}{M_2} \frac{\partial^2}{\partial X_2^2} + \text{similar terms in } Y_1, Y_2, Z_1, Z_2 \right) \tag{42}$$

is the corresponding operator for the nuclei, and

$$H_{\text{pot}} = H_{\text{pot}}(x, X) \tag{43}$$

denotes the potential energy associated with the Coulomb forces inside the molecule. Such forces act, of course, between any two particles of our system of electrons and nuclei.

Due to the fact that H_{pot} contains terms linking coordinates from the set x inextricably with coordinates from the set X, the electronic coordinates x are not strictly separable from the nuclear coordinates X. To some degree of approximation, however, they are separable. We shall soon amplify this statement. But let us first concentrate upon $H_{\text{nuclei}}^{\text{kin}}$, in order to examine a convenient separation of degrees of freedom in regard to the motions of the nuclei.

Suppose X', Y', Z' are the *relative* coordinates of the nuclei and X_0, Y_0, Z_0 the coordinates of their center of mass. This means, in symbols, that

$$X' = X_2 - X_1, \quad Y' = Y_2 - Y_1, \quad Z' = Z_2 - Z_1$$
$$\tag{44a, b, c}$$

and

$$MX_0 = M_1 X_1 + M_2 X_2, \tag{45a}$$
$$MY_0 = M_1 Y_1 + M_2 Y_2, \tag{45b}$$
$$MZ_0 = M_1 Z_1 + M_2 Z_2, \tag{45c}$$

if $M = M_1 + M_2$ is the total mass of the nuclei.

Equations (44a) and (45a) imply that

$$\frac{\partial}{\partial X_1} = -\frac{\partial}{\partial X'} + \frac{M_1}{M} \frac{\partial}{\partial X_0}$$

and hence that

$$\frac{\partial^2}{\partial X_1^2} = \frac{\partial^2}{\partial X'^2} - 2\frac{M_1}{M}\frac{\partial^2}{\partial X'\partial X_0} + \left(\frac{M_1}{M}\right)^2\frac{\partial^2}{\partial X_0^2}.$$

In the same manner one gets

$$\frac{\partial^2}{\partial X_2^2} = \frac{\partial^2}{\partial X'^2} + 2\frac{M_2}{M}\frac{\partial^2}{\partial X'\partial X_0} + \left(\frac{M_2}{M}\right)^2\frac{\partial^2}{\partial X_0^2}.$$

On substitution of the last two equations in Eq. (42), it transforms into

$$H^{\text{kin}}_{\text{nuclei}} = -\frac{\hbar^2}{2M}\nabla_0^2 - \frac{\hbar^2}{2\mu}\nabla'^2; \tag{46}$$

here the Laplace operators ∇_0^2 and ∇'^2 are defined by

$$\nabla_0^2 = \frac{\partial^2}{\partial X_0^2} + \frac{\partial^2}{\partial Y_0^2} + \frac{\partial^2}{\partial Z_0^2}$$

and

$$\nabla'^2 = \frac{\partial^2}{\partial X'^2} + \frac{\partial^2}{\partial Y'^2} + \frac{\partial^2}{\partial Z'^2},$$

while

$$\mu = \frac{M_1 M_2}{M} \tag{47}$$

is the so-called *reduced mass* of the nuclei.

Since the first term on the right-hand side of Eq. (46) involves only the coordinates X_0, Y_0, Z_0 and the second term only X', Y', Z', the transformations (44) and (45) have brought about a separation of the center-of-mass (or translational) coordinates from the relative coordinates. We may write Eq. (46) accordingly as

$$H^{\text{kin}}_{\text{nuclei}} = H_{\text{tr}} + H_{\text{rel}}, \tag{48}$$

where

$$H_{\text{tr}} = -\frac{\hbar^2}{2M}\nabla_0^2 \tag{49}$$

and

$$H_{\text{rel}} = -\frac{\hbar^2}{2\mu}\nabla'^2. \tag{50}$$

Inspection of Eq. (50) shows that the relative motion of the two nuclei is equivalent to the motion of a single particle of mass μ. Moreover, Eq. (48), in conjunction with Eqs. (49) and (50), states explicitly, for a system of two particles, a theorem that has already been invoked in Eq. (20). It is obvious indeed that H_{tr} is the operator representing the kinetic energy of the total mass M moving with the velocity of the center of mass; while one may verify by the following argument that H_{rel} is the operator for the kinetic energy of the nuclei calculated relative to a nonrotating set of axes anchored in the center of mass.

On combining Eqs. (44a) and (45a), we obtain

$$X_1 - X_0 = -\frac{M_2}{M} X' \tag{51}$$

and

$$X_2 - X_0 = \frac{M_1}{M} X' \tag{52}$$

for the x-components pertaining to the displacements of the nuclei 1 and 2 with respect to their center of mass; analogous relations hold for the y- and z-components. If all these relations are substituted in the expression

$$\tfrac{1}{2}M_1(\dot{X}_1 - \dot{X}_0)^2 + \tfrac{1}{2}M_2(\dot{X}_2 - \dot{X}_0)^2 + \text{similar terms for the } y\text{-} \\ \text{and } z\text{-direction,}$$

which furnishes the kinetic energy relative to a set of axes with origin at the center of mass, one finds

$$\tfrac{1}{2}\mu(\dot{X}'^2 + \dot{Y}'^2 + \dot{Z}'^2).$$

And if in this result we replace $\dot{X}'$ by $-(i\hbar/\mu)\partial/\partial X'$, and so on, it goes over into H_{rel} of Eq. (50)—which proves our original assertion.

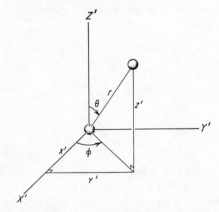

FIGURE 4–1. Relation between cartesian and polar coordinates.

We continue our analysis of H_{rel} by transforming from the rectangular cartesian coordinates X', Y', Z' to the spherical polar coordinates r, θ, ϕ, which are illustrated in Figure 4–1, with the aid of the equations

$$X' = r \sin \theta \cos \phi, \tag{53a}$$
$$Y' = r \sin \theta \sin \phi, \tag{53b}$$
$$Z' = r \cos \theta. \tag{53c}$$

The physical significance of the polar coordinates is clear: r stands for the length of the line segment joining the nuclei, whilst the angles θ and ϕ specify the direction of this (molecular) axis. Accordingly, when these coordinates vary, the resulting modes of motion can be thought of as *vibration* of the nuclei along the molecular axis, accompanied by *rotation* of this axis about the center of mass. The reader may confirm that, in terms of polar coordinates, the Laplace operator is

$$\nabla'^2 = \frac{1}{r^2} \frac{\partial}{\partial r} \left(r^2 \frac{\partial}{\partial r} \right) + \frac{1}{r^2} D_{\theta\phi}, \tag{54}$$

where

$$D_{\theta\phi} = \frac{1}{\sin \theta} \frac{\partial}{\partial \theta} \left(\sin \theta \frac{\partial}{\partial \theta} \right) + \frac{1}{\sin^2 \theta} \frac{\partial^2}{\partial \phi^2}. \tag{55}$$

If Eq. (54) is substituted in Eq. (50), our findings up to this point can be summarized by the equation

$$H = H_{nuc} + H_{el}^{kin} + H_{pot} + H_{tr} - \frac{\hbar^2}{2\mu} \left[\frac{1}{r^2} \frac{\partial}{\partial r} \left(r^2 \frac{\partial}{\partial r} \right) + \frac{1}{r^2} D_{\theta\phi} \right]. \tag{56}$$

We recall that H_{el}^{kin} is composed of the operators $\partial/\partial x$ and H_{tr} of the operators $\partial/\partial X_0$, $\partial/\partial Y_0$, $\partial/\partial Z_0$, while H_{pot} is a function of the electronic coordinates x as well as the coordinates X_0, Y_0, Z_0 and r, θ, ϕ. This means that none of the mentioned coordinates make a purely additive contribution to H in Eq. (56)—the electronic, translational, vibrational, and rotational motions of a diatomic molecule are interdependent.

Nevertheless, as Born and Oppenheimer (1927) first demonstrated, it is possible, to a high degree of accuracy, to rewrite Eq. (56) formally as

$$H = H_{nuc} + H_{el} + H_{vib} + H_{rot} + H_{tr}, \tag{57}$$

so that in each term on the right-hand side only the coordinates indicated by the subscripts are treated as variables. The energy eigenvalues of a molecule,

$$\varepsilon = \varepsilon^{nuc} + \varepsilon^{el} + \varepsilon^{vib} + \varepsilon^{rot} + \varepsilon^{tr}, \tag{58}$$

are consequently found by adding the eigenvalues ε^{nuc}, ε^{el}, etc., of the operators H_{nuc}, H_{el}, etc. The corresponding energy eigenfunctions are of the form

$$\psi = \psi^{nuc}\psi^{el}\psi^{vib}\psi^{rot}\psi^{tr}. \tag{59}$$

To express quantitatively the approximation assumed in Eq. (57), we introduce the parameter

$$\kappa = \left(\frac{m}{M}\right)^{1/4}. \tag{60}$$

Born and Oppenheimer now showed that Eq. (58) represents an expansion of the energy $\varepsilon - \varepsilon^{nuc}$ in powers of κ. More specifically, $\varepsilon^{el} \sim \kappa^0$, $\varepsilon^{vib} \sim \kappa^2$, while both ε^{rot} and $\varepsilon^{tr} \sim \kappa^4$. The energies due to couplings between the electronic, vibrational, and rotational motions are of orders higher than the fourth in κ, and are neglected in our approximation.

Subsequent analysis will bear out the correctness of the foregoing estimates up to the fourth order. Here it will suffice to demonstrate that the cited orders of magnitude are consistent with spectroscopic data.

Let us first get an idea as to the size of the electronic energy by considering a valence electron, whose motions cover more or less the whole volume occupied by the molecule. One can treat such an electron roughly as a free point particle confined to a box with a volume equal to that of a molecule. Hence, by Eq. (27), Chapter 3,

$$\varepsilon^{el} \sim \frac{h^2}{8ma^2}$$

for moderately excited states, if a signifies the size of the linear dimensions of the molecule. This means that $\varepsilon^{el} \sim 10$ ev for $a \sim 1$ angstrom, as an easy calculation would show. When all this energy is spent in a radiation process, it is seen, on division by h, to produce radiation whose frequency is possibly of the order 10^{15} sec^{-1}, that is, visible or ultraviolet light.

To find the frequencies characterizing the vibrational and rotational energies, we note that κ^2 is about $1/61$ for a hydrogen molecule, and less for heavier molecules. Suppose that $\kappa^2 \sim 10^{-2}$, then, from the hypothesis above,

$$\varepsilon^{vib} \sim 10^{-2} \times 10 = 10^{-1}\,\text{ev} \qquad \text{and} \qquad \varepsilon^{rot} \sim 10^{-4} \times 10 = 10^{-3}\,\text{ev}.$$

To such energies correspond frequencies of the order 10^{13} sec^{-1} and 10^{11} sec^{-1}, respectively, which lie in the infrared and microwave regions of the frequency spectrum.

Now experiment confirms that the spectrum of every diatomic molecule can be resolved into sets of lines arising from quantum transitions in which changes occur mainly in either ε^{el} (electronic band spectrum) or ε^{vib}

(vibration-rotation band spectrum) or ε^{rot} (pure rotation spectrum). And these sets occupy indeed the regions of the spectrum delimited in the preceding paragraphs.

After this brief digression, we will give a meaning to each of the terms into which H is split according to Eq. (57). The operators H_{nuc} and H_{tr} have already been defined and are physically explained without difficulty. Interpretation of the remaining operators in Eq. (57) is less direct.

Consider first H_{el}, which is defined as

$$H_{el} = H_{el}^{kin} + H_{pot} \ (X = \text{const.}) \tag{61}$$

Since $H_{el}^{kin} \sim 1/m$ and $1/\mu \sim \kappa^4/m$, one notices that, if intranuclear and translational motions are neglected, H_{el} is the form taken on by H in Eq. (56) when κ tends to zero.

The important fact about H_{el} in the present context is that $H_{el} = H_{el}(x, \partial/\partial x; X)$. In other words, the nuclear coordinates X in H_{el} may be treated as parameters, to which one can assign any fixed values. Accordingly, we regard here the eigenvalue equation

$$H_{el}\psi^{el} = u\psi^{el} \tag{62}$$

as a differential equation in the electronic coordinates x alone. The function ψ^{el} evidently describes an eigenstate of H_{el}, belonging to the energy u, for the electrons when the nuclei are held fixed. Complete solution of Eq. (62) provides us with a set of eigenfunctions ψ_i^{el} and a corresponding set of eigenvalues u_i. Although the ψ_i^{el} will in general depend not only on x but also on X, a moment's reflection will show that, whatever our choice of coordinate axes, the eigenvalues u_i can be functions only of the internuclear distance r, that is,

$$u_i = u_i(r). \tag{63}$$

An electronic energy level scheme is thus obtained in which the positions of the levels vary with the value assigned to r.

In principle, it is possible to compute the functions (63) for every diatomic molecule. In practice, though, the calculations are complicated and have consequently so far been restricted mainly to H_2 and one- and two-electron ions. One therefore generally postulates that u_i has a particular functional form whose constants are then adjusted to suit the available spectroscopic data. If the lowest energy value u_0 is plotted against r for a simple molecule, one gets a curve of the type illustrated in Figure 4–2. The values of the ordinates in this drawing are dependent upon our convention: $u_0 = 0$ when the nuclei are at an infinite distance from one another. The curves for excited states would lie above the curve shown in the diagram and have the same general appearance provided they belong to a stable molecule.

To aid the reader in consulting literature on molecular spectroscopy, we may point out that the notation appropriate to electronic energy levels of diatomic molecules is different from that explained in Section 4–2 for monatomic molecules. In the latter case, the spherical symmetry of H_{el} led to the rigorous commutation of $\mathbf{J}$ with H_{el} and, if the spin-orbit interactions are weak, to the approximate commutation of $\mathbf{L}$ with H_{el}; hence the admissibility of the quantum number L in the level notation. In diatomic molecules, H_{el} is no longer spherically symmetric. But axial symmetry still obtains, as H_{el} will

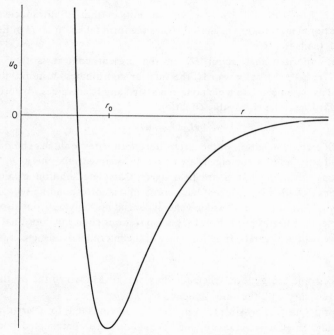

FIGURE 4–2. Typical functional dependence of the lowest electronic energy on the distance between nuclei.

clearly not change when the entire system of electrons is rotated through any angle about the molecular axis. One infers that the component of $\mathbf{L}$ along this axis, which possesses the eigenvalues $\pm \Lambda \hbar$ such that $\Lambda = 0, 1, 2, \ldots$, commutes with H_{el}. Thus the quantum number Λ can be used to label the electronic energy levels. It is customary to specify the given values of Λ by the Greek capital letters $\Sigma, \Pi, \Delta, \ldots$, in analogy to the code $S, P, D, \ldots$

employed in Section 4–2. A particular value of Λ will on the whole be applicable to more than one level, so that additional labels are required to uniquely identify the energy levels: these labels are affixed to the Greek capitals as sub- or superscripts. To explain their nature will take us too far afield.

As implied earlier, the eigenfunctions ψ_i^{el} are functions of the nuclear coordinates r, θ, ϕ, X_0, Y_0, Z_0 as well as of the electronic coordinates x. Since the translational coordinates X_0, Y_0, Z_0 can be separated out, we conveniently suppose for the remainder of this section that they are held fixed. We may thus write

$$\psi_i^{el} = \psi_i^{el}(x; r, \theta, \phi). \qquad (64)$$

Due to the occurrence in H_{pot} of terms "mixing" the coordinates x with the coordinates r, θ, ϕ, the motions of the electrons and nuclei are coupled. This means that one is, strictly speaking, not allowed to assume the electrons to be in one of the eigenstates (64) when the molecule as a whole has a precise energy. But in the fourth-order approximation here employed, it is permissible to reason that they are in any one of these eigenstates with r having a constant value r_0, where r_0 will be defined in the second paragraph below. The physical justification for this is that when one studies electrons, which (classically speaking) perform rapid periodic motions, the relatively slow-moving nuclei may be regarded as being stationary.

We next examine the motions of the nuclei and the significance of H_{vib} and H_{rot} in this connection. Despite the existence of H_{pot}, an inquiry into these motions will in our approximation not involve the instantaneous values of the coordinates x. Indeed, the nuclei will experience only the average effect of the electric field produced by the fast-moving electrons; so that the forces exerted by the electrons upon the nuclei depend merely on the state ψ_i^{el} of the electrons and not on their coordinates x. The potential function describing these forces together with the Coulomb repulsion between the nuclei is none other than—as Born and Oppenheimer proved—the function $u_i(r)$. Our task is to investigate the behavior of the nuclei in the central field $u_i(r)$.

For every stable state i, the function u_i exhibits a minimum (see Figure 4–2). It occurs where $du_i/dr = 0$, that is, at the point $r = r_0$ determined by

$$u_i'(r_0) = 0. \qquad (65)$$

This implies that when $r = r_0$, the forces on the nuclei vanish and hence the equilibrium configuration of the nuclei is realized. In a comprehensive treatment of our problem, one should know the form of u_i for all values of r, but such information is only rarely available. However, in the second-order approximation, for which the assertion holds that the function $u_i(r)$ represents the internuclear potential, it suffices to know u_i and its second-order derivative at $r = r_0$, as the following reasoning will show.

It is plausible to assume that along the molecular axis the nuclei execute only small oscillations, compared with r_0, about their equilibrium positions over intervals that shrink to zero when κ vanishes. We therefore write

$$r = r_0 + \kappa q \tag{66}$$

(so that q measures the deviation of r from r_0 in units of κ) and develop the potential function u_i as a power series in $\kappa q \ll r_0$. Breaking this series off at the second-order term, and remembering Eq. (65), one gets

$$u_i(r_0 + \kappa q) = u_i(r_0) + \tfrac{1}{2}\kappa^2 q^2 u_i''(r_0). \tag{67}$$

The fifth, or purely radial, term in the Hamiltonian (56) can also be expanded in powers of κ. Up to terms of the second order, one finds that

$$-\frac{\hbar^2}{2\mu}\frac{1}{r^2}\frac{\partial}{\partial r}\left(r^2\frac{\partial}{\partial r}\right) = -\frac{\hbar^2}{2\mu}\frac{1}{\kappa^2}\frac{\partial^2}{\partial q^2}, \tag{68}$$

since $1/\mu \sim \kappa^4/m$ and $\partial/\partial r = (1/\kappa)\partial/\partial q$. We accordingly define

$$H_{\text{vib}} = -\frac{\hbar^2}{2\mu\kappa^2}\frac{\partial^2}{\partial q^2} + \tfrac{1}{2}\kappa^2 q^2 u_i''(r_0) \tag{69}$$

as the Hamiltonian describing the (internal) radial, or vibrational, motion of the molecule. It is seen on inspection of Eq. (69) that formally H_{vib} is the Hamiltonian of a linear harmonic oscillator with the coordinate κq and having a mass μ, a force constant $u_i''(r_0)$, and hence a classical frequency

$$\nu_i = \frac{1}{2\pi}\left(\frac{u_i''(r_0)}{\mu}\right)^{1/2}. \tag{70}$$

We finally write down the leading term in the expansion of the last, i.e., angular, term of the Hamiltonian Eq. (56):

$$H_{\text{rot}} = -\frac{\hbar^2}{2\mu r_0^2}D_{\theta\phi}. \tag{71}$$

H_{rot} is of the fourth order in κ, and obviously represents the Hamiltonian of the nuclei if they are conceived of as staying at a fixed distance r_0 from one another. The physical justification for assuming the nuclei to be "frozen" in their equilibrium positions is based on an argument analogous to that which led to the adoption of the internuclear potential: since the frequency of vibration is much higher than that of rotation, in a treatment of the latter one may argue that the nuclei practically occupy their average positions corresponding to $r = r_0$.

H_{rot} resembles the Hamiltonian of a particle that has a mass μ and is constrained to move on the surface of a (geometrical) sphere with radius r_0. A system of this kind is called a *rigid rotator*. We may thus say that the neglect of higher-order terms in Eqs. (69) and (71) amounts to our simply using a harmonic oscillator and a rigid rotator as models for the study of (internal) molecular vibrations and rotations.

4–4. Thermodynamic Properties of Diatomic Ideal Gases

Having interpreted the separate contributions in Eq. (57) to the molecular Hamiltonian, we shall now investigate their eigenvalues in Eq. (58) and the effect of each set of eigenvalues on the corresponding factor in the molecular partition function

$$Z_1 = \zeta_{\text{nuc}}\zeta_{\text{el}}\zeta_{\text{vib}}\zeta_{\text{rot}}\zeta_{\text{tr}}. \qquad (72)$$

Here, as in the case of monatomic molecules, the intranuclear degrees of freedom are unexcited. They therefore give rise to a partition function of the form Eq. (36) and make no contribution to the heat capacity. The electronic degrees of freedom too will again be unexcited and hence produce a partition function like Eq. (34) and a zero heat capacity, except for those special cases in which the ground electronic level belongs to a set of some very closely spaced levels. In our approximation (to κ^4), the electronic energies have the values

$$\varepsilon_i^{\text{el}} = u_i(r_0), \qquad (73)$$

which are the eigenvalues associated with the eigenfunctions $\psi_i^{\text{el}}(r_0)$.

The translational motion is also readily dealt with by analogy. Because the degrees of freedom described by the coordinates X_0, Y_0, Z_0 are evidently classical, ζ_{tr} is once more furnished by Eq. (26), provided $M = M_1 + M_2$ is substituted for m. They consequently add the amount

$$\boxed{C_V^{tr} = \frac{3k}{2}} \qquad (74)$$

to the molecular heat capacity.

The eigenvalues of the vibrational Hamiltonian Eq. (69) are derived in most textbooks of quantum mechanics. They are

$$\varepsilon_n^{\text{vib}} = h\nu_i(n + \tfrac{1}{2}). \qquad (n = 0, 1, 2, \ldots) \qquad (75)$$

In order to compute the vibrational partition function, we posit the frequencies ν_i to have approximately the same value, namely ν, for all electronic energy eigenstates. Since all the levels of Eq. (75) are nondegenerate, one then simply has by Eq. (9),

$$\zeta_{\text{vib}} = \sum_{n=0}^{\infty} e^{-\beta \varepsilon_n^{\text{vib}}} = e^{-\frac{1}{2}\beta h\nu} \sum_{n=0}^{\infty} e^{-n\beta h\nu}. \tag{76}$$

The sum appearing here is a geometric series whose value is found on application of the formula

$$1 + x + x^2 + \cdots = (1 - x)^{-1}.$$

Hence,

$$\zeta_{\text{vib}} = e^{-\Theta_{\text{v}}/2T}(1 - e^{-\Theta_{\text{v}}/T})^{-1} \tag{77}$$

if the so-called *characteristic temperature for vibration* Θ_{v} is defined as

$$\boxed{\Theta_{\text{v}} = \frac{h\nu}{k}}. \tag{78}$$

After multiplying numerator and denominator on the right-hand side of Eq. (77) by $\exp \Theta_{\text{v}}/2T$, one can rewrite this formula briefly as

$$\zeta_{\text{vib}} = \left(2 \sinh \frac{\Theta_{\text{v}}}{2T}\right)^{-1}. \tag{79}$$

We are now able to calculate the vibrational contribution to any thermodynamic property of the gas. Consider in particular its internal energy. By virtue of Eq. (11),

$$U_{\text{vib}} = NkT^2 \frac{d}{dT} \log \zeta_{\text{vib}}$$

and thus, from Eq. (79),

$$U_{\text{vib}} = \frac{1}{2}Nk\Theta_{\text{v}} \coth \frac{\Theta_{\text{v}}}{2T}, \tag{80}$$

or

$$U_{\text{vib}} = Nk\Theta_{\text{v}}[\frac{1}{2} + (e^{\Theta_{\text{v}}/T} - 1)^{-1}]. \tag{81}$$

With the aid of Eq. (81), the values of the vibrational energy for extreme temperatures are easily obtained: when $T \ll \Theta_{\text{v}}$, the function $\exp \Theta_{\text{v}}/T$ is very large, so that the second term in the brackets of Eq. (81) becomes negligible. Therefore,

$$U_{\text{vib}} \approx \frac{1}{2}Nk\Theta_{\text{v}} = \frac{1}{2}Nh\nu; \tag{82}$$

this means that the gas possesses a finite zero-point energy of vibration. The result Eq. (82) was to be expected: as T approaches zero, each of the N conceptual oscillators settles in its ground state, for which the energy is $\frac{1}{2}h$ by Eq. (75).

On the other hand, when $T \gg \Theta_{\mathrm{v}}$, $\exp \Theta_{\mathrm{v}}/T$ can be approximated by $1 + \Theta_{\mathrm{v}}/T$ and hence the second term in the brackets of Eq. (81) by T/Θ_{v}. And since $\frac{1}{2}$ is negligible compared with T/Θ_{v}, Eq. (81) reduces to

$$U_{\mathrm{vib}} \approx NkT. \tag{83}$$

Therefore, at high temperatures the average energy per oscillator is kT; in other words, precisely the value predicted by the equipartition theorem because of the classical Hamiltonian H_{vib} comprising two squared terms.

Theoretically, quantum mechanics enables us to compute the internuclear potential $u_i(r)$ and thus, owing to Eqs. (70) and (78), the frequency ν and the temperature Θ_{v}—both of which might from their definitions be expected on the whole to increase as the molecular mass ($\approx M$) decreases. In practice, however, ν and consequently Θ_{v} of a molecule are usually determined empirically from its vibration spectrum. This has been done for a variety of diatomic molecules, and the results show that Θ_{v} ranges from approximately 6300°K (for H_2) to about 300°K (for I_2).

Once Θ_{v} is known, it is possible to calculate the fraction x^* of molecules occupying the excited vibrational states, for which $n > 0$; clearly,

$$x^* = 1 - \zeta_{\mathrm{vib}}^{-1} \exp -\beta \varepsilon_0^{\mathrm{vib}} = \exp -\frac{\Theta_{\mathrm{v}}}{T}, \tag{84}$$

where Eq. (77) has been invoked in the last step. We infer: when $T = \Theta_{\mathrm{v}}$, $x^* = e^{-1}$, i.e., about 37 per cent of the molecules reside in excited states. As T is lowered, x^* diminishes rapidly, such that when, for example, $T = \Theta_{\mathrm{v}}/7$, x^* reaches a value less than 0.1 per cent. This kind of situation, with $T \ll \Theta_{\mathrm{v}}$, is contemplated when we say that the vibrational degree of freedom is unexcited. Apart from some exceptions, Θ_{v} is a few thousand degrees Kelvin, so that generally the vibrational motion will be unexcited at room temperature.

With an appeal to Eq. (81), the heat capacity due to vibration, dU_{vib}/dT, can immediately be written down:

$$C_V^{\mathrm{vib}} = Nk\left(\frac{\Theta_{\mathrm{v}}}{T}\right)^2 e^{\Theta_{\mathrm{v}}/T}(e^{\Theta_{\mathrm{v}}/T} - 1)^{-2}. \tag{85}$$

It is easily seen that, as T/Θ_{v} tends to zero, this heat capacity becomes zero, while it takes on the classical value Nk when T/Θ_{v} by far exceeds unity.

Examination of Eqs. (81) and (85) reveals that $U_{vib}/Nk\Theta_v$ and C_V^{vib}/Nk are universal functions of the dimensionless parameter T/Θ_v. Accordingly we find it convenient to plot the first two quantities against the last in Figure 4–3. The broken lines indicate the classical values approached by the quantum curves when the temperature becomes very high compared with Θ_v.

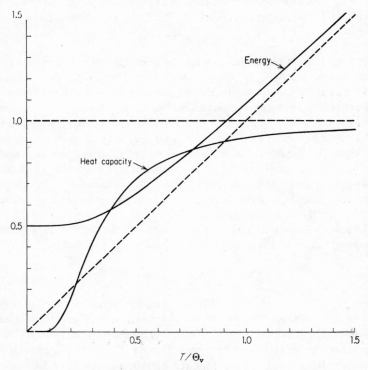

FIGURE 4–3. Energy U_{vib}/N and heat capacity C_V^{vib}/N of a linear harmonic oscillator in units of $k\Theta_v$ and k, respectively.

We lastly consider the rotational motion. The computation of the energy eigenvalues of the rigid rotator, whose Hamiltonian H_{rot} is given by Eq. (71), is a familiar problem in quantum mechanics. They turn out to be

$$\varepsilon_j^{rot} = \frac{j(j+1)\hbar^2}{2I_0}, \qquad (j = 0, 1, 2, \ldots) \tag{86}$$

where

$$I_0 = \mu r_0^2, \tag{87}$$

that is, the value of $I = \mu r^2$ when the nuclei are in vibrational equilibrium.

I is the moment of inertia of the nuclei about an axis that is perpendicular to the line joining them and that passes through their center of mass. This can readily be verified as follows. Per definition,

$$I = M_1(X_1 - X_0)^2 + M_2(X_2 - X_0)^2 + \text{similar terms in } Y_1, Y_2, Z_1, Z_2.$$

If in this equation one replaces $X_1 - X_0$, $X_2 - X_0$, etc., by their values according to Eqs. (51) and (52), one gets

$$I = M_1\left(\frac{M_2}{M}\right)^2 X'^2 + M_2\left(\frac{M_1}{M}\right)^2 X'^2 + \text{similar terms in } Y' \text{ and } Z'$$

$$= \frac{M_1 M_2}{M}(X'^2 + Y'^2 + Z'^2) = \mu r^2;$$

in the last step use has been made of the definition (47) and the transformation equations (53).

The rotational partition function is simply

$$\zeta_{\text{rot}} = \sum e^{-\beta \varepsilon_j^{\text{rot}}}, \tag{88}$$

yet it must be remembered that this sum extends not over values of j, but over the eigenstates of H_{rot}. To convert the right-hand side of Eq. (88) into a sum with respect to j, we must point out that each of the eigenvalues (86) is $(2j + 1)$-fold degenerate. One may consequently write

$$\zeta_{\text{rot}} = \sum_{j=0}^{\infty} (2j + 1)e^{-j(j+1)\Theta_r/T}; \tag{89}$$

here Θ_r signifies the *characteristic temperature for rotation* defined as

$$\boxed{\Theta_r = \frac{\hbar^2}{2I_0 k}}. \tag{90}$$

The sum (89), in contrast to the sum (76), can unfortunately not be expressed as a simple function. However, in the cases of extreme temperatures, an analysis of the sum (89) is an easy matter. At low temperatures, for which $T \ll \Theta_r$, this sum can be approximated by its first few terms. At high temperatures, on the other hand, where $T \gg \Theta_r$, the exponential function in Eq. (89) increases only by a small amount when j advances by unity, so that the sum over the discrete j approaches an integral over the continuous variable j. Thus in the limit $T/\Theta_r \to \infty$, ζ_{rot} tends to

$$\zeta_{\text{rot class}} = \int_0^{\infty} (2j + 1)e^{-j(j+1)\Theta_r/T} \, dj$$

$$= \int_0^{\infty} e^{-y\Theta_r/T} \, dy,$$

or

$$\zeta_{\text{rot class}} = \frac{T}{\Theta_r}. \tag{91}$$

The result (91), we might digress here to note, can also be obtained without appealing to quantum mechanics if we apply our prescription (13). To find the classical Hamiltonian $H_{rot}(q,p)$ required in this method, we proceed in the following manner. The energy associated with the rotation of the two nuclei is evidently

$$\varepsilon = \tfrac{1}{2}\mu(\dot{X}'^2 + \dot{Y}'^2 + \dot{Z}'^2)$$

with $X'^2 + Y'^2 + Z'^2 = r_0^2$. If one substitutes for the time derivatives in the first equation their values from Eq. (53), it becomes

$$\varepsilon = \tfrac{1}{2}I_0(\dot{\theta}^2 + \dot{\phi}^2 \sin^2 \theta).$$

The momenta canonically conjugate to the coordinates θ and ϕ are therefore

$$p_\theta = \frac{\partial \varepsilon}{\partial \dot{\theta}} = I_0 \dot{\theta} \qquad \text{and} \qquad p_\phi = \frac{\partial \varepsilon}{\partial \dot{\phi}} = I_0 \dot{\phi} \sin^2 \theta.$$

If these definitions are employed to eliminate $\dot{\theta}$ and $\dot{\phi}$, the expression for ε transforms into

$$H_{rot}(q,p) = \frac{1}{2I_0} \left(p_\theta^2 + \frac{p_\phi^2}{\sin^2 \theta} \right).$$

It is now left to the reader to confirm that if this Hamiltonian is substituted in the integral

$$\zeta_{rot\,class} = \frac{1}{h^2} \int_0^\pi \int_0^{2\pi} \int_{-\infty}^{\infty} \int_{-\infty}^{\infty} \exp -\beta H_{rot}(q,p) \, d\theta d\phi dp_\theta dp_\phi$$

and the integrations are carried out, Eq. (91) is recovered.

In our discussion of nuclear motions up to this point, we have tacitly assumed that we are dealing with *heteronuclear* molecules, that is, molecules having unlike nuclei, such as HCl and CO. In *homonuclear* molecules, exemplified by H_2 and D_2 (deuterium), Eq. (89) in particular ceases to be valid. Worse still, it is even no longer possible to split off the factors ζ_{nuc} and ζ_{rot} from the partition function Z_1, as we did in Eq. (72). One has instead to work with a combined partition function, denoted by, say, ζ_{nr}, that relates to both the intranuclear and rotational motions.

The failure of ζ_{nr} to resolve into factors is due to the quantum-mechanical demand that any wave function representing a physically realizable state of a molecule must be *antisymmetric* in the coordinates of its protons and its neutrons; this means that whenever two protons or two neutrons exchange their position and spin coordinates, ψ must merely alter its sign. It follows that for a homonuclear molecule any physically possible ψ will be symmetric or antisymmetric in the nuclei (that is, $\psi \rightarrow \psi$ or $\psi \rightarrow -\psi$ when the nuclei are exchanged), depending on whether each nucleus contains an even or odd number of nucleons.

Let us apply this requirement to the energy eigenfunctions in Eq. (59) while positing that the electronic, and thus *a fortiori* the intranuclear, motions are unexcited. The eigenfunctions ψ^{vib} and ψ^{tr}, which depend upon r and X_0, Y_0, Z_0, respectively, are clearly not affected by an exchange of the nuclei. If we postulate that the ground state ψ_0^{el} too is symmetric in the nuclei (as is mostly the case), then the nuclear symmetry of ψ will be given by that of the product $\psi_0^{\text{nuc}}\psi^{\text{rot}}$. We conclude: (i) for nuclei with *even* mass numbers, symmetric (antisymmetric) ψ^{rot} must be combined with symmetric (antisymmetric) ψ_0^{nuc}; (ii) for *odd* mass numbers, symmetric (antisymmetric) ψ^{rot} must be combined with antisymmetric (symmetric) ψ_0^{nuc}. One consequently knows that when ψ_0^{nuc}, for instance, is specified, ψ^{rot} and therefore ε^{rot} cannot be chosen arbitrarily. This means: in spite of the postulated absence of interaction between the intranuclear and rotational motions, the corresponding energy eigenfunctions and eigenvalues are not independent—a fact that prevents the factorization of ζ_{nr}.

The form taken on by ζ_{nr} is in general quite complicated and hence it will not be presented here. In the classical situation $T \gg \Theta_r$ though, a considerable simplification takes place: once again one may speak of a rotational partition function, and the forementioned symmetry requirements manifest themselves only in the appearance of an additional factor $\frac{1}{2}$ in front of the sum in Eq. (89). When treating a homonuclear molecule, one has accordingly to replace Eq. (91) by

$$\zeta_{\text{rot class}} = \frac{T}{2\Theta_r}. \tag{92}$$

The division by 2 in Eq. (92) is most easily justified with reference to the penultimate equation. In the multiple integral on its right-hand side equal contributions arise from the direction (θ, ϕ) and from the direction $(\pi - \theta, \phi + \pi)$ which results from the former when the molecule is rotated through 180°. But since these two configurations of a homonuclear molecule are indistinguishable from one another, they should be counted only once. Hence we must divide the above integral by 2 in order to obtain the correct answer.

In theory, quantum mechanics equips us to calculate r_0, and thus I_0 and Θ_r from Eqs. (87) and (90). In practice, however, these quantities are ordinarily determined for any given molecule from measurements on its vibration-rotation or rotation spectrum. So it is found that Θ_r equals 85.4, 64.1, 42.5 degrees Kelvin for H_2, HD, D_2; it equals 15.2, 12.1, 9.0 degrees Kelvin for HCl, HBr, HI; and is much less for diatomic molecules not containing hydrogen. It is thus evident that $T \gg \Theta_r$ for all diatomic molecules, other than H_2, HD, D_2, in the gaseous phase. This means that the rotational degrees of freedom of real gases are on the whole classical, so that the partition function ζ_{rot} is given by either Eq. (91) or (92).

Independent of whether Eq. (91) or (92) applies, the internal energy and heat capacity are clearly

$$U_{\text{rot class}} = NkT^2 \frac{d}{dT} \log T = NkT \qquad (93)$$

and

$$\boxed{C_{V\,\text{class}}^{\text{rot}} = Nk} \; ; \qquad (94)$$

these relations could, of course, have been written down immediately with the aid of the equipartition theorem. On the other hand, when T/Θ_r tends to zero, ζ_{rot} approaches unity by virtue of Eq. (89), and U_{rot} and C_V^{rot} become therefore zero. At temperatures lying between $T = \Theta_r$ and $T \gg \Theta_r$, one may compute C_V^{rot} in the case of heteronuclear molecules by appealing to the approximation formula of Mulholland (1928), to wit,

$$\zeta_{\text{rot}} = \frac{1}{y} \left(1 + \frac{y}{3} + \frac{y^2}{15} + \frac{4y^3}{315} + \cdots \right), \qquad (95)$$

where $y = \Theta_r/T$, which is valid to within circa 1 per cent for $y \leqslant 1$; at lower temperatures, i.e., $y > 1$, one must resort to the initial series in Eq. (89) interrupted after a sufficient number of terms. [For the derivation of Eq. (95), see Problem 3.]

The foregoing considerations lead to the heat capacity curve in Figure 4–4. The most remarkable feature of C_V^{rot} displayed by this graph is: at $T \sim \Theta_r$ it goes through a maximum, where it exceeds its classical value Nk, and then

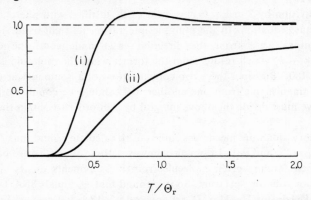

FIGURE 4–4. (i) Molecular heat capacity C_V^{rot}/N and (ii) molecular energy U_{rot}/N, in units k and kT, respectively.

tends to Nk from above as T increases. Before T has become equal to $2\Theta_r$, C_V^{rot} will have approached the limiting value Nk to within less than 1 per cent.

This theoretical curve has been confirmed by experiments carried out on HD gas. With regard to all other diatomic gases consisting of heteronuclear molecules, observation of the variation with temperature of C_V^{rot} is out of the question, because they would be in the liquid or solid phase well before temperatures comparable with their Θ_r were realized.

Coordinating the results of this section, we note that our theory predicts an ideal diatomic gas to behave roughly in the following manner when its temperature is raised. At very low temperatures, where $T \ll \Theta_r$, nearly all molecules occupy their rotational and vibrational states of lowest energy, and any heat entering the gas augments only its translational energy. In consequence, if this energy already has its classical value, the heat capacity per molecule, C_V, is simply $3k/2$. With rising temperature a stage is reached where molecules begin to populate states of higher rotational energy in appreciable numbers. C_V therefore increases until, at a temperature equal to a few times Θ_r, it attains practically the value $5k/2$ corresponding to fully excited, or classical, rotational as well as translational motions. At a much larger temperature, the molecules begin to crowd significantly into states of higher vibrational energy; and this process continues until, at some temperature exceeding Θ_v, the vibrational degrees of freedom too have become classical. C_V then has the value $7k/2$.

We are thus led to expect that over the temperature range wherein neither condensation nor dissociation occurs, a plot of C_V versus T of a diatomic gas will resemble a staircase with steps appearing at the levels $3k/2$, $5k/2$, and $7k/2$. This prediction has been borne out by the experimental C_V curves of the hydrogen gases H_2, HD, D_2. At room temperature, where the rotational but generally not the vibrational degrees of freedom are fully excited, our theory requires that $C_p = C_V + k = 7k/2$ and $\gamma = C_p/C_V = 7/5$. Also these predictions are satisfactorily confirmed by observation for a variety of gases.

4–5. Normal Vibrations of Monatomic Crystalline Solids

Our applications of statistical theory to material systems have so far stayed on a relatively elementary level only because we deliberately confined ourselves to dilute gases, for which the interactions between molecules can largely be ignored. It is to be expected that if we were to extend our study to denser gases and finally to liquids and solids, the intermolecular forces would become increasingly more important, as the molecules come to lie closer to one another. Due to the preponderance of interactions in denser matter, one might assume at first sight the statistical treatment to be the most complex for solid systems. Fortunately, however, the periodicity characterizing the structure of such systems greatly simplifies the nature of our physical assumptions. For these reasons, we omit any discussion of dense gases and liquids but examine the main thermodynamic properties of the simplest kind of solid in this and the next sections.

It is a well-known fact that all solids in stable thermostatic equilibrium are crystals or, more often, consist of numerous small crystals. The amorphous solids form no exception to this rule if we regard them as metastable substances which, given sufficient time, will eventually crystallize. X-ray analysis shows that the symmetry outwardly distinguishing every macroscopic crystal, arises microscopically from the arrangement of atoms (ions or molecules) at the corners of a strictly periodic three-dimensional lattice. The complete lattice is generated by repetition of a small region, the so-called *elementary cell*. Since the atoms are not static, we ought to add that the lattice corners correspond to the equilibrium sites of the atoms. These sites are, per definition, so chosen that when the atoms are in the equilibrium configuration, the forces exerted on any atom by the remaining atoms will exactly cancel. Because we stipulate that the crystal as a whole undergoes neither translation nor rotation, the equilibrium positions are fixed in space. The dynamical description of a crystal is thus as follows: the atoms execute vibrations about fixed lattice points, while the electrons and nucleons perform motions inside the atoms. The first type of motion is known as *lattice vibrations*. In metals one should moreover also consider the electrons that become detached from the atoms and thereafter function as conduction electrons. These were discussed earlier, in Chapter 3.

In our subsequent analysis we shall disregard mention of electronic and nuclear motions. After all, it should be realized that any solid will melt or decompose chemically before kT reaches a value comparable with that of the interaction energy between its atoms. This means: all atoms in solids are in their nuclear ground states and only a small fraction of atoms in general occupies excited electronic states. The contributions to the thermodynamic properties made by bound electrons will therefore normally be small and those due to nucleons even smaller or zero (as in the case of heat capacity). A similar claim cannot be upheld concerning the translational motions of the free conduction electrons in metals. At low temperatures their contributions can no longer be discounted as insignificant in comparison with those stemming from the lattice vibrations. In this instance, we shall tacitly suppose that any electronic contribution has already been subtracted, so that merely the pure lattice part of any thermodynamic property remains.

To facilitate the study of lattice vibrations as much as possible, let us restrict our inquiry to a monatomic substance with a cubic crystal structure. As a model for treating this system, we posit that one, and only one, of its atoms occupies each corner of a cubic lattice with volume equal to that of the given substance. These atoms will carry out vibrations about the lattice corners as equilibrium positions. In order to describe the configuration of a system of N atoms at any particular time, we may employ the cartesian components ξ_i ($i = 1, 2, \ldots, 3N$) of the displacements of the atoms from their equilibrium sites. The classical Hamiltonian function of the crystal then becomes

$$H = \sum_{i=1}^{3N} \frac{P_i^2}{2m} + \phi(\xi_1, \xi_2, \ldots, \xi_{3N}), \tag{96}$$

where the momenta P_i are defined by $P_i = m\dot{\xi}_i$ and ϕ signifies the potential energy associated with the forces between the atoms.

Even without knowing the precise manner in which ϕ depends on the ξ_i, we are still able to make some useful assertions about it. Note first that one can measure the potential energy with respect to the equilibrium configuration $\xi_1 = \xi_2 = \cdots = \xi_{3N} = 0$ as a standard situation; hence, $\phi_0 = \phi(0, 0, \ldots, 0) = 0$. Furthermore, since the net force on any atom is zero for the equilibrium configuration, the latter must correspond to a minimum value of ϕ, that is,

$$\left(\frac{\partial \phi}{\partial \xi_i}\right)_0 = 0, \quad \text{(all } i) \tag{97}$$

where the subscript o indicates that the derivatives are calculated at $\xi_1 = \xi_2 = \cdots = \xi_{3N} = 0$. We thus infer that the Taylor series expansion of ϕ begins with second-order terms:

$$\phi = \frac{1}{2} \sum_i \sum_j \phi_{ij} \xi_i \xi_j + \cdots, \tag{98}$$

with $\phi_{ij} = (\partial^2 \phi / \partial \xi_i \partial \xi_j)_0$. If one now makes use of the fact that the displacements ξ_i are small compared with the interatomic distances, it is clear that the third- and higher-order terms in the expansion (98) may be neglected. The Hamiltonian, Eq. (96), consequently reduces to a homogeneous quadratic function of the ξ_i:

$$H = \sum_i \frac{P_i^2}{2m} + \frac{1}{2} \sum_i \sum_j \phi_{ij} \xi_i \xi_j. \tag{99}$$

The first part of this Hamiltonian, which represents the kinetic energy, is obviously separable in terms such that each refers to only one of the co-ordinates ξ_i. But this is not true for the second, or potential energy, part, owing to the appearance of cross terms of the type $\xi_i\xi_j$. It is therefore certainly not permissible to treat the atoms of a crystal as independent entities, as we did in the case of the molecules of a dilute gas. The situation does, however, not present a deadlock. For, it is still possible to analyze the crystal conceptually into a set of independent subsystems, provided one formulates its dynamics in the language of a very special set of coordinates q_r ($r = 1, 2, \ldots, 3N$) known as the *normal coordinates*. The q_r are distinguishable from any other coordinates by the fact that their use renders the potential energy, as well as the kinetic energy, a sum solely of squared terms. They result from a unique linear combination of the ξ_i that we shall now examine.

For the potential energy stated in Eq. (99), the classical equations of motion of the lattice vibrations, $m\ddot{\xi}_i = -\partial\phi/\partial\xi_i$, read:

$$m\ddot{\xi}_i = -\sum_j \phi_{ij}\xi_j, \qquad \text{(all } i\text{)} \qquad (100)$$

since $\phi_{ij} = \phi_{ji}$. A solution of this system of equations is found if we postulate that all atoms perform simple harmonic vibrations with the same angular frequency ω in the x, y, and z directions. In other words, we put

$$\xi_i = a_i \sin \omega t, \qquad \text{(all } i\text{)} \qquad (101)$$

supposing that the atoms pass through their equilibrium positions at the time $t = 0$. Substitution of Eqs. (101) in Eqs. (100) easily gives the time-independent set of simultaneous linear equations for the amplitudes a_i:

$$m\omega^2 a_i = \sum_j \phi_{ij} a_j. \qquad \text{(all } i\text{)} \qquad (102)$$

It is well known that a set of equations such as Eqs. (102) admits of a solution other than the trivial one $a_1 = a_2 = \cdots = a_{3N} = 0$ only if the determinant formed by the coefficients of the a_i vanishes, i.e., if

$$\begin{vmatrix} \phi_{11} - m\omega^2 & \phi_{12} & \phi_{13} & \cdots & \phi_{1,3N} \\ \phi_{21} & \phi_{22} - m\omega^2 & \phi_{23} & \cdots & \phi_{2,3N} \\ \vdots & \vdots & \vdots & & \vdots \\ \phi_{3N,1} & \phi_{3N,2} & \phi_{3N,3} & \cdots & \phi_{3N,3N} - m\omega^2 \end{vmatrix} = 0. \qquad (103)$$

This is obviously an equation of the degree $3N$ in ω^2. It could be solved, in principle at least, to furnish $3N$ possible values ω_r for ω in the postulate Eqs. (101). The quantities $\nu_r = \omega_r/2\pi$ are commonly referred to as the *normal frequencies* or *eigenfrequencies* of the crystal.

Suppose any one of the ω_r is substituted in Eqs. (102). They can then, in theory at least, be solved to supply a set of amplitudes $a_1^{(r)}, a_2^{(r)}, \ldots, a_{3N}^{(r)}$, which depends upon ω_r. It will be noticed though that Eqs. (102) determine only the ratios of these amplitudes; one is thus free to multiply each of them by the same arbitrary constant. This constant we now choose such that

$$\sum_i a_i^{(r)} a_i^{(r)} = 1. \qquad \text{(all } r) \tag{104}$$

Furthermore, we know from the theory of linear equations that the $a_i^{(r)}$ satisfy, or can be made to satisfy, also the conditions

$$\sum_i a_i^{(r)} a_i^{(s)} = \delta_{rs} \qquad \text{(all } r \text{ and } s) \tag{105}$$

and

$$\sum_r a_i^{(r)} a_j^{(r)} = \delta_{ij}, \qquad \text{(all } i \text{ and } j) \tag{106}$$

where $\delta_{rs} = 1$ when $r = s$, and is 0 otherwise.

The normal coordinates q_r are now defined by the transformation

$$q_r = \sum_i a_i^{(r)} \xi_i. \qquad \text{(all } r) \tag{107}$$

From this follows, with the aid of Eqs. (106), that

$$\sum_s a_j^{(s)} q_s = \sum_s \sum_i a_j^{(s)} a_i^{(s)} \xi_i = \sum_i \delta_{ji} \xi_i = \xi_j,$$

so that the inverse transformation to Eqs. (107) is provided by

$$\xi_i = \sum_r a_i^{(r)} q_r. \qquad \text{(all } i) \tag{108}$$

We leave it as an exercise to the reader to verify, using Eqs. (102), (105), (106), and (108), that the equations of motion (100) reduce to

$$m\ddot{q}_r = -m\omega_r^2 q_r, \tag{109}$$

while the Hamiltonian Eq. (99) transforms into a sum of squared terms, viz.,

$$H(q,p) = \frac{1}{2} \sum_{r=1}^{3N} \left(\frac{p_r^2}{m} + m\omega_r^2 q_r^2 \right), \tag{110}$$

with

$$p_r = m\dot{q}_r. \tag{111}$$

It should be added that the sum (110 will actually contain not $3N$ but $3N - 6$ terms. The reason is that six of the normal vibrations—all having $\omega = 0$—correspond to the translation and rotation of the crystal as a whole; and these modes of motion are absent by hypothesis. However, since $3N$ is an enormously large number, the difference with the sum for $3N - 6$ is trivial.

As no terms of the type $q_r q_s$ ($r \neq s$) appear in Eq. (110), the lattice energy has been resolved into the sum of $3N$ independent terms, one for each q_r, or for each normal vibration r. These normal vibrations, involving the whole crystal, rather than the individual atoms, are the entities which we are going to treat as independent subsystems. Our statistical analysis is made easy by the fact that the energy associated with a vibration r, namely $p_r^2/2m + \frac{1}{2}m\omega_r^2 q_r^2$, is identical in form with that of a simple harmonic oscillator of mass m and angular frequency ω_r. We may consequently proceed as if we were dealing with a system of $3N$ independent harmonic oscillators possessing frequencies equal to the eigenfrequencies of the crystal.

But before we pursue this line of reasoning any further, we note that Eq. (110) allows us forthwith to write down the classical values of the internal energy and the heat capacity of the crystal. Indeed, according to the equipartition theorem, each one of the $6N$ quadratic terms occurring in the Hamiltonian Eq. (110) contributes an amount $\frac{1}{2}kT$ to the internal energy, so that

$$U_{\text{class}} = 3NkT \tag{112}$$

and

$$C_{V\,\text{class}} = 3Nk. \tag{113}$$

The molar heat capacity of a monatomic solid at sufficiently high temperature should therefore be $3R = 5.96$ calories. This represents the law of Dulong and Petit (1818), which experiment shows to be well obeyed for most monatomic solids and ionic crystals even at moderate temperatures.

A general treatment of the heat capacities and other properties of solids requires a knowledge of the eigenfrequencies and, as Einstein (1907) first realized, recourse to quantum theory. A quantum-mechanical attack on our virtual set of oscillators may start from the assertion that their canonical partition function Z equals the product of the partition functions $Z_1, Z_2, \ldots,$ Z_{3N} of the individual oscillators, that is,

$$Z = Z_1 Z_2 \ldots Z_{3N}. \tag{114}$$

This formula is essentially the same as Eq. (5), which holds for independent gas molecules, except that here the product is not divided by a permutation factor. The difference is due to the circumstance that the oscillators, unlike the molecules, are distinguishable from one another.

The quantum partition functions Z_r of the single oscillators can be written down immediately with the help of Eqs. (77) and (78):

$$Z_r = e^{-h\nu_r/2kT}(1 - e^{-h\nu_r/kT})^{-1}, \qquad (r = 1, 2, \ldots, 3N) \tag{115}$$

where $\nu_r = \omega_r/2\pi$. One consequently gets

$$Z = \prod_{r=1}^{3N} e^{-h\nu_r/2kT}(1 - e^{-h\nu_r/kT})^{-1}, \qquad (116)$$

while the Helmholtz free energy $F = -kT \log Z$ of the crystal becomes

$$F = U_0 + kT \sum_r \log (1 - e^{-h\nu_r/kT}), \qquad (117)$$

in which

$$U_0 = \sum_r \tfrac{1}{2}h\nu_r \qquad (118)$$

is the zero-point energy of the crystal. U_0 obtains at $T = 0$ when every oscillator occupies its ground, or unexcited, quantum state.

In principle, our initially stated aim has herewith been achieved. For, once the eigenfrequencies are inserted on the right-hand side of Eq. (117) as functions of T, V, and N, the missing thermodynamic parameters can be found in the customary manner. In practice however it is exactly at this point that our real difficulties begin, because it is well-nigh impossible to determine these frequencies precisely. Historically, attempts at determination were based on the use of simplified models of the lattice vibrations. They will be the subject of the following section.

4–6. Heat-Capacity Theories of Einstein and Debye

Einstein (1907) assumed that in a solid the atoms themselves can be treated as independent units capable of performing isotropic oscillations of the same frequency. He accordingly replaced a monatomic crystal by a set of $3N$ linear harmonic oscillators, all having the frequency ν_E. The effect of this procedure on the internal energy and the heat capacity can be seen at once, if ν_E is substituted for every ν_r in Eq. (117). Introducing the symbol

$$\boxed{\Theta_E = \frac{h\nu_E}{k}} \qquad (119)$$

for the *Einstein temperature*, one obtains

$$F = \tfrac{3}{2}Nk\,\Theta_E + 3NkT \log (1 - e^{-\Theta_E/T}), \qquad (120)$$

so that

$$U = F - T\left(\frac{\partial F}{\partial T}\right)_{V,N} = \tfrac{3}{2}Nk\,\Theta_E + 3Nk\,\Theta_E(e^{\Theta_E/T} - 1)^{-1} \qquad (121)$$

and

$$C_V = \left(\frac{\partial U}{\partial T}\right)_{V,N} = 3Nk\left(\frac{\Theta_E}{T}\right)^2 e^{\Theta_E/T}(e^{\Theta_E/T} - 1)^{-2}.$$ (122)

Equation (122) shows that at high temperatures (Θ_E/T approaches zero), C_V tends to the empirical value $3Nk$. Moreover, C_V is seen to become zero as $T \to 0$, and to be in general a function only of the ratio Θ_E/T; these facts too are borne out by observation. On the other hand, while Eq. (122) predicts that the decline of C_V to zero (as $T \to 0$) will occur more or less exponentially, experiment reveals instead a much slower decrease near absolute zero—approximately in proportion to T^3. The physical reason for this discrepancy lies in Einstein's replacement of the wide spectrum of eigenfrequencies ν_r by a single representative frequency ν_E. This approximation implies that all normal vibrations de-excite simultaneously as the temperature diminishes, whereas in reality the lower frequencies persist after the higher frequencies have faded out.

Realizing the inadequacy of the Einstein model, Born and von Kármán jointly (1912, 1913), and Debye (1912) independently, proposed that one should admit not a singular frequency but a spectrum of frequencies, three per atom —in agreement with the number $3N$ of eigenfrequencies. To compute this spectrum, these workers followed widely different methods.

Although less faithful, the Debye model of a crystal is the simpler one, and we therefore discuss it first. Rather than getting involved in a complicated consideration of lattice dynamics, Debye ingeniously ventured the following (partly correct) hypothesis: the required frequencies are none other than those of the standing elastic waves that can be excited in a continuous solid having the shape and size of the given crystal. Of course, since the number of such waves in a continuous medium is infinite (though enumerable), the number of allowed frequencies in a crystal would likewise be infinite. To avoid this conclusion, Debye demanded that no frequencies exist above a certain maximum value ν_D. This cutoff point is chosen such that the number of frequencies having values less than ν_D exactly equals $3N$.

Let us now with Debye examine the nature of elastic waves in an isotropic continuum. The displacement $u(x,y,z,t)$ of any of these waves must satisfy the *wave equation*

$$\frac{\partial^2 u}{\partial x^2} + \frac{\partial^2 u}{\partial y^2} + \frac{\partial^2 u}{\partial z^2} = \frac{1}{c^2}\frac{\partial^2 u}{\partial t^2},$$ (123)

c being the velocity of propagation. [For the derivation of Eq. (123) the reader is referred to a textbook on sound.] Equation (123) is satisfied by solutions of the kind

$$u = A \sin 2\pi(\boldsymbol{\sigma} \cdot \mathbf{r} - \nu t), \tag{124}$$

provided

$$\sigma^2 = \frac{\nu^2}{c^2}, \tag{125}$$

where A is an arbitrary constant and $\mathbf{r} = (x, y, z)$. One may easily verify Eq. (124) by differentiating it with respect to each of the variables x, y, z, t and substituting the results in Eq. (123).

A moment's reflection will show that the solution (124) describes a plane wave of frequency ν and wavelength $\lambda = 1/\sigma$ traveling with the velocity c in a direction specified by the *wave number vector* $\boldsymbol{\sigma}$. Indeed, $(\boldsymbol{\sigma}/\sigma) \cdot \mathbf{r} = s$ obviously defines a plane surface at a distance s from the origin, on which u in Eq. (124) has everywhere the same value, say u_0, at time $t = 0$. Moreover, u will clearly retain the value u_0 if the rate of change of s is such that $(d/dt)(s/c - t) = 0$, i.e., if $ds/dt = c$.

From Eq. (124) a set of altogether eight plane waves can be obtained, all having the frequency ν and the velocity c but propagated in different (symmetrically arranged) directions, when one considers the wave number components $\pm\sigma_x$, $\pm\sigma_y$, $\pm\sigma_z$. The reader may now convince himself (see Problem 4) that appropriate additions and subtractions of these waves will yield the standing wave

$$u = 8A \sin 2\pi\sigma_x x \sin 2\pi\sigma_y y \sin 2\pi\sigma_z z \cos 2\pi\nu t. \tag{126}$$

Suppose that the continuous solid under investigation has the shape of a parallelepiped whose edge-lengths are L_x, L_y, L_z and whose faces are the planes $x = 0$, $x = L_x$, $y = 0$, $y = L_y$, $z = 0$, $z = L_z$. Then all the standing waves capable of occurring in this body when its faces remain fixed, are those members of the set (126) that exhibit nodes ($u = 0$ for all t) not only at $x = 0$, $y = 0$, $z = 0$ but also at $x = L_x$, $y = L_y$, $z = L_z$. Thus, the wave number vectors are required to obey the restrictions

$$2\sigma_x L_x = n_x, \qquad 2\sigma_y L_y = n_y, \qquad 2\sigma_z L_z = n_z. \qquad (n_x, n_y, n_z = 1, 2, \ldots) \tag{127}$$

Equations (127) can be visualized if we write, e.g., the first of them, as $(\sigma_x/\sigma)(2L_x/\lambda) = n_x$, and note that the quantity on the left-hand side, and hence n_x, signifies the number of nodes outside the origin, that appear in the range $(0, L_x)$.

We discover the frequencies allowed in an elastic continuum on elimination of the wave number components in Eqs. (127) with the aid of Eq. (125). Since $\sigma^2 = \sigma_x^2 + \sigma_y^2 + \sigma_z^2$, one gets

$$\nu = \frac{c}{2} \left(\frac{n_x^2}{L_x^2} + \frac{n_y^2}{L_y^2} + \frac{n_z^2}{L_z^2} \right)^{1/2}. \tag{128}$$

In the further discussion of Debye's method, we need not concern ourselves with the values of Eq. (128). It suffices to know how many standing waves have frequencies less than any given value ν. The reason is that when the integers n_x, n_y, n_z are large enough—which is the case for nearly all the waves of interest to us—the fractional increase of ν caused by unit increase of any of these integers is so extremely small that it may be regarded as infinitesimal. One is therefore permitted to treat the discrete *elastic spectrum* of frequencies as continuous. This spectrum is defined by a *spectral density* (or *distribution*) *function* $g(\nu)$ such that $g(\nu)d\nu$ gives the number of frequencies lying between ν and $\nu + d\nu$.

We determine the function $g(\nu)$ by a procedure analogous to that which enabled us in Section 3–3 to ascertain the density of free particle quantum states. On substituting Eq. (128) for Eq. (49) of Section 3–3 and modifying the argument that follows Eq. (49) accordingly, one readily finds

$$g(\nu) = V\frac{4\pi\nu^2}{c^3}. \tag{129}$$

It is worth pointing out that this spectral density is half the density of photon states in blackbody radiation, as expressed by Eq. (188), Chapter 3. This is not surprising because a photon is endowed with two directions of polarization, while we have (so far) assumed only one possible polarization for elastic waves.

At this stage, we must rectify an omission: in actual fact, an isotropic elastic continuum transmits both longitudinal waves and transverse waves with two independent directions of polarization. This requires that we write down a result like Eq. (129) for the longitudinal waves as well as for each of the two sets of transverse waves. But since the velocity c_l of the longitudinal waves differs from the velocity c_t of the transverse waves, the sum of the distribution functions is not simply three times the quantity cited in Eq. (129). Instead it is

$$g(\nu) = 4\pi V\left(\frac{1}{c_l^3} + \frac{2}{c_t^3}\right)\nu^2. \tag{130}$$

Formula (130), Debye claims, is valid for standing waves not merely in a continuous medium but in an isotropic crystalline solid as well, despite the solid's discrete structure, provided one disallows all frequencies exceeding ν_D. Per definition, this cutoff frequency satisfies the equation

$$\int_0^{\nu_D} g(\nu)d\nu = 3N, \tag{131}$$

so that, after insertion of $g(\nu)$ from Eq. (130),

$$\nu_D^3 = \frac{9N}{4\pi V}\left(\frac{1}{c_l^3} + \frac{2}{c_t^3}\right)^{-1}. \tag{132}$$

With the use of this result, Eq. (130) can be stated more briefly as

$$g(\nu) = \frac{9N}{\nu_D^3}\nu^2. \tag{133}$$

For the distribution of eigenfrequencies given by Eq. (133), the central formula (117) should obviously be changed to read

$$F = \frac{9N}{\nu_D^3}\int_0^{\nu_D}[\tfrac{1}{2}h\nu + kT\log(1 - e^{-h\nu/kT})]\nu^2\,d\nu. \tag{134}$$

On defining the *Debye temperature* by

$$\boxed{\Theta_D = \frac{h\nu_D}{k}} \tag{135}$$

and employing the new integration variable $x = h\nu/kT$, one can rewrite Eq. (134) as

$$F = \tfrac{9}{8}Nk\Theta_D + 9NkT\left(\frac{T}{\Theta_D}\right)^3\int_0^{\Theta_D/T}\log(1 - e^{-x})x^2\,dx. \tag{136}$$

On integration by parts, this transforms into

$$F = \tfrac{9}{8}Nk\Theta_D + 3NkT\log(1 - e^{-\Theta_D/T}) - 3NkT\left(\frac{T}{\Theta_D}\right)^3 F_D(\Theta_D/T), \tag{137}$$

in which, for the sake of brevity, we have used the function

$$F_D(\Theta_D/T) = \int_0^{\Theta_D/T} x^3(e^x - 1)^{-1}\,dx. \tag{138}$$

The integral (138) can be evaluated numerically; but as $F_D(\Theta_D/T)$ is multiplied by $3(T/\Theta_D)^3$ in Eq. (137), it is more advantageous to know the values of the so-called *Debye function* $D(y) = (3/y^3)F_D(y)$. A list of such values appears, for example, in the Landolt-Börnstein Tables.

From the expression (137) for $F = F(T,V,N)$, the thermodynamic parameters now follow in a routine manner. The energy $U = F - T(\partial F/\partial T)$, in particular, is found to be

$$U = \tfrac{9}{8}Nk\Theta_D + 9NkT\left(\frac{T}{\Theta_D}\right)^3 F_D\,(\Theta_D/T) \tag{139}$$

if one notes that

$$\frac{\partial F_D}{\partial T} = -\frac{\Theta_D}{T^2}\left(\frac{\Theta_D}{T}\right)^3 (e^{\Theta_D/T} - 1)^{-1}.$$

And the heat capacity follows on differentiation of Eq. (139) with respect to T:

$$\boxed{C_V = 9Nk\left[4\left(\frac{T}{\Theta_D}\right)^3 F_D\,(\Theta_D/T) - \frac{\Theta_D}{T}\,(e^{\Theta_D/T} - 1)^{-1}\right]}. \tag{140}$$

The values of the heat capacity given by this formula are likewise tabulated. It is remarkable that the molar heat capacity according to Eq. (140) is a universal function of T/Θ_D. In other words, in the theory of Debye, as in that of Einstein, the curves of C_V/N versus T/Θ_D for different solids are coincident—notwithstanding the variation of Θ_D with density and atomic species. Monatomic solids thus obey a *law of corresponding states*; whenever substances have the same value of T/Θ_D, they are said to be in *corresponding states*.

Of special interest to us are the limiting forms of the energy and heat capacity predicted by the present theory for high and low temperatures, respectively. For this purpose, we need to establish the values assumed by the function F_D at these temperature extremes.

When $T \gg \Theta_D$, one has $x \ll 1$ in the integrand of Eq. (138), so that it can be approximated by $x^3/x = x^2$. Since the integral of x^2 is $x^3/3$, Eq. (138) becomes

$$F_D\,(\Theta_D/T) \approx \frac{1}{3}\left(\frac{\Theta_D}{T}\right)^3. \qquad (T \gg \Theta_D) \tag{141}$$

Substitution of this result in Eqs. (139) and (140) yields $U \approx 3NkT$ and $C_V \approx 3Nk$, respectively, if one neglects the first term in (139) and employs the approximation $\exp \Theta_D/T \approx 1 + \Theta_D/T$ in Eq. (140). We thus obtain once more the empirically verified laws (112) and (113).

For the opposite extreme $T \ll \Theta_D$, no serious error is made when one extends the upper limit of the integral (138) to infinity. Furthermore, the integrand is identical with the (convergent) series $x^3 \sum_{n=1}^{\infty} e^{-nx}$, whose termwise integration, with the aid of the lemma

$$\int_0^\infty x^3 e^{-nx}\,dx = -\frac{d^3}{dn^3}\int_0^\infty e^{-nx}\,dx = \frac{6}{n^4},$$

leads to

$$F_D(\Theta_D/T) \approx 6 \sum_{n=1}^{\infty} n^{-4} = \frac{\pi^4}{15}. \qquad (T \ll \Theta_D) \qquad (142)$$

Inserting Eq. (142) in Eqs. (139) and (140), one finds, when the approach to zero of the second term in Eqs. (140) is taken into account, that

$$U \approx \tfrac{9}{8} N k \Theta_D + 9NkT\left(\frac{T}{\Theta_D}\right)^3 \frac{\pi^4}{15} \qquad (T \ll \Theta_D) \qquad (143)$$

and

$$\boxed{C_V \approx 3Nk\,\frac{4\pi^4}{5}\left(\frac{T}{\Theta_D}\right)^3,} \qquad (T \ll \Theta_D) \qquad (144)$$

respectively. The result Eq. (144) is the celebrated *Debye's T^3*, or *cube, law*.

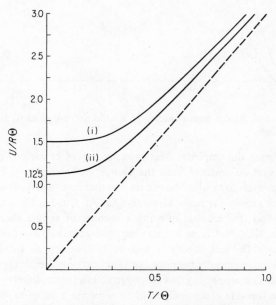

FIGURE 4–5. Molar energy of a solid according to (i) Einstein and (ii) Debye.

The proportionality between C_V and T^3 asserted by this law should theoretically hold accurately within less than 1 per cent for all $T < \Theta_D/12$.

The formulas for the energy and the heat capacity, propounded up to this point, are summarized pictorially in Figure 4-5 and Figure 4-6. To facilitate comparison, the curves representing the expressions of Einstein and Debye are drawn relative to the same set of axes.

The interpretation of experimental data with a view to testing the validity of Debye's theory is far from straightforward. Suppose his Eq. (140) is correct at all T; one should then be able, by selecting the proper value of Θ_D in each

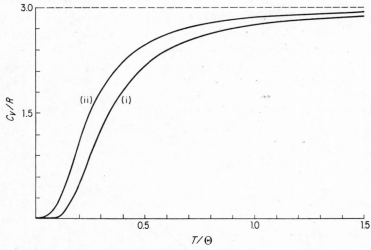

FIGURE 4-6. Molar heat capacity of a solid according to (i) Einstein and (ii) Debye.

instance, to bring the empirical heat capacity curves of various monatomic solids into exact coincidence with the Debye curve shown in Figure 4-6. Early experimenters arrived at the conclusion that such a procedure is indeed successful, not merely for many elements (Ag, Al, Cu, Fe, Pb, Zn, etc.), but also, surprisingly, for crystals of quite a number of simple chemical compounds (KBr, KCl, NaCl, etc.). Later inquiries revealed, however, that the agreement with Debye's theory is not as satisfactory as was previously believed, and that especially the cube law is at best only seemingly confirmed. The main evidence supporting this judgment follows immediately.

The Debye formula (140) enables us to compute a value of Θ_D for each pair of measured values of T and C_V, and hence to establish empirically the dependence of Θ_D upon T. Now, although the derivation of Eq. (140) rests on the assumption that Θ_D is independent of T (at fixed N/V), it is also true that Θ_D, as defined by Eq. (135), can be expected to exhibit a slow monotonic change with increase of temperature. We infer that if the Debye theory were essentially correct, the empirical function $\Theta_D(T)$ would vary only weakly (or not at all) with T and have no extrema. But the real behavior of $\Theta_D(T)$ is markedly different. As a matter of fact, for many solids, $\Theta_D(T)$ changes rapidly at low temperatures and frequently traverses a maximum or minimum. Denoting by Θ_∞ the average value of Θ_D for high temperatures, one finds generally this extremum to lie at a temperature $\hat{T} \sim \Theta_\infty/50$. This fact alone constitutes a refutation of the Debye cube law. Indeed, on the basis of the cube law, C_V would start decreasing toward zero like T^3 at temperatures as high as $\Theta_\infty/10$, whereas the cited experimental pecularities of Θ_D exclude such a monotonic decline until T has fallen below $\hat{T}$.

To illustrate the remarks of the foregoing paragraph, we quote numerical values characterizing the Θ_D versus T curves for KCl and C (diamond). According to measurements carried out by Keesom and Clark (1935), the curve for KCl displays a maximum at $T \approx 4.5°$K, while Θ_D varies between circa 220°K and 235°K in the temperature range extending from 1°K to 10°K. The data for carbon are due to de Sorbo (1953); they give a maximum at $T \approx 60°$K and a variation of Θ_D between about 1850°K and 2250°K in the range from 30°K to 300°K.

At this point it should have become clear that any instance, in which C_V/T^3 takes on a constant value in some temperature interval, must be regarded as fortuitous and not as evidence in favor of Debye's cube law. In this context we might mention the examples of CaF_2 and FeS_2. The quantity C_V/T^3 is for them almost rigorously a constant at all temperatures ranging from $\Theta_D/25$ to $\Theta_D/12$, if one assumes Θ_D to equal 474°K for CaF_2 and 645°K for FeS_2.

Although it cannot be denied that the Debye heat capacity formula describes the experimental data faithfully outside the T^3 region, the preceding discussion shows that the agreement breaks down at lower temperatures. We are thus forced to conclude that the Debye model is unable to predict accurately the complete frequency spectrum of a crystal.

4-7. Lattice Theory of Born and von Kármán and Extensions

The true eigenfrequencies of a crystal are of course the $3N$ positive roots ν_r of Eq. (103). But owing to the extremely high dimensionality of the determinant appearing there, an explicit computation of the ν_r (in terms of the ϕ_{ij})

is in general out of the question. In the hypothetical case of a one-dimensional crystal, however, this problem has a relatively easy solution. It was first worked out by Born and von Kármán (1912, 1913). In the next paragraphs we shall reproduce the main elements of their method, which will afford us some idea of the concepts involved in the lattice theory of heat capacity and of the reasons for the failure of Debye's approach.

Let us consider a large number of similar and structureless atoms labeled $1, 2, \ldots, N$ arranged from left to right along the x-axis, to which we restrict their motions. Denote the equilibrium separation between adjacent atoms by a, so that the instantaneous coordinates of the atoms are $x_j = (j - 1)a + \xi_j$ ($j = 1, 2, \ldots, N$), where ξ_j stands for the displacement of the atom j from its equilibrium position.

On the assumption that the interactions between two atoms depend only upon their distance apart and that interactions between nonadjacent atoms can be neglected, the potential energy of the linear atomic chain is obviously of the form

$$\phi = \sum_{j=1}^{N-1} f(\xi_{j+1} - \xi_j). \tag{145}$$

(Do not mistake the argument of f for a factor!) If ϕ is expanded in a power series broken off at the quadratic terms, as in Eq. (99), one is left with

$$\phi = \frac{1}{2} \sum_{j=1}^{N-1} K(\xi_{j+1} - \xi_j)^2, \tag{146}$$

where

$$K = f''(0). \tag{147}$$

The equations of motion for the atoms $j = 2, 3, \ldots, N - 1$ accordingly become

$$m\ddot{\xi}_j = -K(2\xi_j - \xi_{j-1} - \xi_{j+1}). \tag{148}$$

The atoms at the ends of the chain obey different equations, due to the fact that atom 1 has no neighbor on its left and atom N no neighbor on its right. To make Eq. (148) valid for them as well, we imagine the given chain to be an internal segment of a longer chain. It will further simplify matters if we suppose that atoms 1 and $N + 1$ are in phase, in other words, $\xi_1 = \xi_{N+1}$ at all times. These two assumptions are admissible since (as Born and von Kármán demonstrated), for the large N here contemplated (say $N \sim 10^6$), the eigenfrequencies of our chain will no longer depend on the particular conditions imposed on its end points.

A short calculation would confirm that one can satisfy Eq. (148) for all j by

$$\xi_j = A \sin 2\pi(\sigma ja - \nu t), \tag{149}$$

A being a constant, provided ν bears the following relation to σ:

$$4\pi^2 m\nu^2 = 2K(1 - \cos 2\pi\sigma a) = 4K \sin^2 \pi\sigma a. \tag{150}$$

The solution (149) has the form of a traveling plane wave with wave number σ and frequency ν. On extracting the positive square root of Eq. (150), one gets

$$\nu(\sigma) = \frac{1}{\pi} \left(\frac{K}{m}\right)^{1/2} |\sin \pi\sigma a|. \tag{151}$$

This means that the wave velocity ν/σ varies with the wave number σ, or that the waves show *dispersion*.

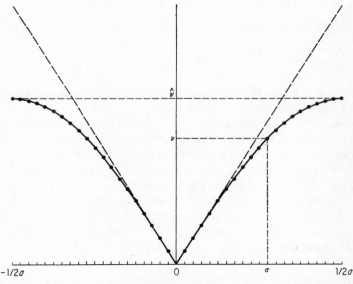

FIGURE 4–7. The relation between frequency and wave number for the normal vibrations in a one-dimensional crystal (i) of infinite length (continuous curve) and (ii) of finite length (dots). The broken curve represents the equation $\nu = c\sigma$.

The graph in Figure 4–7 depicts the function $\nu(\sigma)$. Obviously one does not obtain a new wave if σ is replaced by $\sigma + 1/a$ in Eq. (149). We have therefore conveniently limited σ to the interval $-1/2a < \sigma \leqslant 1/2a$.

With the stated restriction, the dispersion relation (151) refers to a chain of infinite length. If it is to apply to our finite chain, one must further reduce the domain of values of σ by imposing here our earlier periodicity requirement $\xi_1 = \xi_{N+1}$ on the solution (149), which implies that σNa has to be an integer. By virtue of the two foregoing conditions, σ can have only the N values

$$\sigma_r = \frac{r}{Na}, \qquad \left[r = 0, \pm 1, \ldots, \pm\left(\frac{N}{2} - 1\right), +\frac{N}{2}\right] \tag{152}$$

where, for simplicity's sake, N is supposed to be an even number. Thus, wave numbers larger than $\hat\sigma = 1/2a$, or wavelengths shorter than $2a$, are ruled out. The frequencies corresponding to the discrete set of wave numbers (152) are, by Eq. (151),

$$\nu_r = \frac{1}{\pi}\left(\frac{K}{m}\right)^{1/2}\left|\sin\frac{r\pi}{N}\right|, \tag{153}$$

and the maximum frequency, in particular, is seen to be

$$\hat\nu = \frac{1}{\pi}\left(\frac{K}{m}\right)^{1/2}. \tag{154}$$

Notice that in Figure 4–7 we have indicated the ν_r by dots and the associated σ_r by marks (along the horizontal axis).

In Eq. (153) the eigenfrequencies of a finite one-dimensional crystal are enumerated. Inspection of the argument of the sine function reveals that the ν_r lie very close to one another for large N. Once again, the discrete frequency spectrum may therefore be approximated by a continuous spectrum. To determine the density function $g(\nu)$ describing this spectrum, we observe: according to Eq. (153), $Nad\sigma$ normal vibrations possess wave numbers lying between σ and $\sigma + d\sigma$, and an equal number of vibrations exists in the interval $-\sigma$ to $-\sigma - d\sigma$. Since ν is the same for σ and $-\sigma$, it follows that $2Nad\sigma$ frequencies lie between ν and $\nu + d\nu$. That is,

$$g(\nu)d\nu = 2Nad\sigma, \tag{155}$$

or, on division by $d\nu$,

$$g(\nu) = \frac{2Na}{d\nu/d\sigma} = \frac{2N}{\pi}(\hat\nu^2 - \nu^2)^{-1/2}; \tag{156}$$

here $d\nu/d\sigma$ has been substituted from Eq. (151). The function (156), characterizing the so-called *lattice spectrum*, is plotted in Figure 4–8. The main features of this graph are: it is horizontal at $\nu = 0$ and goes to infinity when $\nu \to \hat\nu$.

In order to discuss the connection between the lattice spectrum and the Debye, or elastic, spectrum, let us examine what will happen when σ becomes very small. For long wavelengths, i.e., $\sigma a \ll 1$, the displacement ξ_j in

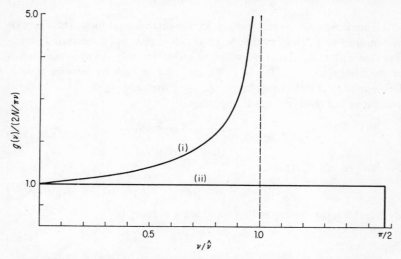

FIGURE 4–8. Density function $g(\nu)$ for (i) the lattice spectrum and (ii) the elastic spectrum of a one-dimensional crystal.

Eq. (149) changes very little from one atom to the next. We are consequently permitted to approximate Eq. (149) by the continuous function

$$\xi = A \sin 2\pi(\sigma x - \nu t) \tag{157}$$

of the position coordinate x. Also, from Eq. (151), making the approximation $\sin \pi\sigma a \approx \pi\sigma a$, we see that the velocity of the disturbance (157) has the same value

$$\frac{\nu}{\sigma} = \hat{\nu}\pi a \qquad (\sigma a \ll 1) \tag{158}$$

for all σ's in question. Equation (157) is therefore identical with a plane wave propagated in a continuous elastic medium. The physical reason for the occurrence of this kind of solution is evident: the waves here considered "see" the linear chain as a continuous string, because their wavelengths are many times longer than the distance a between the atoms. They are known as *acoustic waves* and, when appropriately superimposed, give rise to acoustic vibrations of the crystal. The spectral density of the acoustic vibrations obviously derives from Eq. (156) if within that equation one neglects ν^2 in comparison with $\hat{\nu}^2$; one gets

$$g(\nu) = \frac{2N}{\pi\hat{\nu}}. \qquad (\nu \ll \hat{\nu}) \tag{159}$$

We are now able to state exactly, in one-dimensional form, the approximation implicit in Debye's theory. His method rests upon the tacit assumption that Eqs. (158) and (159), which in reality are only the acoustical limits of the true relations (151) and (156), are valid at high frequencies as well. Debye continues this extrapolation up to the frequency ν_D chosen so that the integral of the resulting elastic spectrum

$$g_D(\nu) = \begin{cases} \dfrac{2N}{\pi\hat{\nu}}, & (\nu \leqslant \nu_D) \\ 0 & (\nu > \nu_D) \end{cases} \tag{160}$$

over all ν equals N. Hence,

$$\nu_D = \frac{\pi}{2}\hat{\nu}. \tag{161}$$

By Eq. (158), the corresponding cutoff wave number is

$$\sigma_D = \frac{1}{2a} = \hat{\sigma}. \tag{162}$$

The last two equations reveal that the Debye theory, while it furnishes the same maximum wave number as lattice theory, has a maximum frequency that is too large by a factor $\pi/2$. This difference reflects the fact that Born and von Kármán employed the known number N of atoms to impose an upper limit on σ rather than on ν. The realization of these workers that the wave number is the more important quantity, represented a considerable advance over the ideas held by Debye.

Since the lattice spectrum agrees asymptotically with the elastic spectrum as ν becomes zero, it follows that Debye's approach will be correct when the acoustic, or low, frequencies alone are excited—in other words, at sufficiently low temperatures.

This conclusion was arrived at on the basis of the simple frequency function Eq. (151), which is valid only if a single atom occupies each lattice point of the given one-dimensional lattice. When two or more atoms are associated with every lattice point, the frequency function acquires essentially new features. Fortunately, however, these features are confined to high frequencies, which are inoperative near $T = 0°K$, so that our conclusion remains true.

To amplify this assertion, let us postulate that one atom of mass m' and another of mass m'' occupy each *primitive*, or smallest unit, cell of a one-dimensional lattice. An analysis similar to that made earlier in relation to singly occupied primitive cells would show that, in the present situation, *two* frequencies, ν_- and ν_+, with $\nu_+ > \nu_-$, belong to each value of the wave number σ (see Problem 6). The two functions $\nu_-(\sigma)$ and $\nu_+(\sigma)$ arising in this manner are commonly referred to as the *acoustic* and *optical branches*, respectively, of the function $\nu(\sigma)$.

The acoustic branch resembles the frequency curve, Eq. (151), to an extent depending upon the values of m', m'' and the interatomic force constant. At small values of σa, the frequency ν_- thus decreases linearly to zero with σ, and the associated constant-velocity waves behave like acoustic waves in a continuous medium; hence the name "acoustic branch." The optical branch, on the other hand, is a symmetrical bell-shaped curve that lies everywhere above the acoustic branch and attains a nonzero value $\nu_+(0)$ (which is also the maximum value of ν_+) at $\sigma = 0$. This branch therefore refers solely to relatively high frequencies, as we noted above.

We might point out another major difference between the two types of lattice vibrations. In the limit $\sigma \to 0$, the atoms m' and m'' vibrate in phase with one another when they partake in an acoustic vibration, whereas they move in opposing directions during an optical vibration. This means that in an ionic crystal, where the atoms m' and m'' carry opposite charges, an optical vibration having (in comparison with the lattice constant a) an appreciable wavelength, will correspond to a dipole wave. Such a wave can be expected to interact with radiation in the infrared region of the electromagnetic spectrum, whose wavelength is likewise long. The optical effect here predicted does indeed manifest itself in many real crystals as a strong selective absorption and reflection of light at the limiting frequencies $\nu(0)$ of optical branches. This explains how the name for these branches originated.

In Born's extension (1923) of the Born-von Kármán theory to three dimensions, the main characteristics of the one-dimensional model are retained and generalized. If one adopts the *harmonic* approximation—that is, terminates the Taylor expansion of a crystal's potential energy in the atomic displacements ξ_j at the second-order terms—he may again decompose the motions of atoms in a crystal into a large number of independent plane waves (as many as there are degrees of freedom). And, once more, we have to distinguish between acoustic and optical modes of vibration. The difficulties of this whole problem are, however, compounded by the fact that for any allowed wave vector σ, the oscillating atoms are capable of undergoing three independent kinds of displacement from their equilibrium positions, instead of the single, longitudinal kind permitted in one dimension. The existence of these three modes of polarization causes the number of branches of the frequency function to treble. A three-dimensional crystal containing two atoms in every primitive cell will consequently exhibit three acoustic and three optical branches. This property has been fully verified experimentally, as, for example, in studies of the elements germanium and silicon.

It is possible to demonstrate that every atom added to the primitive cell after the second one, also increases the number of optical branches by three (by one, in the linear crystal), while leaving the number of acoustic branches unchanged. Born's theory thus predicts that the frequency function $\nu(\sigma)$ for a crystal having, say, r atoms in each primitive cell, will be characterized by three acoustic and $3r - 3$ optical branches. In three dimensions, as in one dimension, it is true that $\nu(\sigma)$ tends to zero linearly with σ in any acoustic branch, so that we are dealing with waves whose velocities are independent of σ. It turns out, moreover, that one of their polarization states is longitudinal, while the remaining two are transverse. And so these waves may be compared with acoustic waves in a continuum. By contrast, the frequencies defined by the optical branches again tend to nonzero values (some of which may coincide) as $\sigma = 0$ is approached. At this limit the optical frequencies belong to vibrations taking place in such a way that the centers of mass of the primitive cells remain at rest.

Because of the finite values of optical frequencies at $\sigma = 0$, acoustic waves alone will be energized at low enough temperatures. It follows that lattice theory too predicts a cube law for the heat capacity of real crystals. We should however add two significant qualifications. The upper limit of the T^3 region must be determined for each crystal individually, and in general it will lie far below the temperature expected on the basis of Debye's theory.

Individual treatment is called for, because the density function $g(\nu)$, on which the detailed behavior of the heat capacity function depends, varies strongly with the nature of the forces between atoms and thus from one crystal to another. The computation of $g(\nu)$ is a very difficult task. The pioneering work in this field was done by Blackman (1937). He calculated $g(\nu)$, and from it the heat capacity C_V, for a simple cubic lattice—which does not correspond to any crystal in nature. His basic assumption was that only (quasi-elastic) forces between closest and next nearest neighboring atoms need to be considered.

Kellermann (1941) extended Blackman's method to real crystals by computing $g(\nu)$ and C_V for NaCl. Several workers continued in the same direction by performing similar calculations for other crystals, such as KCl (Iona, 1941), diamond, and Ag. The comparison between this kind of theoretical results and experimental data is still in progress. We shall accordingly not pursue the matter any further.

4–8. Epilogue: Some Features of Interacting Particle Systems

In this chapter we have studied a few characteristics of ideal classical and quantum-mechanical gases. A surprising result of these investigations is the extent to which certain properties of real systems approximate those of the corresponding independent-particle system. So, for instance, the conception of conduction electrons as forming an ideal gas, proves in more than one way to be an adequate model for treating an actual metal, despite the long-range Coulomb interactions existing between the electrons and between electrons and the metallic ions. Likewise, liquid helium II resembles somewhat a degenerate ideal boson gas.

It must however be recognized that the free-electron model is not at all helpful in explaining many other properties of metals, such as the tremendous range of variation—from 10^8 to 10^{-22} ohm^{-1} cm^{-1}—of electrical conductivity between metals and insulators. Furthermore, the atoms in liquid helium at normal density are, on the average, only 3.6 A apart; and at distances not much less than this (2.7 A), helium atoms will repel each other so strongly that an ideal gas model becomes rather inadequate. A recent statistical theory due to Lee, Huang, and Yang (1957) in fact took into account such interactions with considerable success. Their model might be regarded as a modification of the ideal gas model. But in general the method of attacking the interaction problem has followed a different course, both in respect of conduction electrons and the liquid helium system.

It is instructive in this connection to start with the customary treatment of forces of interaction in solids. Let us remember that, although the ions in a crystal strongly interact with one another, their collective modes of motion, as described by the lattice vibrations, are mutually independent in the harmonic approximation. Any dynamic state of the crystal is a superposition of these normal vibrations, and the energy associated with each normal mode of frequency ν is $h\nu(n_\nu + \frac{1}{2})$, where n_ν is zero or a positive integer that increases with the excitation of the mode. This state of affairs calls to mind a similar result that obtains if one quantizes the plane waves into which an electromagnetic field can be analyzed. A proper quantum-mechanical treatment reveals that not only the energies but also the linear momenta of these waves are quantized—the allowed values of the momentum being $n_\nu h\sigma$ for a wave with a wave vector σ. The appearance of these corpuscular attributes has led physicists to represent an electromagnetic field at times by an assembly of particles, or photons, having energies $h\nu$ and momenta $h\sigma$. This is the viewpoint adopted by us in our earlier discussion of blackbody radiation.

One can now pursue an analogous line of reasoning with regard to lattice waves in solids: every wave of frequency ν and wave vector σ is replaced by a number of particle-like entities, called *phonons*, each possessing an energy $\varepsilon = h\nu$ and a momentum $\mathbf{p} = h\sigma$. And, in the harmonic approximation, any excited state of the vibrating atoms or ions is viewed as a gas of non-interacting phonons, i.e., as an ideal gas.

In parentheses we might caution that the analogy between phonons and material particles ought not to be followed through to the extreme. For one thing, the quasi-momentum $\mathbf{p}$ and the energy ε have been demonstrated to be many-valued functions of σ and p respectively. Moreover, the number of phonons (sum of the n_ν's), unlike that of material particles, in a closed system is not constant, but increases as the temperature rises.

If in a solid one includes the anharmonic terms (of order higher than the second) in the expression for the lattice potential energy, interactions are introduced among the lattice waves, and therefore between phonons. This so-called phonon-phonon interaction—which intensifies as the number of phonons grows—besides providing a mechanism for the attainment of thermal equilibrium, is responsible for thermal expansion and partly for the phenomenon of heat conduction.

Turning now to the conduction electrons in metallic solids, we recall that our discussion in Section 3-5 was based on the Sommerfeld model, which treats electrons as an ideal gas of fermions moving in a constant potential field. We have already noted that this model was successful in describing the electronic heat capacity of metals and some of their thermal and electrical transport properties. The phenomena which Sommerfeld's hypothesis failed to explain can be understood adequately in terms of the electron-electron and electron-ion interactions.

The interactions between the conduction electrons in a metal engender a new phenomenon, which has no analogue in an ideal gas, namely, *plasma oscillations*. These are collective motions where the behavior of the charged particles is correlated over large distances by the Coulomb interactions. Wave motions produced in this manner are comparable with ordinary acoustic waves—which would likewise not exist, were it not for the interactions between the particles of the propagation medium. But it should be pointed out that, owing to the high frequency ω_p of the plasma waves, the energy $\hbar\omega_p$ is so large (10 to 20 ev) compared with kT that these so-called plasma modes cannot be excited thermally. They can be excited though if electrons of a few kilovolt energies are fired into a thin metal film.

One would be inclined to think that the electron-electron interaction will markedly change the Fermi-Dirac distribution governing independent fermions. But, as empirical evidence has confirmed, the opposite is true, and for the following reason. Due to their mutual repulsion, the electrons "shun" one another, so that every electron is effectively surrounded by a "cloud" of positive charge. The electron together with its cloud behaves somewhat like a particle. It interacts with any other such *quasi-particle* through a *screened Coulomb* force—in which r^{-2} is multiplied by an exponential factor decreasing rapidly with the interelectron separation r. In this manner, we obtain an assembly of virtually independent entities approximately obeying the original distribution law.

The motions of conduction electrons is affected more significantly by their interactions with the periodically arrayed positive ions. The force field of this ion lattice causes the electronic energy states to be arranged in quasi-continuous groups, or *energy bands*, separated from one another by finite intervals. The energy-momentum relationship of an electron is thus no longer that of a free electron. This modification may be taken into account partly if one replaces the ordinary electron mass by an appropriate *effective mass* and introduces corresponding changes in various other electronic properties.

By using the concepts of effective mass and quasi-particle, one may reinterpret the parameters appearing in Sommerfeld's theory and thereby retain its sheer formalism. It can then be appreciated why his free-electron model was successful to the extent explained above.

The strict periodicity of the ion lattice hitherto assumed is disturbed by the thermal vibrations of the ions, which always occur at $T > 0°$K. These imperfections scatter electrons and thus give rise to electrical resistance. One commonly treats this scattering as an electron-phonon interaction, in which an electron either emits or absorbs a phonon.

Suppose the phonon emitted by one electron is subsequently absorbed by another electron. Such a compound event will generate a weak virtual attractive interaction between the two electrons. Processes of this type are important at low temperatures, where they are responsible for *superconductivity*. This phenomenon, discovered by Kamerlingh Onnes as early as 1911, is the property of vanishing electrical resistance appearing in a number of metals and some of their alloys at very low (but still finite) temperatures. It is only during the last decade however that a physical understanding of superconductivity has been achieved in terms of the Bardeen-Cooper-Schrieffer theory (1957), which is founded upon the aforementioned mechanism of pair interaction between electrons.

As a final instance of the application of statistical theory to a system where the interactions between particles play a prominent role, we will consider certain aspects of the helium four problem, which we briefly referred to in Section 3–8.

Kamerlingh Onnes liquefied helium gas in the year 1908; since then the liquid He^4 isotope has been found to possess several highly peculiar properties. It has its normal boiling point at 4.216°K and like He^3, but unlike any other substance, remains liquid down to the lowest temperatures ever reached, provided the pressure does not exceed about 25 atm (29 atm for He^3). As originally observed by Keesom (1932), He^4 undergoes at the lambda point $T_\lambda = 2.186°K$ a phase transition from a high-temperature form, He I, to a low-temperature form, He II. While ordinarily phase transitions are of the *first order*—that is, accompanied by finite changes in volume and entropy— the phase change of helium at T_λ resembles a transition of the *second order*, which is characterized instead by jumps in the specific heats and expansion coefficients. Below the lambda point. the specific heat decreases rapidly: first in a roughly exponential manner and then, from 0.6°K downwards, strictly proportional to T^3. Indubitably, however, the most fascinating trait of He II, discovered by Kapitza (1938), is its *superfluidity*, by which we mean the absence of viscosity in the low-speed flow of He II through narrow capillaries.

The first attempt to explain the strange properties of He II was made by F. London (1938), who related the lambda transition to the phenomenon of Bose-Einstein condensation. He showed that this approach leads to a transition temperature for helium of the correct order of 3°K (see Section 3–8). The ideas of London were further pursued by Tisza (1938, 1940), who proposed a *two-fluid model* to understand the behavior of liquid helium. In the phenomenological theory of this model, one visualizes He II as a mixture of two interpenetrating fluids, viz., a *normal fluid*, which is viscous, and a *super-fluid*, which has zero entropy and flows without any viscosity. The relative amounts of these two components are assumed to vary with the temperature in such a manner that the liquid consists of pure superfluid at $T = 0°K$ and of pure normal fluid at $T = T_\lambda$. In conformity with London's hypothesis, the superfluid is supposedly made up of helium atoms in the condensed (zero-momentum) state, while the normal fluid consists of those atoms still occupying the excited states.

In spite of the seeming success of the London-Tisza theory, it must be remembered that the specific heat curve of a boson gas is peaked at $T = T_c$, whereas the curve for helium is discontinuous at $T = T_\lambda$.* It turns out more-over that the computed derivative dT_λ/dp has the wrong, i.e., positive, sign. For these and other reasons, the relatively simple interpretations of the two-fluid model presented by this theory proved untenable, although the model itself has remained formally valid.

* Recent work suggests a logarithmic singularity at T_λ.

This negative appraisal should not surprise us, for it is conceivable that the not unappreciable forces between atoms of liquid helium could cause fundamental deviations from the behavior of an ideal boson gas. The breakthrough in the helium problem occurred quintessentially with the recognition of this very fact by Landau (1941). Realizing the primacy of the forces in interaction, he gave up any attempt to describe the motions of individual particles—as was done heretofore—and instead inquired into the

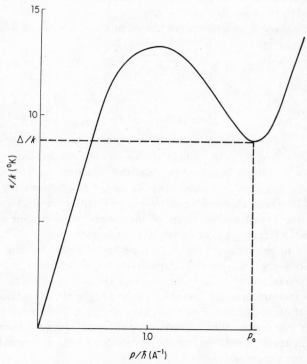

FIGURE 4–9. Energy-momentum relation of an elementary excitation.

quantum states of the helium liquid taken as a whole. To this end he proposed that helium atoms be treated as a real liquid (interacting particles), that might be better modeled on a solid system rather than on a gaseous system (non-interacting particles). His theory upheld the two-fluid model, but interpreted it in a much more plausible manner—albeit without demonstrative rigor.

By a quantization procedure that involves the density ρ and the velocity v of the liquid as quantum operators, Landau (1941, 1947) arrived at the following conclusions. At $T = 0°K$, helium can be pictured as an ideal fluid which is capable of performing frictionless potential flow (curl $\mathbf{v} = 0$). On addition of heat, excitations are created in this fluid, whose energy quanta, known as *elementary excitations*, increase in number as the temperature rises. These elementary excitations may be regarded as quasi-particles since each of them possesses a definite momentum $\mathbf{p}$ and energy ε. They move through the liquid in all directions and undergo viscous effects in colliding with one another and the walls of the container. Theoretical arguments and experimental evidence show that the relation between ε and p has the form represented by the curve in Figure 4–9.

From the graph it is seen that in the vicinities of $p = 0$ and $p = p_0$ the energy is given by

$$\varepsilon = cp \tag{163}$$

and

$$\varepsilon = \Delta + \frac{(p - p_0)^2}{2\mu}, \tag{164}$$

respectively, where c, Δ, p_0, and μ are empirically determined constants. Elementary excitations described by these two equations have been named *phonons* (by Landau) and *rotons* (by Tamm). The phonons are merely quanta of longitudinal sound waves having a velocity c (at $0°K$) and correspond to the lowest excited states of the system, while rotons probably correspond to certain types of vortex motions (curl $\mathbf{v} \neq 0$).

In order to calculate the thermal properties of liquid helium, Landau conceives of every low-lying excited quantum state of helium as an assembly of weakly interacting elementary excitations. If the density of this gas is small, i.e., at low temperatures, the interactions will be negligible, so that one has an ideal gas of quasi-particles. From the curve of $\varepsilon(p)$ it is also evident that at sufficiently low temperatures, mainly phonons, and only to a lesser extent rotons, will appear, as the excitations represented by the upper parts of the curve are not yet generated.

At temperatures below $0.6°K$, not even the rotons are excited, so that only phonons need be considered. The equation for the specific heat of helium can then be written down immediately, either from Eq. (208), Chapter 3, which holds for radiation quanta, or from Debye's cube law, Eq. (144), Chapter 4, provided one corrects for the absence of transverse phonons. We get

$$C_{\mathrm{ph}} = \frac{16\pi^5 k^4}{15 h^3 \rho c^3} T^3, \qquad (T < 0.6°K) \tag{165}$$

where ρ is the density of the liquid. Equation (165) reproduces exactly the specific heat curve, $C_V = (0.0204 \pm 0.0004)T^3 j$ gm^{-1} deg^{-4}, found experimentally (1957), if one takes $c = (239 \pm 2)$ m/sec.

As the temperature is raised above 0.6°K, more and more rotons are created; they make a contribution C_r to the specific heat, which has to be added to C_{ph}. Now, rotons (like phonons) are bosons. But at the temperatures prevalent in He II, the minimum roton energy Δ is so large compared with kT [see Eq. (169)] that we are entitled to treat rotons by means of classical, instead of *BE*, statistics.

It follows, according to Eq. (13), that in the partition function $Z = Z_1^N/N!$ of the roton gas, the partition function for a single roton, Z_1, is given by

$$Z_1 = \frac{V}{h^3} \int_0^\infty e^{-\varepsilon/kT} 4\pi p^2 \, dp,$$

wherein ε must be substituted from Eq. (164). In consequence,

$$Z_1 = 2V\left(\frac{2\pi}{h^2}\right)^{3/2} p_0^2 (\mu kT)^{1/2} e^{-\Delta/kT}. \tag{166}$$

To get Eq. (166), we replaced the factor p^2 in the integrand by p_0^2; this approximation is permissible, since $p_0^2 \gg \mu kT$ [by Eq. (169)].

In Section 3–9 it was shown that the variability of the number of photons forming a radiation gas causes their Gibbs function G to vanish. The same conclusion holds for rotons, whose number N is likewise not constant. Hence, by Eq. (2), $Z_1 = N$, and the Helmholtz free energy, $F = -kT \log Z = -kT(N \log Z_1 - N \log N + N)$, reduces to

$$F = -kTZ_1. \tag{167}$$

If in this equation one inserts the value (166) of Z_1 and differentiates the result twice with respect to T, the roton part of the specific heat, viz., $-T(\partial^2 F/\partial T^2)_V$, reads:

$$C_r = \frac{2(2\pi)^{3/2}\mu^{1/2}p_0^2\Delta^2}{k^{1/2}h^3\rho T^{3/2}}\left[1 + \frac{kT}{\Delta} + \frac{3}{4}\left(\frac{kT}{\Delta}\right)^2\right]e^{-\Delta/kT}. \tag{168}$$

Due to the exponential factor appearing in Eq. (168), C_r will be negligible in relation to C_{ph} at temperatures sufficiently close to $T = 0$°K. But at some higher value of T, C_r will begin to exceed C_{ph}. In any event, the sum $C_{ph} + C_r$ defined by Eqs. (165) and (168), fits accurately the known experimental specific heat curve of helium four (1957) for all temperatures up to roughly 1.3°K, provided one postulates that

$$\frac{\Delta}{k} = 8.8°\text{K}, \qquad \frac{p_0}{\hbar} = 1.96\,\text{A}^{-1}, \qquad \mu = 0.23m, \tag{169}$$

where m denotes the mass of the He⁴ atom. These values are in fairly good agreement with those obtained independently from recent (1959, 1961) neutron scattering experiments.

When the temperature rises, naturally more and more phonons and rotons are created, and in addition excitations corresponding to the remaining parts of Landau's curve (Figure 4–9) make their appearance. Elementary excitations of all kinds therefore become so numerous that it is no longer permissible to neglect the interactions among them; these excitations thus lose their heuristic value.

The merit of Landau's approach lies very much in the fact that he established a one-to-one correspondence between the quantum states of the helium liquid on one hand, and an ideal gas system composed of elementary excitations on the other. This approximation is, of course, not applicable to systems with strong interactions. The concept of elementary excitations was introduced by Landau on intuitive grounds, but subsequently more rigorous theories have corroborated his ideas. An advantage stemming from his novel viewpoint is that the elementary excitations are visualizable as particle-like entities: phonons possess definite momenta and energies, while rotons have moreover an effective mass μ.

In Landau's theory, the superfluid component of the two-fluid model is interpreted to be synonymous with his ideal fluid, which constitutes liquid helium at $T = 0°K$; whereas the excitations, created in the ideal fluid when the temperature is raised, exhibit some of the properties of the normal fluid component, notably viscosity. According to Landau, excitations can appear in helium only for flow velocities exceeding the minimum value of the ratio $\varepsilon(p)/p$. This in his reasoning explains why superfluidity sets in when the flow velocity falls below some definite value, the so-called *critical velocity*. We notice further that for non-viscous flow to occur at all, the ratio $(\varepsilon/p)_{min}$ must be nonzero. In the case of an ideal gas, this ratio is zero, so that the phenomenon of superfluidity is ruled out—contrary to the expectation of Tisza. Against Landau's conception of the two-fluid model at least two objections could be raised.

First, experiment suggests the existence of excitations even in the superfluid component. Onsager (1949) and Feynman (1955) submitted that this defect may be remedied by the hypothesis of quantized vortex lines: the *strength K* of every vortex in liquid helium is some integral multiple n of $\hbar/m$. Here K is defined by $mK = mvr$, where mvr is the angular momentum of any helium atom in the vortex.

Secondly, the predicted value of the critical velocity, viz., ≈ 60 m sec⁻¹ (for rotons), is very much larger than the observed critical velocity, which is less than ≈ 50 cm sec^{-1}. Thus far no satisfactory explication for this discrepancy has been proposed.

As pointed out before, Landau's theory fails to assign numerical values to the parameters characterizing the energy spectrum of elementary excitations. This shortcoming was inevitable, since the spectrum obviously depends on the atomic properties of helium, whereas his description of helium is based upon a few macroscopic parameters, such as density and flow velocity. It was an ingenious achievement of Feynman (1955) to devise the appropriate microscopic treatment: by examining some general properties of the wave functions satisfying the Schrödinger equation for an assembly of helium atoms, he established (i) that no excitations other than those postulated by Landau exist, and (ii) that they will display quantitatively the spectrum found in an empirical manner. Any further discussion of Feynman's exciting conclusions would however transcend the scope of this book.

REFERENCES

ABRIKOSOV, A. A., L. P. GORKOV, and I. E. DZYALOSHINSKI. *Methods of Quantum Field Theory in Statistical Physics.* Translated from the Russian and edited by R. A. Silverman. Englewood Cliffs, N.J.: Prentice-Hall, 1963.

BARDEEN, J., L. N. COOPER, and J. R. SCHRIEFFER. *Phys. Rev.*, **108**, 1175 (1957).

BLACKMAN, M. *Proc. Roy. Soc. (London)*, **A159**, 416 (1937).

BLACKMAN, M. "Spezifische Wärme der Kristalle," in *Handbuch der Physik*, Vol. VII/1. Berlin: Springer, 1956.

BOLTZMANN, L. *Sitz.-Ber. Akad. Wiss. (Wien)*, **63**, 712 (1871).

DE BOER, J. "Excitation Model for Liquid Helium II," in G. Careri (ed.), *Liquid Helium.* New York: Academic Press, 1963.

BORN, M., and T. VON KÁRMÁN. *Physikal. Zeitschr.*, **13**, 297 (1912); **14**, 15 (1913).

BORN, M., and J. R. OPPENHEIMER. *Ann. Phys.*, **84**, 457 (1927).

BORN, M., and K. HUANG. *Dynamical Theory of Crystal Lattices.* New York: Oxford U.P., 1954.

BUCKINGHAM, M. J., and W. M. FAIRBANK, in Vol. 3, Chap. III, C. J. Gorter (ed.), *Progress in Low Temperature Physics.* Amsterdam: North-Holland, 1961.

CLAUSIUS, R. *Ann. Phys.*, **141**, 124 (1870).

CRAWFORD, F. H. *Heat, Thermodynamics, and Statistical Physics.* New York: Harcourt, 1963.

DAVIDSON, N. *Statistical Mechanics.* New York: McGraw-Hill, 1962.

DEBYE, P. *Ann. Phys.*, **39**, 789 (1912).

EINSTEIN, A. *Ann. Phys.*, **22**, 180 (1907).

FEYNMAN, R. P. *Phys. Rev.*, **91**, 1301 (1953).

FEYNMAN, R. P. *Phys. Rev.*, **94**, 262 (1954).

FEYNMAN, R. P., in Vol. 1, Chap. II, C. J. Gorter (ed.), *Progress in Low Temperature Physics*. Amsterdam: North-Holland, 1955.

FOWLER, R., and E. A. GUGGENHEIM. *Statistical Thermodynamics*. New York: Cambridge U.P., 1960.

GORTER, C. J., in Vol. 1, Chap. I, C. J. Gorter (ed.), *Progress in Low Temperature Physics*. Amsterdam: North-Holland, 1955.

HENSHAW, D. G., and A. D. B. WOODS. *Phys. Rev.*, **121**, 1266 (1961).

HERZBERG, G. *Atomic Spectra and Atomic Structure*. Translated from the German by J. W. T. Spinks. New York: Dover, 1944.

IONA, M. *Phys. Rev.*, **60**, 822 (1941).

KAPITZA, P. O. *Nature*, **141**, 74 (1938).

KEESOM, W. H., and C. W. CLARK. *Physica*, **2**, 698 (1935).

KELLERMANN, E. W. *Proc. Roy. Soc. (London)*, **A178**, 17 (1941).

LANDAU, L. D. *J. Phys. (Moscow)*, **5**, 71 (1941).

LANDAU, L. D. *J. Phys. (Moscow)*, **11**, 91 (1947).

LANDAU, L. D., and E. M. LIFSHITZ. *Statistical Physics*. Translated from the Russian by E. Peierls and R. F. Peierls. Reading, Mass.: Addison-Wesley, 1958.

LEE, T. D., K. HUANG, and C. N. YANG. *Phys. Rev.*, **106**, 1135 (1957).

LONDON, F. *Nature*, **141**, 643 (1938).

LONDON, F. *Phys. Rev.*, **54**, 948 (1938).

LONDON, F. *J. Phys. Chem.*, **43**, 49 (1939).

LONDON, F. *Superfluids*. Vol. II, 1954 (republished by Dover, 1964).

MAYER, J. E., and M. G. MAYER. *Statistical Mechanics*. New York: Wiley, 1940.

MULHOLLAND, H. P. *Proc. Cambridge Phil. Soc.*, **24**, 280 (1928).

ONSAGER, L. *Nuovo Cimento*, **6**, Suppl. 2, 249 (1949).

SEITZ, F. *Modern Theory of Solids*. New York: McGraw-Hill, 1940.

DE SORBO, W. *J. Chem. Phys.*, **21**, 876 (1953).

TISZA, L. *Nature*, **141**, 913 (1938).

TISZA, L. *J. Phys. et Radium*, **1**, 164, 359 (1940).

TISZA, L. *Phys. Rev.*, **72**, 838 (1947).

TOLMAN, R. C. *Phys. Rev.*, **11**, 261 (1918).

WIEBES, J., C. G. NIELS-HAKKENBERG, and H. C. KRAMERS. *Physica*, **23**, 625 (1957).

WILSON, A. H. *Thermodynamics and Statistical Mechanics*. New York: Cambridge U.P., 1960.

YARNELL, J. L., G. P. ARNOLD, P. J. BENDT, and E. C. KERR. *Phys. Rev.*, **113**, 1379 (1959).

Appendix

THE GIBBS ENTROPY PARADOX

THROUGHOUT our statistical treatment of a material gas it was generally postulated that all its molecules belong to the same chemical substance. The theory can however easily be extended to a dilute mixture of different, mutually inert, ideal gases. We shall here consider only the entropy of the mixture, because its behavior has a unique aspect that gave rise to a famous and much debated paradox of classical physics.

In phenomenological thermodynamics, the difference between the entropy of a mixture of two noninteracting ideal gases, say A and B, and that of the pure, separate gases is ordinarily determined by the following procedure. Let N_A molecules of A occupy a volume V_A at a definite pressure and at a temperature T, and let N_B molecules of B fill a volume V_B at the same pressure and temperature. This implies, by the ideal gas law, that V_A is proportional to N_A and V_B to N_B. The gases A and B are kept apart by a partition impermeable to both gases, and the gases together with partition and container form an isolated system. If one now removes the partition, the result is a spontaneous mixing of the two gases. After completion of this interdiffusion process, the internal energy $U(T)$, and hence the temperature T, will be the same as before. The final entropy S_{AB}, however, is required by the second law of thermodynamics to be greater than the initial entropy $S_A + S_B$ of the unmixed gases.

To compute the *entropy of mixing*, $\Delta S = S_{AB} - (S_A + S_B)$, we replace the given diffusion process conceptually by a reversible isothermal process connecting the very same initial and final states; these two processes thus exhibit equal values of ΔS. Imagine that in the isothermal process the quasistatic expansion of each gas is controlled by a so-called *semipermeable* piston, or movable membrane, that is impenetrable to the molecules of the expanding gas, while it freely lets through all the molecules of the other gas. Each gas therefore expands as if the other gas were not present, and one can write for the work performed by the gases during every infinitesimal step of the reversible process:

$$dW = (pdV)_A + (pdV)_B = N_A kT\left(\frac{dV}{V}\right)_A + N_B kT\left(\frac{dV}{V}\right)_B.$$

If this expression is inserted into the relation $TdS = dU + dW = dW$ and the result integrated with respect to V between the lower limits V_A (for gas A) and V_B (for gas B) and the upper limit $V_A + V_B$, we obtain the formula

$$\Delta S = N_A k \log \frac{V_A + V_B}{V_A} + N_B k \log \frac{V_A + V_B}{V_B}. \tag{A1}$$

Since $V_A/V_B = N_A/N_B$, this can also be written as

$$\Delta S = N_A k \log \frac{N_A + N_B}{N_A} + N_B k \log \frac{N_A + N_B}{N_B}. \tag{A2}$$

To eliminate unessential features in our further discussion, let us assume that A and B have the same number of molecules, say N; then Eq. (A2) reduces to

$$\boxed{\Delta S = 2Nk \log 2} \quad . \quad (A \neq B) \tag{A3}$$

It is seen that ΔS is positive, as we anticipated.

Equation (A3) obviously ceases to be valid when the gases A and B become identical, as they are no longer separable by a membrane of any kind. In fact, we know that the diffusion of a gas into itself is not accompanied by a change in any of its thermodynamic parameters, including the entropy. Thus, for gases of the same type,

$$\boxed{\Delta S = 0} \quad . \quad (A = B) \tag{A4}$$

Equation (A4) could not be accounted for by means of classical statistics. Quantum statistics, however, is capable of deducing Eq. (A3) as well as Eq. (A4) within a unified theory. The point of departure is the ideal-gas partition function $Z = Z_1^N/N!$ [Eq. (5), Chapter 4], where Z_1 denotes the molecular partition function.

Consider first the case of unlike gases, $A \neq B$. Before diffusion the Helmholtz free energies of A and B are, respectively,

$$F_A = -kT \log \frac{Z_{1A}^N}{N!} \tag{A5}$$

and

$$F_B = -kT \log \frac{Z_{1B}^N}{N!}. \tag{A6}$$

Noting that the partition functions of the (independent) systems A and B are to be multiplied and the quantum states of the A and B are mutually exclusive, we have, after diffusion,

$$F_{AB} = -kT \log \frac{\tilde{Z}_{1A}^N}{N!} \frac{\tilde{Z}_{1B}^N}{N!} \qquad (A \neq B) \qquad (A7)$$

for the free energy of the joint system. The tildes of $\tilde{Z}_{1A}$ and $\tilde{Z}_{1B}$ indicate the crucial fact that these partition functions must be computed for the volume $2V = 2V_A$ throughout which the molecules of A and B are finally distributed—and not for the volume V which is initially accessible to the gases A and B. This means, in view of Sections 2 and 3 of Chapter 4, that $\tilde{Z}_{1A}$ and $\tilde{Z}_{1B}$ are both proportional to $2V$, whereas Z_{1A} and Z_{1B} are both proportional to V. Consequently,

$$\Delta F = F_{AB} - (F_A + F_B) = -2NkT \log 2V + 2NkT \log V.$$

If one applies to this equation the thermodynamic relation $S = -(\partial F / \partial T)_{V,N}$, one recovers the formula (A3).

For gases of the same molecular species, $A = B$, Eqs. (A5) and (A6) are retained, but Eq. (A7) must be replaced by

$$F_{AA} = -kT \log \frac{\tilde{Z}_{1A}^{2N}}{(2N)!}, \qquad (A = B) \qquad (A8)$$

in recognition of the fact that the molecules are now distributed over a single set of quantum states rather than over two sets. Combination of (A8) with (A6) and (A5) leads to

$$\Delta F = F_{AA} - (F_A + F_B) = -2NkT \log 2V + 2NkT \log 2N \\ + 2NkT \log V - 2NkT \log N = 0,$$

and thus to $\Delta S = 0$, that is, to the formula (A4).

Quantum statistics therefore confirms the predictions of phenomenological thermodynamics. The reason for the failure of Boltzmann statistics to achieve the same, lies in its omission of the factorial appearing in Eq. (A8); this factorial is, of course, introduced in quantum theory in order to deal with the indistinguishability of identical molecules.

We are now equipped to treat the main issue. Suppose one is convinced, on the basis of all the foregoing considerations, that the mixing entropy ΔS can assume only the values $2Nk \log 2$ or zero; which means that ΔS remains finite and constant as long as there is any discernible difference between the gases A and B, but drops abruptly to zero when A and B become identical! Then we are clearly confronted with a *discontinuity paradox*, which was first noted by Gibbs in his famous memoir, *On the Equilibrium of Heterogeneous Substances*. To paraphrase Gibbs: one may suppose other gases to exist than those actually existent, and there seems to be no limit to the resemblance that two of these gases might display. But the increase of entropy due to their mixing at given T and p would be independent of the degree of similarity or dissimilarity between them.

Gibbs' contention could have gained plausibility in the light of later evidence, which indicated that apparently $\Delta S = 2Nk \log 2$ not only for some atoms near each other in the periodic table but also for isotopes of the same element. This holds even for a mixture of orthohydrogen and parahydrogen (whose components differ in total spin quantum number alone) and for mixtures of similar molecules which are partly in the ground state and partly in some excited state.

Gibbs was not able to resolve his paradox in the form stated—although he recognized that a modification, whereby the classical entropy formula $S = k \log W$ becomes $S = k \log W - Nk \log N$, would prevent the unwanted result $\Delta S \neq 0$ for $A = B$. Since the advent of quantum mechanics however various resolutions of the Gibbs paradox have been suggested.

Among the most widely supported proposals, subscribed to by Sommerfeld and Fong, has been the claim that the concept of continuous transition of molecular properties—as envisioned by Gibbs—is invalid. In any event, it is devoid of physical significance because we know from experiment that one or more properties of atoms and of their isotopes (e.g., the number of protons or neutrons) vary in discrete amounts from one particle to the next. And even in the same atom or molecule, quantities such as energy and spin exhibit a discrete rather than a continuous behavior.

Another physically meaningful attempt to solve the paradox was developed by Bridgman. He examined the instrumental operations by which the dissimilarity of two gases A and B could be established when the limit of identical gases, $A = B$, is approached. One readily appreciates that as $A \to B$, a set of particular, verbally formulated operations becomes less and less performable. But at no stage do these operations fail to be consistent with the known laws of nature, and thus they remain valid at least in theory. At the limit $A = B$, however, the situation changes suddenly. We must no longer ask: what are the physical properties of a given molecule in the mixture AB? Instead the question is: what is its history? In other words, we want to know what part of our container the molecule occupied before diffusion started. Needless to say, according to the principles of quantum mechanics no laboratory operations could ever be performed to answer this question. Briefly then, the instrumental procedure suffers a discontinuity at $A = B$—and Bridgman therefore concludes, "the argument for the continuity of any function, such as the entropy, fails."

The advocates of the above resolutions of Gibbs' paradox accept the discontinuity of ΔS at $A = B$ as a basic premiss, and solve the paradox by maintaining either that it has no empirical implications at all or that it was theoretically to be expected. One may however challenge both the asserted discontinuity and the proposed solutions which rest upon it.

Starting with the solutions, we note that even though the operational argument demonstrates that it is unnecessary (indeed unlikely) for a ΔS to vary continuously, it does at the same time not seem to rule out continuous behavior either. On the other hand, reasoning from the discontinuity of atomic properties, one cannot deny that no gradual transition occurs between atoms or molecules of different gases A and B. But the argument loses its cogency when A and B represent different quantum states of the same particle.

In order to clarify this contention, let us investigate what we ordinarily mean in thermodynamics by the statement that two gases A and B are different or identical. A proper analysis, which was first carried out by von Neumann and elaborated by Landé, leads incontrovertibly to a complete resolution of the Gibbs paradox. The device commonly employed in thermo-dynamics to decide whether two gases are similar or dissimilar is the semi-permeable membrane. If it is at all possible to construct such a membrane that allows every molecule of gas A to pass through but reflects every molecule of gas B, then one can infer that $A \neq B$; if it is not possible, then one says that $A = B$. We have therefore made the important assumption that any two gases are either strictly separable by a filter or strictly inseparable.

Yet this assumption is definitely false when the gases are alike, but the mole-cules of A are all in an arbitrary quantum state ϕ and the molecules of B are all in some state ψ. In explanation, let us first designate by η the inner product (ϕ,ψ) of the two functions, i.e., the integral over the whole of space of the function $\phi^*\psi$. It has now been proved by von Neumann that to avoid conflict with the second law of thermodynamics one can postulate complete separ-ability of A and B only when $\eta = 0$, while complete inseparability requires $\eta = 1$. For all the intermediate states with $0 < \eta < 1$, lying between the extremes indicated, the gases are neither separable ($A \neq B$) nor inseparable ($A = B$). This situation corresponds to the fact that an A-molecule, for example, may sometimes be transmitted and sometimes be reflected on interaction with the membrane. Such gases Landé denotes as *fractionally equal*, symbolized by $A \sim B$. In classical theory they are entirely ignored.

This is the essential point: von Neumann demonstrated powerfully that the value of the mixing entropy ΔS decreases continuously from $2Nk \log 2$ to zero, as η varies from zero to unity. He thus removed the basic premiss of Gibbs' paradox, and therefore the paradox itself, in a single stroke.

The expression for ΔS proposed by von Neumann is general and does not contain the parameter η explicitly. However, in relation to molecular states ϕ and ψ belonging to the same energy value, his formula may be easily specialized to read

$$\frac{\Delta S}{Nk} = -(1 + \eta) \log (1 + \eta) - (1 - \eta) \log (1 - \eta) + 2 \log 2. \quad (A9)$$

This result, first derived by M. J. Klein, displays in a straightforward manner the predicted continuous variation of ΔS with η.

We can assert in summary that the entropy associated with the mixing of two gases A and B has the following characteristics. Should A and B differ in at least one permanent property, say P (such as molecular mass), the entropy of mixing, ΔS, is invariably $2Nk \log 2$—however small the physical difference $\delta P = P_A - P_B$. When on the contrary no permanent difference exists, so that $A = B$ obtains, $\Delta S = 2Nk \log 2$ only if the A- and B-molecules are prepared in mutually orthogonal states ϕ and ψ. Otherwise ΔS will be less than this standard value and smoothly diminish to zero as the states ϕ and ψ become identical.

The merits of the arguments deployed here are hardly open to dispute: the paradoxical aspect of the entropy in a mixing process has been eliminated. None the less, there is still the possible query why ΔS depends in no way upon the size of the permanent difference δP. With regard to this point, the following purely nonquantal considerations, to which P. G. Bergmann directed our attention, may be illuminating.

If gases A and B are distinct in respect to some permanent property P, this parameter will enter into the Hamiltonian H_{AB} of the combined system in the form P_A for gas A and P_B for gas B. We now suppose that A and B mix and that we introduce in H_{AB} a small interaction with the surroundings, which renders the attainment of equilibrium possible. The system must eventually relax into an equilibrium state described by a canonical phase density $\rho = C \exp -H_{AB}/kT$ in gamma space. One will then immediately grant that the relaxation time depends on the difference δP: it is short for large, and long for small, δP, and it might become extremely long for a minute δP. But—to epitomize Bergmann's suggestion—the results of classical statistics, including the value of ΔS, will not be affected at all. For they pertain merely to the eventual equilibrium state, regardless of how long it takes to establish that equilibrium.

A contrasting situation arises where $\delta P = 0$ for all P, so that A and B are actually the very same gas A. Here one cannot find any term in H_{AB} (not even an interaction with the environment) that would permit the density-in-phase ρ finally to be symmetric in the permutation of any two (similar) molecules. The only exception would occur when the density is symmetric at the outset. All this can be deduced from Liouville's theorem, Eq. (6), Chapter 2, which demonstrates that complete symmetry at any time (past or future) entails complete symmetry at any other time. In closing our discussion, we thus see that there is no possibility for the relaxation to occur, and accordingly one encounters a jump in the (classical) value of ΔS when $A = B$.

REFERENCES

BERGMANN, P. G. Personal Communication, July 5, 1964.

BRIDGMAN, P. W. *The Nature of Thermodynamics*, p. 169. Cambridge, Mass.: Harvard U.P., 1943.

FONG, P. *Foundations of Thermodynamics*. New York: Oxford U.P., 1963.

GIBBS, J. W. *The Scientific Papers*, vol. I, p. 167. Dover, 1961 (first published in 1906).

KLEIN, M. J. *Ned. T. Natuurk.*, **25**, 73 (1959).

LANDÉ, A. *From Dualism to Unity in Quantum Physics*. Cambridge U.P., 1960.

VON NEUMANN, J. *Mathematical Foundations of Quantum Mechanics*, Chap. V, translation of *Mathematische Grundlagen der Quantenmechanik* (1932) by R. T. Beyer. Princeton U.P., 1955.

SOMMERFELD, A. *Thermodynamics and Statistical Mechanics*, translated from the German by J. Kestin. New York: Academic Press, 1956.

Problems

CHAPTER 1

1. Given be a closed system in diathermal contact with a heat reservoir having a temperature T_0. Let, in this system, an irreversible process occur, at the beginning and the end of which equilibrium obtains.

(a) Write down the first and second laws of thermodynamics for such a process and combine them to get

$$T_0 \Delta S = \Delta U + W + T_0 \Delta_i S;$$

here W is the work performed by, and $\Delta_i S$ the entropy created in, the system.

(b) Remembering that in our process both the initial and final temperatures are T_0, prove from the result in (a) that

$$W = -\Delta F - T_0 \Delta_i S,$$

with $F = U - TS$.

(c) Furthermore, if throughout the process the system is subjected to the same pressure p_0, show that

$$W' = -\Delta G - T_0 \Delta_i S,$$

where $G = U - TS + pV$ and W' denotes the work done over and above the work against the outside pressure p_0.

(d) What physical interpretation of $\Delta_i S$ is suggested by the formulas in (b) and (c)?

2. Let us suppose the amounts of heat $Q_1, Q_2, \ldots, Q_j, \ldots$ are absorbed by a closed system at different temperatures $T_1, T_2, \ldots, T_j, \ldots$. Extend the relation in (1a) to this more general case, and demonstrate that for a cyclic process one finds

$$W = -T_1 \Delta_i S + \sum_j (T_j - T_1) \frac{Q_j}{T_j}.$$

(b) Restricting the heat exchange only to reservoirs 1 and 2, verify that in the limit of a reversible process, the result in (2a) reduces to the familiar efficiency equation

$$\frac{W}{Q_1} = 1 - \frac{T_2}{T_1}. \qquad (T_2 < T_1)$$

3. Given is a one-component fluid enclosed in two contiguous vessels 1 and 2 connected by a small orifice. The temperature and pressure in vessel 1 are held constant at the values T,p and in vessel 2 at $T + \Delta T$, $p + \Delta p$.

(a) With the aid of Eq. (19) of our text in the special form $\sigma = \mathbf{J}_u \cdot \text{grad} \, (1/T) - \mathbf{J}_m \cdot \text{grad} \, (\mu/T)$, establish that the entropy production $d_iS/dt = \int \sigma dV$ associated with the resulting flows of mass and energy is

$$\frac{d_iS}{dt} = \tilde{J}_m X_m + \tilde{J}_u X_u,$$

where the mass current $\tilde{J}_m = -dm/dt$, the energy current $\tilde{J}_u = -dU/dt$, and $X_m = -\Delta(\mu/T)$, $X_u = \Delta(1/T)$ stand for the corresponding forces; m is the mass and U the internal energy of the fluid in vessel 1.

[*Hint:* Note that $\sigma = 0$ everywhere except in a small region of thickness Δx extending by equal amounts on either side of the orifice; there, $\mathbf{J}_m$ and $\mathbf{J}_u$ are constant, while grad μ and grad T may be replaced by $\Delta\mu/\Delta x$ and $\Delta T/\Delta x$, respectively.]

(b) From the result in (a), deduce the phenomenological equations

$$\tilde{J}_m = -L_{mm}v \frac{\Delta p}{T} + (L_{mm}h - L_{mu}) \frac{\Delta T}{T^2}$$

and

$$\tilde{J}_u = -L_{um}v \frac{\Delta p}{T} + (L_{um}h - L_{uu}) \frac{\Delta T}{T^2}.$$

[*Hint:* $\Delta\mu = v\Delta p - s\Delta T$ and the specific enthalpy $h = \mu + Ts$; the quantities v and s are the specific volume and entropy.]

(c) Using the Onsager relation, $L_{mu} = L_{um}$, derive the formula

$$\left(\frac{\Delta p}{\Delta T}\right)_{J_m = 0} = \frac{h - u^*}{Tv},$$

with $u^* = (J_u/J_m)_{\Delta T = 0}$.

(This significant result expresses the so-called *thermomolecular pressure difference* for zero flow of matter. The quantity u^*, representing the energy transported from vessel 1 to vessel 2 per unit mass, is known as the *energy of transfer*.)

(d) In order to realize the condition of uniform temperature required in the definition of u^*, it may be necessary to supply the heat q^* per unit mass to the vessel 1 and to extract the same amount from vessel 2.

Apply the first law of thermodynamics to show that the *heat of transfer* q^* equals $u^* - h$, and hence that the thermomolecular pressure difference becomes $-q^*/vT$.

4. Imagine that the system treated in Problem 3 is an ideal gas whose pressure is low enough for the mean free path of its molecules to be large compared with the dimensions of the orifice. We then speak of a *Knudsen gas*. The molecules of such a gas will pass through the aperture without colliding with one another; thus a pure *molecular flow* is maintained between vessels 1 and 2.

(a) By sheer kinetic theory considerations, find that, in the case of monatomic molecules, the energy of transfer is

$$u^* = \frac{1}{2} \frac{\overline{c^3}}{\bar{c}},$$

where c is the speed of a molecule and the bars indicate average values.

(b) Compute $\bar{c}$ and $\overline{c^3}$ according to the Maxwell speed distribution (see Problem 2, Chapter 2), and insert their values in the above formula to obtain

$$u^* = \frac{2RT}{M}$$

and consequently the heat of transfer

$$q^* = -\frac{RT}{2M}.$$

(c) Substitution of this value of q^* into the expression for the thermomolecular pressure difference derived in Problem 3d, yields $(\Delta p / \Delta T) = R/2Mv$. Prove that this equation, combined with the ideal gas law, leads on integration to

$$\frac{p_1}{p_2} = \left(\frac{T_1}{T_2}\right)^{1/2}.$$

(This relation has been confirmed experimentally for several systems.)

5. Verify the last equation in Problem 4c by kinetic theory arguments alone—that is, without appealing to irreversible thermodynamics.

[*Hint:* Zero mass flow implies $n_1 \bar{c}_1 = n_2 \bar{c}_2$, if n signifies the number of molecules per unit volume. Also, $p = \frac{1}{3} mn\overline{c^2}$ and $p = nkT$, where m is the molecular mass.]

6. If the aperture between two vessels 1 and 2 containing a fluid becomes large compared with the mean free path of the molecules, the molecular flow—characteristic of a Knudsen gas (see Problem 4)—will be replaced by an ordinary bulk flow of matter. This holds not only for an ideal gas, but for an arbitrary fluid.

Ascertain that, under these conditions, the energy of transfer u^* is simply h, the specific enthalpy, and thus the heat of transfer $q^* = 0$, so that the thermomolecular pressure effect vanishes. Was this result to be expected?

7. Consider a system with uniform temperature T, consisting of charged components $1, 2, \ldots, j, \ldots$, whose concentrations are likewise constant throughout the system. A porous diaphragm divides the system into two compartments 1 and 2. The pressures of phases 1 and 2 are p and $p + \Delta p$ and the electrical potentials are ϕ and $\phi + \Delta\phi$, respectively. If Δp and $\Delta\phi$ are nonzero, a coupled flow of mass and electricity will take place between 1 and 2.

(a) According to Eq. (19) of the text, the entropy production per unit volume accompanying this process is

$$\sigma = -\sum_j \mathbf{J}_j \cdot \text{grad}\, \frac{\mu_j}{T} - \mathbf{J}_e \cdot \text{grad}\, \frac{\phi}{T}.$$

Show that the entropy production $\int \sigma dV$ is given by

$$\frac{d_i S}{dt} = \frac{1}{T} \sum_j (M_j \mu_j + z_j \mathfrak{F} \phi)\, \frac{dn_j}{dt},$$

where M_j is the molar mass of component j, z_j its electrovalency, n_j its molar number in phase 1, and $\mathfrak{F}$ the Faraday constant (96,490 coulomb).

[*Hint:* Replace the gradients in μ_j and ϕ by the corresponding increments per unit length in the vicinity of the diaphragm; cf. Problem 3a.]

(b) Observing the definitions

$$\tilde{J}_v = -\sum_j v_j \frac{dn_j}{dt} \qquad \text{and} \qquad \tilde{J}_e = -\sum_j z_j \mathfrak{F}\, \frac{dn_j}{dt}$$

of the total volume and charge currents from container 1 to container 2, in which v_j denotes the partial molar volume of component j, cast the result (a) in the form

$$\frac{d_i S}{dt} = -\tilde{J}_v \frac{\Delta p}{T} - \tilde{J}_e \frac{\Delta \phi}{T}.$$

[*Hint:* The thermodynamic relation $dG = -SdT + Vdp + \sum_j M_j \mu_j\, dn_j$ implies $(\partial M_j \mu_j / \partial p)_{T,n_1,n_2,\ldots} = v_j$—that is, $\Delta M_j \mu_j \approx v_j \Delta p$.]

(c) Write down the phenomenological relations corresponding to the above entropy production, and from them in combination with Onsager's theorem derive the connections

and

$$\left(\frac{\Delta \phi}{\Delta p}\right)_{J_e = 0} = -\left(\frac{J_v}{J_e}\right)_{\Delta p = 0} \qquad (Sax\acute{e}n's\ relation)$$

$$\left(\frac{\Delta p}{\Delta \phi}\right)_{J_v = 0} = -\left(\frac{J_e}{J_v}\right)_{\Delta \phi = 0}.$$

8. Applying Eqs. (1) and (25), prove that

$$\frac{d_i S}{dt} = -\frac{1}{T} \sum_j \mu_j \frac{dm_j}{dt}$$

for a process in which the masses m_j of the chemical substances vary.

Suppose now that this variation is due to the chemical reaction

$$-\nu_1 B_1 - \nu_2 B_2 - \cdots - \nu_k B_k \rightleftharpoons \nu_{k+1} B_{k+1} + \nu_{k+2} B_{k+2} + \cdots + \nu_{k+l} B_{k+l},$$

where $B_1, B_2, \ldots, B_k$ are the symbols for the reactants and $B_{k+1}, B_{k+2}, \ldots,$ B_{k+l} denote the products, while $\nu_1, \nu_2, \ldots, \nu_{k+l}$ stand for their stoichiometric coefficients. With the definitions $dm_j = \nu_j M_j d\xi$ $(j = 1, 2, \ldots, k + l)$ and $A = -\sum_{j=1}^{k+l} M_j \mu_j \nu_j$ of the extent of reaction ξ and of the affinity A, show that

$$\frac{d_i S}{dt} = \frac{A}{T}\frac{d\xi}{dt},$$

and hence that the entropy source density for a chemical reaction is $\sigma = \nu A/T$, as asserted in Eq. (19) of the text.

9. Let two systems 1 and 2 be isolated from their environment, but in thermal contact with one another. At equilibrium their common temperature is T_0 and their internal energies are U'_0 and U''_0. In a situation deviating slightly from equilibrium, the temperature and internal energy are T, $U'_0 - \varepsilon$ for 1 and $T + \Delta T$, $U''_0 + \varepsilon$ for 2.

By expanding the total entropy $S = S' + S''$ in a Taylor series up to second-order terms in ε, demonstrate that the entropy production associated with the heat exchange between systems 1 and 2 is given by

$$\dot{S} = \dot{\varepsilon}\Delta\frac{1}{T}.$$

[*Hint:* $1/T = \partial S'/\partial U'$ and $1/T_0 = (\partial S'/\partial U')_{U' = U'_0}$.]

Confirm that $\dot{S} > 0$ implies that heat flows from high to low temperature regions, whereas $\dot{S} < 0$ entails a heat flow in the opposite direction.

10. Envisage a particle of mass m moving along the x-axis while being immersed in a viscous fluid with volume V, internal energy U, and entropy S. The fluid offers a retarding force $m\beta v$ to the particle when it has the speed v, $m\beta$ being a proportionality constant. Suppose further that the particle is acted upon also by another force derivable from a positive potential energy $\phi(x)$ such that $\phi(0) = 0$. The equation of motion is therefore $m\ddot{x} = -m\beta\dot{x} - \partial\phi/\partial x$, or, if $|\ddot{x}| \ll \beta|\dot{x}|$, $\dot{x} = -(1/m\beta)(\partial\phi/\partial x)$. Since the system "fluid + particle" is assumed to be isolated, its energy remains constant at the value, say, U_0. The state of maximum entropy obtains when $x = 0$, $v = 0$, and hence $U = U_0$.

Using the customary definitions $J = \dot{x}$ and $F = \partial\Delta S/\partial x$ [see Eq. (89)], prove that the above equation of motion can be written as $J = LF$, provided one puts $L = T/m\beta$.

[*Hint:* $1/T = (\partial S/\partial U)_{U = U_0}$.]

11. Given be a microscopically small particle of mass m suspended in a fluid that is otherwise isolated. As the speed v of the particle decreases to zero, the entropy S of the fluid increases to the value S_0 corresponding to the maximal energy U_0 of the fluid. According to the second law of thermodynamics, a process in which the particle acquires kinetic energy at the expense of the internal energy U of the fluid, is strictly forbidden, as the entropy S would decrease. However, for the minute energies associated with the motion of the particle, such a process is

allowed. Consequently, small fluctuations of S about its average value $\bar{S}$ continually occur; they give rise to the experimentally observed *Brownian movement*.

(a) Establish that the irreversible entropy production $d_iS/dt = m v \dot{v}/T$ accompanies the fluctuation of $S(U)$ about $\bar{S} = S(\bar{U})$, where $\bar{U} = U_0 - \frac{1}{2}m v^2$.

Supposing that the particle is slowed down by the frictional force $-m\beta v$, what conclusion can you draw concerning d_iS/dt? Verify further that

$$\mathbf{J} \equiv \dot{\mathbf{v}} = \frac{\beta T}{m} \mathbf{F},$$

if the components F_x, F_y, F_z are the Onsager forces corresponding to the Onsager coordinates v_x, v_y, v_z.

(b) Note that the function f in Eq. (82) may be approximated by f_0 defined in Eq. (84) (on what grounds?), and then show that the Brownian particle obeys the Maxwell velocity distribution law

$$W(v_x, v_y, v_z)\, dv_x dv_y dv_z = C e^{-(1/kT)(\frac{1}{2}mv_x^2 + \frac{1}{2}mv_y^2 + \frac{1}{2}mv_z^2)}\, dv_x dv_y dv_z,$$

C being a normalizing constant.

(c) The corresponding speed distribution is clearly

$$W(v)dv = C e^{-mv^2/2kT} 4\pi v^2\, dv.$$

Use this law to compute, for $m = 0.001$ gm and $T = 290°$K, the relative probability of a 0.001% deviation of the particle's kinetic energy from its average value $\frac{1}{2}m\bar{v^2} = \frac{3}{2}kT$.   0.254. *Ans.*

12. Given be a gas in a state of macroscopic equilibrium described by the temperature T, pressure p_0, and mass density ρ_0. Due to the random motions of its molecules, however, the density ρ at any point of the system will fluctuate about the average value ρ_0.

To study these fluctuations, consider an element of the gas containing a large fixed number n of molecules, but having a small variable volume V. For example, let $n \sim 10^{16}$ and correspondingly $V \sim 1$ mm^3. Classical statistics predicts that the relative frequency with which a deviation $\Delta\rho = \rho - \rho_0$ in the density occurs, is proportional to $\exp -\Delta U/kT$, where $\Delta U = U(\rho) - U(\rho_0)$ denotes the energy difference of the n molecules for the densities ρ and ρ_0.

After these remarks, demonstrate that:

(a) $\Delta U = \dfrac{1}{2\kappa_0 V_0} (\Delta V)^2$,

if κ is the isothermal compressibility $-(1/V)(\partial V/\partial p)_T$.

[*Hint:* $\Delta U = -\int_{V_0}^{V}(p - p_0)\, dV$, i.e., ΔU is the work done on our system when its volume changes by $\Delta V = V - V_0$.]

(b) $\overline{(\Delta V)^2} = kT\kappa_0 V_0$.

[*Hint:* $\exp -ax^2$ integrated between $-\infty$ and $+\infty$ yields $(\pi/a)^{1/2}$.]

(c) $\overline{\Delta U} = \frac{1}{2}kT$.

(d) $\overline{\left(\dfrac{\Delta\rho}{\rho_0}\right)^2} = \dfrac{kT\kappa_0}{V_0}$.

(e) $\overline{\left(\dfrac{\Delta\rho}{\rho_0}\right)^2} = \dfrac{1}{n}$.

13. It is commonly believed that a current passing through a thermionic tube can be maintained at a constant value. In reality, however, since the emission of electrons from the cathode proceeds in a random fashion, the current I will exhibit minute fluctuations about an average value I_0. This phenomenon is known as the *shot effect* (discovered by Schottky) and contributes to background noise in amplifiers.

Let n be the (variable) number of electrons given off by the cathode in a finite time interval τ whose magnitude is such that n is large enough for statistical treatment. Then, if e is the electron charge, $I = ne/\tau$ and $I_0 = n_0 e/\tau$. Assuming that the result in Problem 12e with $n = n_0$ is applicable to the electrons, ascertain that

$$\overline{(\Delta I)^2} = \frac{eI_0}{\tau}$$

characterizes the fluctuations $\Delta I = I - I_0$ of the thermionic current.

CHAPTER 2

1. Appealing to the canonical distribution function, Eq (15), show that the probability for a system of N noninteracting point particles in contact with a heat reservoir at temperature T to have an energy between E and $E + dE$, is given by

$$P(E)dE = Ce^{-E/kT}E^{3N/2-1}\,dE,$$

C being a normalizing constant.

Find, with the aid of this distribution, the most probable value $\hat{E}$ of the energy, and verify that the average energy

$$\bar{E} = \tfrac{3}{2}NkT \approx \hat{E}.$$

Sketch the function $P(E)$ for a few small values of N. What do you conclude?

2. Again from Eq. (15), derive the Maxwell distribution of velocities as expressed by Eq. (58) if $v_0 = 0$ and $C = (m/2\pi kT)^{3/2}$.

[*Hint:* $\int_{-\infty}^{\infty} e^{-x^2}\,dx = \pi^{1/2}$. See Problem 1a, Chapter 3.]

Further prove that this velocity distribution implies the speed distribution

$$F(v)dv = \frac{4}{\pi^{1/2}}\left(\frac{m}{2kT}\right)^{3/2}v^2 e^{-mv^2/2kT}\,dv.$$

3. The function $\Phi(E,V,N)$, defined in Section 2–8, can be approximated in the classical limit by

$$\Phi = \frac{1}{N!h^{3N}} \int \cdots \int dq_1 \, dq_2 \ldots dq_{3N} \, dp_1 dp_2 \ldots dp_{3N}$$

when applied to a system of N particles; the integration is to be extended over that part of γ-space for which $H(q,p) \leqslant E$. Moreover, the volume of a unit sphere in $3N$-dimensional space is $\pi^{3N/2}/(3N/2)!$ (see H. and B. S. Jeffreys. *Mathematical Physics*. Cambridge U.P., 1956, p. 470) and $N! \approx (N/e)^N$ (Stirling's formula).

Establish that

$$\Phi = \frac{1}{h^{3N}} \left(\frac{4\pi mE}{3N}\right)^{3N/2} \left(\frac{V}{N}\right)^N e^{5N/2}$$

for an ideal gas occupying a volume V. Combine this result with the formula $S = k \log \Phi$, Eq. (51), to obtain the entropy of the gas.

4. It is obvious that, for $n \gg 1$,

$$\log n! = \log 1 \times 2 \times 3 \times \cdots \times n = \log 1 + \log 2 + \cdots + \log n$$

may be approximated by the area between the curve $y = \log x$ and the segment $1 \leqslant x \leqslant n$ of the x-axis. Use this fact to derive Stirling's formula, viz., $\log n! \approx n \log n - n$, or, alternatively, $n! \approx (n/e)^n$ $(n \gg 1)$.

Confirm with the help of mathematical tables that the error involved in Stirling's approximation is about 13 per cent for $n = 10$ and 1 per cent for $n = 50$.

5. Let $P(q,p)$ be the probability of finding a phase point (that represents the state of an N-particle system) in the element $dqdp = dq_1 \, dq_2 \ldots dq_{3N} \, dp_1 \, dp_2 \ldots dp_{3N}$ of γ-space. In the case of a canonical distribution of phase points, one can, starting from Eq. (100), formulate the entropy of the system in terms of the function $P(q,p)$. However, in classical theory it is necessary to take Z in Eq. (100) to be $Z = (1/h_0^{3N}) \int \int \exp -\beta H(q,p) \, dqdp$, where h_0 is an arbitrary constant having the dimensions of action and ensuring that Z is dimensionless.

(a) Demonstrate that the entropy is

$$S = -k \int \int P \log (Ph_0^{3N}) \, dqdp.$$

(This is Gibbs' statistical definition of entropy.)

(b) Verify that for an ideal gas of identical molecules, each characterized by the (normalized) position-momentum distribution function $f(\mathbf{r},\mathbf{p})$,

$$S = -NkH,$$

in which H is Boltzmann's H-function

$$H = \int \cdots \int f \log (fh_0^3) \, dxdydzdp_x dp_y dp_z;$$

$\mathbf{r} = (x,y,z)$ and $\mathbf{p} = (p_x,p_y,p_z)$.

[*Hint:* $P(q,p) = \prod_{i=1}^{N} f(\mathbf{r}_i, \mathbf{p}_i)$, with $\mathbf{r}_i$ and $\mathbf{p}_i$ denoting the position and momentum vectors of the molecule i.]

(c) Which function $f(\mathbf{r},\mathbf{p})$ corresponds to the Maxwell distribution of velocities? Insert this function in the result (b) to get

$$\frac{S}{Nk} = \frac{3}{2} + \log V + \frac{3}{2} \log \frac{2\pi mkT}{h_0^2}$$

for a monatomic ideal gas.

[*Hint:* $\int_{-\infty}^{\infty} u^2 e^{-au^2}\, du = \frac{1}{2}(\pi/a^3)^{1/2}$. Cf. Problem 1, Chapter 3.]

(d) Introduction of an extra divisor $N!$ in the above definition of Z will cause S/Nk in (c) to increase by the amount $1 - \log N$ (and thus make S/Nk an intensive property, as it should be). Confirm this statement.

6. Prove that for any thermodynamic system whose ground level is Ω_0-fold degenerate,

$$S \to k \log \Omega_0, \quad \text{i.e.,} \quad \Delta S_T \to 0, \quad \text{as} \quad T \to 0°\text{K}$$

(third law).

[*Hint:* Refer to Eq. (100) and use $\log(1 + x) \approx x$, $(1 + x)^{-1} \approx 1 - x$ $(x \ll 1)$.]

7. It is possible to replace the sum over N in

$$\mathfrak{Z} = \sum_{N} \sum_{E(N)} e^{-\beta[E(N) - N\mu]} = \sum_{N} Z(T,V,N)e^{N\beta\mu}$$

by its maximum term, say $N = \hat{N}$, and the $o(\hat{N}^{1/2})$ terms comparable with it, provided $\mathfrak{Z}$ has no singularity at any finite value of $\beta\mu$. Consequently, if one neglects terms $\sim \log \hat{N}$ relative to those $\sim \hat{N}$, the single term $\log Z(T,V,\hat{N})e^{N\beta\mu}$ may be substituted for $\log \mathfrak{Z}$. This approach is called the *maximum-term method*.

(a) Find the following implicit equation for $\hat{N}$:

$$\mu = -\frac{1}{\beta} \frac{\partial}{\partial \hat{N}} \log Z(T,V,\hat{N}).$$

(b) Using the maximum-term method, deduce that

$$F(T,V,\hat{N}) = -kT \log Z(T,V,\hat{N});$$

in other words, for thermodynamic systems the grand canonical ensemble is equivalent to the canonical ensemble (with a fixed number $\hat{N}$ of molecules).

[*Hint:* Consult Eq. (145).]

(c) Prove that in the special case $Z = Z_1^N(T,V)$, where Z_1 is the partition function for a single molecule, this equivalence breaks down.

CHAPTER 3

1. The gamma function, frequently encountered in kinetic and statistical theory, is defined by the integral

$$\Gamma(n) = \int_{0}^{\infty} e^{-x}x^{n-1}\, dx. \qquad (n > 0)$$

Prove that

(a) $\Gamma(1) = 1$;

(b) $\Gamma(\tfrac{1}{2}) = \pi^{1/2}$;

(c) $\Gamma(n + 1) = n\,\Gamma(n)$;

(d) $\Gamma(n + 1) = n!$, for $n = 1, 2, \ldots$.

[*Hint* for (b): Show first that $\Gamma(\tfrac{1}{2})$ can be written as $\Gamma(\tfrac{1}{2}) = \int_{-\infty}^{\infty} e^{-u^2}\, du$ by suitable transformation of the integration variable. Then introduce polar coordinates in $\Gamma(\tfrac{1}{2})^2 = \int_{-\infty}^{\infty} \int_{-\infty}^{\infty} e^{-(u^2 + v^2)}\, du\,dv$ according to the equations $u = r\cos\theta$ and $v = r\sin\theta$.]

[*Hint* for (c): Apply integration by parts to the integral $\Gamma(n)$.]

2. (a) Establish that the Fermi-Dirac distribution law, Eq. (18f), gives rise to the continuous speed distribution function

$$\frac{d\bar{n}(v)}{dv} \equiv \frac{8\pi m^3 V}{h^3}\, v^2 \left[1 + \exp\frac{1}{kT}\left(\tfrac{1}{2}\,mv^2 - \mu\right)\right]^{-1}$$

for a particle with mass m, confined to a volume V, when $V \to \infty$.

[*Hint:* Use the density of quantum states expressed by Eq. (50).]

(b) Plot this distribution function for $T = 0$ and some $T \neq 0$.

(c) Finally, verify that for large kT the Fermi-Dirac distribution law goes over into the Maxwell speed distribution law (referred to in Problem 2, Chapter 2). What is the appropriate value of μ?

3. (a) Derive the equation

$$\varepsilon_0 = 0.625 \times 10^{-8} \rho^{2/3} \text{ gm}^{-2/3} \text{ cm}^2 \text{ erg}$$

for the Fermi energy, defined in Eq. (51), belonging to an electron gas of mass density ρ.

(b) Find the numerical value of ε_0 for electrons in silver (density 10.6 gm cm^{-3}), assuming one free electron per Ag atom. 8.9×10^{-12} erg. *Ans.*

(c) Show that, up to $T \sim 10^{4\circ}$K, the molar heat capacity of these electrons obeys the linear relation

$$C_{el} \approx 1.5 \times 10^{-4} T \text{ cal mole}^{-1} \text{ deg}^{-2}$$

if one takes $R = 1.987$ cal deg^{-1}.

[*Hint:* Consult Eq. (93).]

(d) Ascertain that at $15°$C, C_{el} amounts to only 1.5 per cent of the classical electronic heat capacity.

(e) Let C_{lat} denote the molar heat capacity due to the lattice vibrations of the silver ions. What is the ratio of C_{el} to C_{lat} at $T = 1°$K?

[*Hint:* Invoke Eq. (95).]   3.5. *Ans.*

4. Prove that Eq. (55), determining the chemical potential of fermions, can be reformulated briefly as

$$\eta = f_{3/2}(\beta\mu),$$

where, per definition,

$$\eta = \frac{4}{3\pi^{1/2}} (\beta\varepsilon_0)^{3/2} \quad \text{and} \quad f_{3/2}(\beta\mu) = \Gamma(\tfrac{3}{2})^{-1} \int_0^\infty \frac{x^{1/2}\, dx}{e^{x-\beta\mu} + 1}.$$

Expanding the integrand as a geometric series and integrating term by term, deduce that the expansion

$$f_{3/2}(\beta\mu) = \sum_{r=1}^\infty (-1)^{r+1} r^{-3/2} e^{r\beta\mu}$$

is valid for $\mu < 0$.

5. Start from Eq. (56) and show that the internal energy and the equation of state of an ideal fermion gas are given by

$$U = \tfrac{3}{2} pV = \frac{N\beta}{\eta} f_{5/2}(\beta\mu),$$

where

$$f_{5/2}(\beta\mu) = \Gamma(\tfrac{5}{2})^{-1} \int_0^\infty \frac{x^{3/2}\, dx}{e^{x-\beta\mu} + 1}.$$

Obtain the series expansion

$$f_{5/2}(\beta\mu) = \sum_{r=1}^\infty (-1)^{r+1} r^{-5/2} e^{r\beta\mu}. \qquad (\mu < 0)$$

6. On the basis of the results in Problems 4 and 5, arrive at the following formulas valid for sufficiently high temperatures:

$$\beta\mu = \log\eta + 2^{-3/2}\eta - 3(3^{-5/2} - 2^{-4})\eta^2 + \cdots, \qquad (\eta < 1)$$

$$\frac{S}{Nk} = -\log\eta + \frac{5}{2} + 2^{-7/2}\eta - 2(3^{-5/2} - 2^{-4})\eta^2 + \cdots, \qquad (\eta < 1)$$

$$\frac{C_V}{\tfrac{3}{2}Nk} = 1 - 2^{-7/2}\eta + 4(3^{-5/2} - 2^{-4})\eta^2 - \cdots. \qquad (\eta < 1)$$

[*Hints:* Prove first that

$$e^{\beta\mu} = \eta + 2^{-3/2}\eta^2 + (2^{-2} - 3^{-3/2})\eta^3 + \cdots. \qquad (\eta < 1)$$

Note further that $S = (1/T)(U + pV - N\mu)$ and $C_V = T(dS/dT)_V = -\tfrac{3}{2}\eta(dS/d\eta)$.]

What is the heat capacity for $\eta = 0.1$ and $\eta = 0.75$?

$$0.989 \text{ and } 0.936 \text{ in units } \tfrac{3}{2}Nk. \ Ans.$$

7. Deduce the equation

$$\frac{S}{Nk} \approx \frac{5}{2} + \frac{3}{2}\log\frac{2\pi mkT}{h^2} + \log\frac{V}{N} - 0.2309\left(\frac{T_0}{T}\right)^{3/2}$$

$$- 0.0225\left(\frac{T_0}{T}\right)^3 - 0.0023\left(\frac{T_0}{T}\right)^{9/2}$$

for the entropy of an ideal boson gas at temperatures T exceeding T_0 [see Eq. (133)].

Verify that at high temperatures and low densities one recovers the Sackur-Tetrode formula, Eq. (37).

8. (a) From the supposition that the photons of a radiation gas propagate in all directions with equal probability, it follows that a fraction $\frac{1}{2}\sin\theta d\theta$ of photons will proceed in directions forming angles, with any coordinate axis, that range from θ to $\theta + d\theta$. Prove!

(b) Combine this result with the fact that a photon of frequency ν has a linear momentum $h\nu/c$ and an energy $h\nu$, to demonstrate that the pressure exerted by radiation of energy density u (per cm³) on a perfectly reflecting surface is given by $p = u/3$, Eq. (198).

9. Estimate, with the aid of Wien's displacement law, Eq. (223), the surface temperature of a star that emits radiation with maximum intensity appearing at an approximate wavelength 0.4×10^{-4} cm.   7245°K. *Ans.*

CHAPTER 4

1. Let $q_1, q_2, \ldots, q_f$ be the generalized coordinates of a mechanical system and $p_1, p_2, \ldots, p_f$ their conjugate momenta, and denote the classical canonical ensemble average of any function $L(q,p)$ of these quantities by $\bar{L}$. Assume further that the Hamiltonian function $H(q,p)$ of the system is such that $[q_i e^{-\beta H}]^{q_i''}_{q_i'} = 0$ and $[p_j e^{-\beta H}]^{p_j''}_{p_j'} = 0$, where q_i', p_j' and q_i'', p_j'' are the lower and upper limits, respectively, of q_i and p_j.

(a) Prove that for q_i and p_j the equipartition theorem

$$\overline{q_i \frac{\partial H}{\partial q_i}} = kT, \qquad \overline{p_j \frac{\partial H}{\partial p_j}} = kT$$

is satisfied (Tolman, 1918).

(b) Suppose H obeys the requirement $[p_j e^{-\beta H}]^{p_j''}_{p_j'} = 0$ for all j and that the kinetic energy part of $H = H_{\text{kin}}(q,p) + H_{\text{pot}}(q)$ is a homogeneous quadratic function of the p_j. Show that

$$\bar{H}_{\text{kin}} = f\tfrac{1}{2}kT.$$

(c) Regarding q_1, q_2, etc., as the cartesian coordinates $x_1, y_1, z_1, \ldots, x_N, y_N, z_N$ of a system of N point particles, derive from (a) the so-called *virial theorem*:

$$\sum_{n=1}^{N} \overline{\mathbf{r}_n \cdot \mathbf{F}_n} = -3NkT,$$

where $\mathbf{r}_n$ signifies the position vector of, and $\mathbf{F}_n$ the force acting upon, the particle n.

[*Hints:* (a) Use the definition of $\bar{L}$ implied by Eq. (12), Chapter 2, transform the integrand appropriately, and then integrate by parts. (b) Begin by showing that $\sum_j p_j(\partial H_{\text{kin}}/\partial p_j) = 2H_{\text{kin}}$. (c) Sum the first equation in (a) over i.]

2. The characteristic temperature for vibration of chlorine is $\Theta_v = 810°K$. Compute its molar heat capacity C_V at $15°C$, taking the gas constant $R = 1.987$ cal deg^{-1} mole^{-1}. Compare the result with the experimental value of 5.93 cal deg^{-1} mole^{-1}. What value of C_V is predicted by classical theory?

Calculate the fractions of chlorine molecules occupying the ground and first excited vibrational states.

94.0 per cent and 5.6 per cent.

3. If $\sum_{j=0}^{\infty} f(j) \equiv f(0) + f(1) + f(2) + \cdots$ is a convergent series, its value can be approximated by the *Euler-Maclaurin summation formula*

$$\sum_{j=0}^{\infty} f(j) = \int_0^{\infty} f(x)dx + \frac{1}{2} f(0) - \frac{1}{12} f'(0) + \frac{1}{720} f'''(0)$$
$$- \frac{1}{30,240} f^{(v)}(0) + \cdots,$$

where $f'(0) = df/dx$ at $x = 0$, and so on. (See H. Margenau and G. M. Murphy. *The Mathematics of Physics and Chemistry*. Princeton: Van Nostrand, 1964, p. 475.) Employ this series to derive Mulholland's formula, expressed by Eq. (95) in the text.

4. Prove Eq. (126) of Section 4–6.
[*Hint:*

$$\sin \theta - \sin \phi = 2 \cos \tfrac{1}{2}(\theta + \phi) \sin \tfrac{1}{2}(\theta - \phi),$$
$$\cos \theta - \cos \phi = -2 \sin \tfrac{1}{2}(\theta + \phi) \sin \tfrac{1}{2}(\theta - \phi).]$$

5. In the theory of elasticity it is shown that the velocities of transverse and longitudinal elastic waves in an isotropic solid are given by the formulas

$$c_t = \sqrt{\frac{E}{2\rho(1 + \sigma)}} \quad \text{and} \quad c_. = \sqrt{\frac{E(1 - \sigma)}{\rho(1 + \sigma)(1 - 2\sigma)}},$$

where E is Young's modulus, σ Poisson's ratio, and ρ the mass density. (See A. E. H. Love. *The Mathematical Theory of Elasticity*. New York: Dover, 1944, p. 297.)

With the aid of these formulas, compute c_t and c_l for the elements aluminum, copper, and silver from the following room-temperature values of the constants* (in cgs units):

	Al	Cu	Ag
E	7×10^{11}	12.77×10^{11}	7.75×10^{11}
σ	0.33	0.36	0.37
ρ	2.69	8.95	10.49

By substituting the numerical results into Eqs. (132) and (135), find the Debye temperatures Θ_D for the above elements. Compare them with the data 396°K (Al),

* *American Institute of Physics Handbook* (New York: McGraw-Hill, 1963).

313°K (Cu), and 220°K (Ag) determined from the experimental C_V versus T curve. (M. Blackman, in *Handbuch der Physik*, vol. 7, part 1. Berlin: Springer, 1955, p. 329.) What are your conclusions in regard to the Debye theory?

6. Given is a one-dimensional crystal consisting of atoms with masses $m' = m$ and $m'' = 2m$, arranged alternately, at distances a apart, and having interaction only between adjacent atoms.

Deduce that the optical and acoustic branches of the dispersion relation $\nu(\sigma)$ are described by

$$4\pi^2\nu^2 = \frac{K}{2m}\left(3 \pm \sqrt{5 + 4\cos 4\pi\sigma a}\right),$$

K being the elastic force constant. Sketch these branches for the periodicity interval $-\dfrac{1}{4a} < \sigma \leqslant \dfrac{1}{4a}$.

[*Hint:* Denote the displacements of the atoms m' from their equilibrium positions by

$$\ldots, \xi_{-2}, \xi_0, \xi_2, \ldots, \xi_{2n}, \ldots$$

and those of the atoms m'' by

$$\ldots, \xi_{-1}, \xi_1, \ldots, \xi_{2n+1}, \ldots;$$

then write down the equations of motion for ξ_{2n} and ξ_{2n+1}.]

7. Paramagnetism is a property characterizing certain substances whenever the magnetic moments of their ions (or atoms) are nonzero. Consider an assembly of paramagnetic ions that are sufficiently separated from one another by magnetically nonactive ions so that their mutual interactions can be neglected. The effective magnetic moment μ of an ion is parallel to its total angular momentum $\mathbf{J}$ and has the magnitude $g\mu_B[J(J + 1)]^{1/2}$; here J is the total angular momentum quantum number, the *Bohr magneton* $\mu_B = eh/4\pi m$ (e = charge of the proton), and the *Landé g-factor* is defined by

$$g = 1 + \frac{J(J + 1) + S(S + 1) - L(L + 1)}{2J(J + 1)}.$$

(Note: $1 \leqslant g \leqslant 2$.) When an ion is placed in a magnetic field $\mathfrak{B}$, the component J_z of $\mathbf{J}$ in the direction of $\mathfrak{B}$ is quantized so that the corresponding quantum number M can assume only the values $-J, -J + 1, \ldots, J - 1, J$. And the magnetic energies associated with these M's are

$$\varepsilon_M = Mg\mu_B\mathfrak{B}.$$

(a) Show that the partition function of a paramagnetic ion is given by

$$Z_1 = \frac{\sinh(J + \tfrac{1}{2})gx}{\sinh\tfrac{1}{2}xg}, \quad \text{with} \quad x = \frac{\mu_B\mathfrak{B}}{kT}.$$

$$\left[\textit{Hint:} \quad 1 + e^{gx} + e^{2gx} + \cdots + e^{2Jgx} = \frac{1 - e^{gx(2J+1)}}{1 - e^{gx}}.\right]$$

(b) Signifying the average component of μ in the direction of $\mathfrak{B}$ by $\bar{\mu}$ and the maximum value of the same component by $\mu = gJ\mu_B$, prove that

$$\frac{\bar{\mu}}{\mu} = \frac{J + \frac{1}{2}}{J} \coth (J + \tfrac{1}{2})gx - \frac{1}{2J} \coth \tfrac{1}{2}gx.$$

(This is *Brillouin's formula*; its right-hand side is known as *Brillouin's function*.)

[*Hint:* $\bar{\mu} = \bar{M}g\mu_B = \mu_B(\partial/\partial x) \log Z_1$.]

(c) Investigate Brillouin's formula to establish that $\bar{\mu}$ approaches μ, its so-called *saturation value*, when $x \to \infty$. Interpret this result physically.

[*Hint:* $\coth y \to 1$ if $y \to \infty$.]

(d) Demonstrate that Brillouin's formula reduces to

$$\frac{\bar{\mu}}{\mu} \approx C\frac{\mathfrak{B}}{T} \quad (\textit{Curie's law}),$$

where $C = (J + 1)g\mu_B/3k$, for $x \equiv 6.7 \times 10^{-5}(\mathfrak{B}/T)$ deg gauss$^{-1} \ll 1$.

[*Hint:* $\coth y \approx 1/y + y/3$ if $y \ll 1$.]

(e) Plot $\bar{\mu}/\mu$ as a function of gx for any chosen value of J.

(f) In Brillouin's formula, let $J \to \infty$ and $x \to 0$ (classical limit) to obtain the result

$$\frac{\bar{\mu}}{\mu} = \coth \frac{\mu\mathfrak{B}}{kT} - \frac{kT}{\mu\mathfrak{B}}.$$

(This formula was first deduced by Langevin with the aid of classical statistics; its right side is called *Langevin's function*.)

(g) Confirm that Langevin's formula in the limit $\mu\mathfrak{B} \ll kT$ implies Curie's law in the form

$$\frac{\bar{\mu}}{\mu} \approx C_\infty \frac{\mathfrak{B}}{T},$$

with $C_\infty = \mu/3k$.

8. Consider a dilute ideal gas consisting of N identical molecules, each of which has the same energy spectrum

$$\varepsilon_1, \varepsilon_2, \ldots, \varepsilon_i, \ldots$$

with corresponding degeneracies

$$\omega_1, \omega_2, \ldots, \omega_i, \ldots.$$

The occupation numbers of the energy levels are

$$n_1, n_2, \ldots, n_i, \ldots,$$

such that

$$\sum_i n_i = N.$$

(a) Convince yourself that the number of independent quantum states of the gas associated with a given set $n_1, n_2, \ldots, n_i, \ldots$ is

$$\prod_i \frac{\omega_i^{n_i}}{n_i!}.$$

Hence show that the canonical partition function of the gas can be written as

$$Z = \sum_{n_1} \sum_{n_2} \cdots \prod_i \frac{\omega_i^{n_i}}{n_i!} \, e^{-\beta \Sigma_j n_j \varepsilon_j},$$

where in the summations each n_i assumes the values $0, 1, 2, \ldots, N$.

(b) Prove the equivalence of this function with that determined by $Z = Z_1^N/N!$, Eq. (5).

[*Hint:* Invoke the multinomial theorem

$$(x_1 + x_2 + \cdots + x_i + \cdots)^N = \sum_{n_1} \sum_{n_2} \cdots N! \prod_i \frac{x_i^{n_i}}{n_i!} \qquad \left(\sum_i n_i = N\right),$$

with

$$x_i = \omega_i e^{-\beta \varepsilon_i}.$$

Also note that

$$Z_1 = \sum_i \omega_i e^{-\beta \varepsilon_i}.]$$

9. The grand canonical partition function for a multicomponent thermodynamic system containing N_A molecules of the species A, N_B molecules of species B, etc., may—by an obvious extension of Eq. (134), Chapter 2—be defined as

$$\mathfrak{Z} = \sum_{N_A=0}^{\infty} \sum_{N_B=0}^{\infty} \cdots \sum_{E(N_A)} \sum_{E(N_B)} \cdots e^{-\beta E(N_A, N_B, \cdots)} \lambda_A^{N_A} \lambda_B^{N_B} \ldots;$$

here $\lambda_A = \exp \beta \mu_A$, $\lambda_B = \exp \beta \mu_B, \ldots$ (the *absolute activities* of the species A, B, etc.).

Demonstrate that, at equilibrium:

(a) The average values of the numbers $N_A, N_B, \ldots$ are given by

$$\bar{N}_A = \lambda_A \frac{\partial \log \mathfrak{Z}}{\partial \lambda_A}, \qquad \bar{N}_B = \lambda_B \frac{\partial \log \mathfrak{Z}}{\partial \lambda_B}, \ldots$$

(b) The average energy is given by

$$\bar{E} = -\frac{\partial \log \mathfrak{Z}}{\partial \beta}.$$

10. In the case of a dilute ideal gas mixture composed of the reactants and the product of the simple dissociation reaction

$$A + B \rightleftharpoons AB,$$

the grand partition function is seen to be

$$\mathfrak{Z} = \sum_{n_1^A, n_2^A, \cdots} \sum_{n_1^B, n_2^B, \cdots} \sum_{n_1^{AB}, n_2^{AB}, \cdots} \prod_i \frac{(\omega_i^A)^{n_i^A}}{n_i^A!} \prod_i \frac{(\omega_i^B)^{n_i^B}}{n_i^B!} \prod_i \frac{(\omega_i^{AB})^{n_i^{AB}}}{n_i^{AB}!}$$

$$\times e^{-\beta(\Sigma_i n_i^A \varepsilon_i^A + \Sigma_i n_i^B \varepsilon_i^B + \Sigma_i n_i^{AB} \varepsilon_i^{AB})} \lambda_A^{N_A} \lambda_B^{N_B}.$$

In this expression, the summations over n_i^A, n_i^B, n_i^{AB} are unrestricted; further,

$N_A = N_1 + N_{12}$ and $N_B = N_2 + N_{12}$ if $N_1 = \sum_i n_i^A$ denotes the number of free A-atoms, $N_2 = \sum_i n_i^B$ the number of free B-atoms, and $N_{12} = \sum_i n_i^{AB}$ the number of bound A- and B-atoms in the compound AB.

(a) Now show that $\mathfrak{Z}$ thus defined can be related to the canonical partition functions of the chemical species A, B, and AB by the equation

$$\mathfrak{Z} = e^{\lambda_A Z_A} e^{\lambda_B Z_B} e^{\lambda_{AB} Z_{AB}}.$$

[*Hint:* Insert $x = \lambda \omega e^{-\beta \varepsilon}$ in $\sum_{n=0}^{\infty} x^n / n! = e^x$.]

(b) Combining this result with formulas found in Problem 9, you are now able to prove:

(i) $\bar{N}_A = \lambda_A Z_A + \lambda_A \lambda_B Z_{AB}$,

       $\bar{N}_B = \lambda_B Z_B + \lambda_A \lambda_B Z_{AB}$;

(ii) $\bar{E} = \lambda_A Z_A \overline{\varepsilon^A} + \lambda_B Z_B \overline{\varepsilon^B} + \lambda_A \lambda_B Z_{AB} \overline{\varepsilon^{AB}}$,

       $\overline{\varepsilon^A} = -\dfrac{\partial \log Z_A}{\partial \beta}$,   etc.;

(iii) $\dfrac{\bar{N}_{12}}{\bar{N}_1 \bar{N}_2} = \dfrac{Z_{AB}}{Z_A Z_B}$ = a function only of T and V.

[The result (iii) is the *law of mass action* in its simplest form.]

11. Verify that the minimum value of the ratio ε/p for rotons, that is, the critical flow velocity for helium according to Landau's theory, is equal to

$$\frac{1}{\mu} (\sqrt{2\mu\Delta + p_0^2} - p_0) \approx 60 \text{ m sec}^{-1}.$$

To obtain the numerical result, use the empirical values for Δ, μ, and p_0 cited in Section 19, Chapter 4.

PROBLEMS TO APPENDIX

1. Suppose two cylinders I and II having the same volume V can slide into one another, like the tubes of a telescope, without friction. The end of I lying inside II is assumed to be impermeable to a gas A while allowing a gas B to penetrate it. On the other hand, the end of II lying inside I, permits A to pass through, while totally preventing the flow of B. Finally, the curved surfaces and outer ends of I and II are impermeable to both A and B.

(a) Convince yourself that such a device is capable of reversibly mixing and unmixing two ideal gases A and B without changing their partial pressures p_A and p_B.

(b) Using this apparatus, show by purely thermodynamic reasoning that a mixture of n_A moles of an ideal gas A and n_B moles of an ideal gas B at the temperature T has the entropy

$$S_{AB} = n_A s_A(T,p_A) + n_B s_B(T,p_B),$$

where $s_A(T, p_A)$ is the molar entropy of A at temperature T and pressure p_A, and similarly for $s_B(T, p_B)$. (This equation is Gibbs' *law of partial entropies*.)

2. Apply the thermodynamic formula $s = s_0 + \int c_v(T)/T \; dT + R \log v$ to the result in Problem 1(b) in order to prove that

$$S_{AB} = n_A s_A(T, p) + n_B s_B(T, p) - R\left(n_A \log \frac{n_A}{n_A + n_B} + n_B \log \frac{n_B}{n_A + n_B}\right),$$

with $p = p_A + p_B$.

3. Reproduce the result in Problem 2 by statistical reasoning.
  [*Hint:* Start from $F = -kT \log (Z_A^{N_A}/N_A!)(Z_B^{N_B}/N_B!)$.]

4. On the basis of the formula derived in Problem 2, verify that the entropy of a mixture consisting of one mole of A and one mole of B at absolute zero is $2R \log 2$.
  [*Hint:* $s_A(T, p)$ and $s_B(T, p) \to 0$ as $T \to 0$ (third law for pure substances).]

Index

A CATALOGUE OF
SELECTED DOVER BOOKS
IN ALL FIELDS OF INTEREST

A CATALOGUE OF SELECTED DOVER
BOOKS IN ALL FIELDS OF INTEREST

RACKHAM'S COLOR ILLUSTRATIONS FOR WAGNER'S RING. Rackham's finest mature work—all 64 full-color watercolors in a faithful and lush interpretation of the *Ring*. Full-sized plates on coated stock of the paintings used by opera companies for authentic staging of Wagner. Captions aid in following complete Ring cycle. Introduction. 64 illustrations plus vignettes. 72pp. 8⅝ x 11¼.   23779-6 Pa. $6.00

CONTEMPORARY POLISH POSTERS IN FULL COLOR, edited by Joseph Czestochowski. 46 full-color examples of brilliant school of Polish graphic design, selected from world's first museum (near Warsaw) dedicated to poster art. Posters on circuses, films, plays, concerts all show cosmopolitan influences, free imagination. Introduction. 48pp. 9⅜ x 12¼.
23780-X Pa. $6.00

GRAPHIC WORKS OF EDVARD MUNCH, Edvard Munch. 90 haunting, evocative prints by first major Expressionist artist and one of the greatest graphic artists of his time: *The Scream, Anxiety, Death Chamber, The Kiss, Madonna,* etc. Introduction by Alfred Werner. 90pp. 9 x 12.
23765-6 Pa. $5.00

THE GOLDEN AGE OF THE POSTER, Hayward and Blanche Cirker. 70 extraordinary posters in full colors, from Maitres de l'Affiche, Mucha, Lautrec, Bradley, Cheret, Beardsley, many others. Total of 78pp. 9⅜ x 12¼.   22753-7 Pa. $5.95

THE NOTEBOOKS OF LEONARDO DA VINCI, edited by J. P. Richter. Extracts from manuscripts reveal great genius; on painting, sculpture, anatomy, sciences, geography, etc. Both Italian and English. 186 ms. pages reproduced, plus 500 additional drawings, including studies for *Last Supper,* Sforza monument, etc. 860pp. 7⅞ x 10¾. (Available in U.S. only)
22572-0, 22573-9 Pa., Two-vol. set $15.90

THE CODEX NUTTALL, as first edited by Zelia Nuttall. Only inexpensive edition, in full color, of a pre-Columbian Mexican (Mixtec) book. 88 color plates show kings, gods, heroes, temples, sacrifices. New explanatory, historical introduction by Arthur G. Miller. 96pp. 11⅜ x 8½. (Available in U.S. only)   23168-2 Pa. $7.95

UNE SEMAINE DE BONTÉ, A SURREALISTIC NOVEL IN COLLAGE, Max Ernst. Masterpiece created out of 19th-century periodical illustrations, explores worlds of terror and surprise. Some consider this Ernst's greatest work. 208pp. 8⅛ x 11.   23252-2 Pa. $6.00

DRAWINGS OF WILLIAM BLAKE, William Blake. 92 plates from Book of Job, *Divine Comedy, Paradise Lost,* visionary heads, mythological figures, Laocoon, etc. Selection, introduction, commentary by Sir Geoffrey Keynes. 178pp. 8⅛ x 11. 22303-5 Pa. $4.00

ENGRAVINGS OF HOGARTH, William Hogarth. 101 of Hogarth's greatest works: *Rake's Progress, Harlot's Progress, Illustrations for Hudibras, Before and After, Beer Street and Gin Lane,* many more. Full commentary. 256pp. 11 x 13¾. 22479-1 Pa. $12.95

DAUMIER: 120 GREAT LITHOGRAPHS, Honore Daumier. Wide-ranging collection of lithographs by the greatest caricaturist of the 19th century. Concentrates on eternally popular series on lawyers, on married life, on liberated women, etc. Selection, introduction, and notes on plates by Charles F. Ramus. Total of 158pp. 9⅜ x 12¼. 23512-2 Pa. $6.00

DRAWINGS OF MUCHA, Alphonse Maria Mucha. Work reveals draftsman of highest caliber: studies for famous posters and paintings, renderings for book illustrations and ads, etc. 70 works, 9 in color; including 6 items not drawings. Introduction. List of illustrations. 72pp. 9⅜ x 12¼. (Available in U.S. only) 23672-2 Pa. $4.00

GIOVANNI BATTISTA PIRANESI: DRAWINGS IN THE PIERPONT MORGAN LIBRARY, Giovanni Battista Piranesi. For first time ever all of Morgan Library's collection, world's largest. 167 illustrations of rare Piranesi drawings—archeological, architectural, decorative and visionary. Essay, detailed list of drawings, chronology, captions. Edited by Felice Stampfle. 144pp. 9⅜ x 12¼. 23714-1 Pa. $7.50

NEW YORK ETCHINGS (1905-1949), John Sloan. All of important American artist's N.Y. life etchings. 67 works include some of his best art; also lively historical record—Greenwich Village, tenement scenes. Edited by Sloan's widow. Introduction and captions. 79pp. 8⅜ x 11¼. 23651-X Pa. $4.00

CHINESE PAINTING AND CALLIGRAPHY: A PICTORIAL SURVEY, Wan-go Weng. 69 fine examples from John M. Crawford's matchless private collection: landscapes, birds, flowers, human figures, etc., plus calligraphy. Every basic form included: hanging scrolls, handscrolls, album leaves, fans, etc. 109 illustrations. Introduction. Captions. 192pp. 8⅞ x 11¾. 23707-9 Pa. $7.95

DRAWINGS OF REMBRANDT, edited by Seymour Slive. Updated Lippmann, Hofstede de Groot edition, with definitive scholarly apparatus. All portraits, biblical sketches, landscapes, nudes, Oriental figures, classical studies, together with selection of work by followers. 550 illustrations. Total of 630pp. 9⅛ x 12¼. 21485-0, 21486-9 Pa., Two-vol. set $15.00

THE DISASTERS OF WAR, Francisco Goya. 83 etchings record horrors of Napoleonic wars in Spain and war in general. Reprint of 1st edition, plus 3 additional plates. Introduction by Philip Hofer. 97pp. 9⅜ x 8¼. 21872-4 Pa. $4.00

THE EARLY WORK OF AUBREY BEARDSLEY, Aubrey Beardsley. 157 plates, 2 in color: *Manon Lescaut, Madame Bovary, Morte Darthur, Salome,* other. Introduction by H. Marillier. 182pp. 8⅛ x 11. 21816-3 Pa. $4.50

THE LATER WORK OF AUBREY BEARDSLEY, Aubrey Beardsley. Exotic masterpieces of full maturity: *Venus and Tannhauser, Lysistrata, Rape of the Lock, Volpone,* Savoy material, etc. 174 plates, 2 in color. 186pp. 8⅛ x 11. 21817-1 Pa. $5.95

THOMAS NAST'S CHRISTMAS DRAWINGS, Thomas Nast. Almost all Christmas drawings by creator of image of Santa Claus as we know it, and one of America's foremost illustrators and political cartoonists. 66 illustrations. 3 illustrations in color on covers. 96pp. 8⅜ x 11¼. 23660-9 Pa. $3.50

THE DORÉ ILLUSTRATIONS FOR DANTE'S DIVINE COMEDY, Gustave Doré. All 135 plates from Inferno, Purgatory, Paradise; fantastic tortures, infernal landscapes, celestial wonders. Each plate with appropriate (translated) verses. 141pp. 9 x 12. 23231-X Pa. $4.50

DORÉ'S ILLUSTRATIONS FOR RABELAIS, Gustave Doré. 252 striking illustrations of *Gargantua and Pantagruel* books by foremost 19th-century illustrator. Including 60 plates, 192 delightful smaller illustrations. 153pp. 9 x 12. 23656-0 Pa. $5.00

LONDON: A PILGRIMAGE, Gustave Doré, Blanchard Jerrold. Squalor, riches, misery, beauty of mid-Victorian metropolis; 55 wonderful plates, 125 other illustrations, full social, cultural text by Jerrold. 191pp. of text. 9⅜ x 12¼. 22306-X Pa. $7.00

THE RIME OF THE ANCIENT MARINER, Gustave Doré, S. T. Coleridge. Dore's finest work, 34 plates capture moods, subtleties of poem. Full text. Introduction by Millicent Rose. 77pp. 9¼ x 12. 22305-1 Pa. $3.50

THE DORE BIBLE ILLUSTRATIONS, Gustave Doré. All wonderful, detailed plates: Adam and Eve, Flood, Babylon, Life of Jesus, etc. Brief King James text with each plate. Introduction by Millicent Rose. 241 plates. 241pp. 9 x 12. 23004-X Pa. $6.00

THE COMPLETE ENGRAVINGS, ETCHINGS AND DRYPOINTS OF ALBRECHT DURER. "Knight, Death and Devil"; "Melencolia," and more—all Dürer's known works in all three media, including 6 works formerly attributed to him. 120 plates. 235pp. 8⅜ x 11¼. 22851-7 Pa. $6.50

MECHANICK EXERCISES ON THE WHOLE ART OF PRINTING, Joseph Moxon. First complete book (1683-4) ever written about typography, a compendium of everything known about printing at the latter part of 17th century. Reprint of 2nd (1962) Oxford Univ. Press edition. 74 illustrations. Total of 550pp. 6⅛ x 9¼. 23617-X Pa. $7.95

THE COMPLETE WOODCUTS OF ALBRECHT DURER, edited by Dr. W. Kurth. 346 in all: "Old Testament," "St. Jerome," "Passion," "Life of Virgin," Apocalypse," many others. Introduction by Campbell Dodgson. 285pp. 8½ x 12¼.   21097-9 Pa. $7.50

DRAWINGS OF ALBRECHT DURER, edited by Heinrich Wolfflin. 81 plates show development from youth to full style. Many favorites; many new. Introduction by Alfred Werner. 96pp. 8⅛ x 11. 22352-3 Pa. $5.00

THE HUMAN FIGURE, Albrecht Dürer. Experiments in various techniques—stereometric, progressive proportional, and others. Also life studies that rank among finest ever done. Complete reprinting of *Dresden Sketchbook*. 170 plates. 355pp. 8⅜ x 11¼.   21042-1 Pa. $7.95

OF THE JUST SHAPING OF LETTERS, Albrecht Dürer. Renaissance artist explains design of Roman majuscules by geometry, also Gothic lower and capitals. Grolier Club edition. 43pp. 7⅞ x 10¾   21306-4 Pa. $3.00

TEN BOOKS ON ARCHITECTURE, Vitruvius. The most important book ever written on architecture. Early Roman aesthetics, technology, classical orders, site selection, all other aspects. Stands behind everything since. Morgan translation. 331pp. 5⅜ x 8½.   20645-9 Pa. $4.50

THE FOUR BOOKS OF ARCHITECTURE, Andrea Palladio. 16th-century classic responsible for Palladian movement and style. Covers classical architectural remains, Renaissance revivals, classical orders, etc. 1738 Ware English edition. Introduction by A. Placzek. 216 plates. 110pp. of text. 9½ x 12¾.   21308-0 Pa. $10.00

HORIZONS, Norman Bel Geddes. Great industrialist stage designer, "father of streamlining," on application of aesthetics to transportation, amusement, architecture, etc. 1932 prophetic account; function, theory, specific projects. 222 illustrations. 312pp. 7⅞ x 10¾.   23514-9 Pa. $6.95

FRANK LLOYD WRIGHT'S FALLINGWATER, Donald Hoffmann. Full, illustrated story of conception and building of Wright's masterwork at Bear Run, Pa. 100 photographs of site, construction, and details of completed structure. 112pp. 9¼ x 10.   23671-4 Pa. $5.50

THE ELEMENTS OF DRAWING, John Ruskin. Timeless classic by great Viltorian; starts with basic ideas, works through more difficult. Many practical exercises. 48 illustrations. Introduction by Lawrence Campbell. 228pp. 5⅜ x 8½.   22730-8 Pa. $3.75

GIST OF ART, John Sloan. Greatest modern American teacher, Art Students League, offers innumerable hints, instructions, guided comments to help you in painting. Not a formal course. 46 illustrations. Introduction by Helen Sloan. 200pp. 5⅜ x 8½.   23435-5 Pa. $4.00

THE ANATOMY OF THE HORSE, George Stubbs. Often considered the great masterpiece of animal anatomy. Full reproduction of 1766 edition, plus prospectus; original text and modernized text. 36 plates. Introduction by Eleanor Garvey. 121pp. 11 x 14¾. 23402-9 Pa. $6.00

BRIDGMAN'S LIFE DRAWING, George B. Bridgman. More than 500 illustrative drawings and text teach you to abstract the body into its major masses, use light and shade, proportion; as well as specific areas of anatomy, of which Bridgman is master. 192pp. 6½ x 9¼. (Available in U.S. only) 22710-3 Pa. $3.50

ART NOUVEAU DESIGNS IN COLOR, Alphonse Mucha, Maurice Verneuil, Georges Auriol. Full-color reproduction of *Combinaisons ornementales* (c. 1900) by Art Nouveau masters. Floral, animal, geometric, interlacings, swashes—borders, frames, spots—all incredibly beautiful. 60 plates, hundreds of designs. 9⅜ x 8-1/16. 22885-1 Pa. $4.00

FULL-COLOR FLORAL DESIGNS IN THE ART NOUVEAU STYLE, E. A. Seguy. 166 motifs, on 40 plates, from *Les fleurs et leurs applications decoratives* (1902): borders, circular designs, repeats, allovers, "spots." All in authentic Art Nouveau colors. 48pp. 9⅜ x 12¼.
23439-8 Pa. $5.00

A DIDEROT PICTORIAL ENCYCLOPEDIA OF TRADES AND IN-DUSTRY, edited by Charles C. Gillispie. 485 most interesting plates from the great French Encyclopedia of the 18th century show hundreds of working figures, artifacts, process, land and cityscapes; glassmaking, paper-making, metal extraction, construction, weaving, making furniture, clothing, wigs, dozens of other activities. Plates fully explained. 920pp. 9 x 12.
22284-5, 22285-3 Clothbd., Two-vol. set $40.00

HANDBOOK OF EARLY ADVERTISING ART, Clarence P. Hornung. Largest collection of copyright-free early and antique advertising art ever compiled. Over 6,000 illustrations, from Franklin's time to the 1890's for special effects, novelty. Valuable source, almost inexhaustible.
Pictorial Volume. Agriculture, the zodiac, animals, autos, birds, Christmas, fire engines, flowers, trees, musical instruments, ships, games and sports, much more. Arranged by subject matter and use. 237 plates. 288pp. 9 x 12.
20122-8 Clothbd. $14.50

Typographical Volume. Roman and Gothic faces ranging from 10 point to 300 point, "Barnum," German and Old English faces, script, logotypes, scrolls and flourishes, 1115 ornamental initials, 67 complete alphabets, more. 310 plates. 320pp. 9 x 12. 20123-6 Clothbd. $15.00

CALLIGRAPHY (CALLIGRAPHIA LATINA), J. G. Schwandner. High point of 18th-century ornamental calligraphy. Very ornate initials, scrolls, borders, cherubs, birds, lettered examples. 172pp. 9 x 13.
20475-8 Pa. $7.00

ART FORMS IN NATURE, Ernst Haeckel. Multitude of strangely beautiful natural forms: Radiolaria, Foraminifera, jellyfishes, fungi, turtles, bats, etc. All 100 plates of the 19th-century evolutionist's *Kunstformen der Natur* (1904). 100pp. 9⅜ x 12¼.   22987-4 Pa. $5.00

CHILDREN: A PICTORIAL ARCHIVE FROM NINETEENTH-CENTURY SOURCES, edited by Carol Belanger Grafton. 242 rare, copyright-free wood engravings for artists and designers. Widest such selection available. All illustrations in line. 119pp. 8⅜ x 11¼.
                                                    23694-3 Pa. $4.00

WOMEN: A PICTORIAL ARCHIVE FROM NINETEENTH-CENTURY SOURCES, edited by Jim Harter. 391 copyright-free wood engravings for artists and designers selected from rare periodicals. Most extensive such collection available. All illustrations in line. 128pp. 9 x 12.
                                                    23703-6 Pa. $4.50

ARABIC ART IN COLOR, Prisse d'Avennes. From the greatest ornamentalists of all time—50 plates in color, rarely seen outside the Near East, rich in suggestion and stimulus. Includes 4 plates on covers. 46pp. 9⅜ x 12¼.   23658-7 Pa. $6.00

AUTHENTIC ALGERIAN CARPET DESIGNS AND MOTIFS, edited by June Beveridge. Algerian carpets are world famous. Dozens of geometrical motifs are charted on grids, color-coded, for weavers, needleworkers, craftsmen, designers. 53 illustrations plus 4 in color. 48pp. 8¼ x 11. (Available in U.S. only)   23650-1 Pa. $1.75

DICTIONARY OF AMERICAN PORTRAITS, edited by Hayward and Blanche Cirker. 4000 important Americans, earliest times to 1905, mostly in clear line. Politicians, writers, soldiers, scientists, inventors, industrialists, Indians, Blacks, women, outlaws, etc. Identificatory information. 756pp. 9¼ x 12¾.   21823-6 Clothbd. $40.00

HOW THE OTHER HALF LIVES, Jacob A. Riis. Journalistic record of filth, degradation, upward drive in New York immigrant slums, shops, around 1900. New edition includes 100 original Riis photos, monuments of early photography. 233pp. 10 x 7⅞.   22012-5 Pa. $7.00

NEW YORK IN THE THIRTIES, Berenice Abbott. Noted photographer's fascinating study of city shows new buildings that have become famous and old sights that have disappeared forever. Insightful commentary. 97 photographs. 97pp. 11⅜ x 10.   22967-X Pa. $5.00

MEN AT WORK, Lewis W. Hine. Famous photographic studies of construction workers, railroad men, factory workers and coal miners. New supplement of 18 photos on Empire State building construction. New introduction by Jonathan L. Doherty. Total of 69 photos. 63pp. 8 x 10¾.
                                                    23475-4 Pa. $3.00

THE DEPRESSION YEARS AS PHOTOGRAPHED BY ARTHUR ROTH-STEIN, Arthur Rothstein. First collection devoted entirely to the work of outstanding 1930s photographer: famous dust storm photo, ragged children, unemployed, etc. 120 photographs. Captions. 119pp. 9¼ x 10¾.
23590-4 Pa. $5.00

CAMERA WORK: A PICTORIAL GUIDE, Alfred Stieglitz. All 559 illustrations and plates from the most important periodical in the history of art photography, Camera Work (1903-17). Presented four to a page, reduced in size but still clear, in strict chronological order, with complete captions. Three indexes. Glossary. Bibliography. 176pp. 8⅜ x 11¼.
23591-2 Pa. $6.95

ALVIN LANGDON COBURN, PHOTOGRAPHER, Alvin L. Coburn. Revealing autobiography by one of greatest photographers of 20th century gives insider's version of Photo-Secession, plus comments on his own work. 77 photographs by Coburn. Edited by Helmut and Alison Gernsheim. 160pp. 8⅛ x 11.
23685-4 Pa. $6.00

NEW YORK IN THE FORTIES, Andreas Feininger. 162 brilliant photographs by the well-known photographer, formerly with Life magazine, show commuters, shoppers, Times Square at night, Harlem nightclub, Lower East Side, etc. Introduction and full captions by John von Hartz. 181pp. 9¼ x 10¾.
23585-8 Pa. $6.95

GREAT NEWS PHOTOS AND THE STORIES BEHIND THEM, John Faber. Dramatic volume of 140 great news photos, 1855 through 1976, and revealing stories behind them, with both historical and technical information. Hindenburg disaster, shooting of Oswald, nomination of Jimmy Carter, etc. 160pp. 8¼ x 11.
23667-6 Pa. $5.00

THE ART OF THE CINEMATOGRAPHER, Leonard Maltin. Survey of American cinematography history and anecdotal interviews with 5 masters—Arthur Miller, Hal Mohr, Hal Rosson, Lucien Ballard, and Conrad Hall. Very large selection of behind-the-scenes production photos. 105 photographs. Filmographies. Index. Originally Behind the Camera. 144pp. 8¼ x 11.
23686-2 Pa. $5.00

DESIGNS FOR THE THREE-CORNERED HAT (LE TRICORNE), Pablo Picasso. 32 fabulously rare drawings—including 31 color illustrations of costumes and accessories—for 1919 production of famous ballet. Edited by Parmenia Migel, who has written new introduction. 48pp. 9⅜ x 12¼. (Available in U.S. only)
23709-5 Pa. $5.00

NOTES OF A FILM DIRECTOR, Sergei Eisenstein. Greatest Russian filmmaker explains montage, making of Alexander Nevsky, aesthetics; comments on self, associates, great rivals (Chaplin), similar material. 78 illustrations. 240pp. 5⅜ x 8½.
22392-2 Pa. $4.50

HOLLYWOOD GLAMOUR PORTRAITS, edited by John Kobal. 145 photos capture the stars from 1926-49, the high point in portrait photography. Gable, Harlow, Bogart, Bacall, Hedy Lamarr, Marlene Dietrich, Robert Montgomery, Marlon Brando, Veronica Lake; 94 stars in all. Full background on photographers, technical aspects, much more. Total of 160pp. 8⅜ x 11¼. 23352-9 Pa. $6.00

THE NEW YORK STAGE: FAMOUS PRODUCTIONS IN PHOTO-GRAPHS, edited by Stanley Appelbaum. 148 photographs from Museum of City of New York show 142 plays, 1883-1939. *Peter Pan, The Front Page, Dead End, Our Town,* O'Neill, hundreds of actors and actresses, etc. Full indexes. 154pp. 9½ x 10. 23241-7 Pa. $6.00

DIALOGUES CONCERNING TWO NEW SCIENCES, Galileo Galilei. Encompassing 30 years of experiment and thought, these dialogues deal with geometric demonstrations of fracture of solid bodies, cohesion, leverage, speed of light and sound, pendulums, falling bodies, accelerated motion, etc. 300pp. 5⅜ x 8½. 60099-8 Pa. $4.00

THE GREAT OPERA STARS IN HISTORIC PHOTOGRAPHS, edited by James Camner. 343 portraits from the 1850s to the 1940s: Tamburini, Mario, Caliapin, Jeritza, Melchior, Melba, Patti, Pinza, Schipa, Caruso, Farrar, Steber, Gobbi, and many more—270 performers in all. Index. 199pp. 8⅜ x 11¼. 23575-0 Pa. $7.50

J. S. BACH, Albert Schweitzer. Great full-length study of Bach, life, background to music, music, by foremost modern scholar. Ernest Newman translation. 650 musical examples. Total of 928pp. 5⅜ x 8½. (Available in U.S. only) 21631-4, 21632-2 Pa., Two-vol. set $11.00

COMPLETE PIANO SONATAS, Ludwig van Beethoven. All sonatas in the fine Schenker edition, with fingering, analytical material. One of best modern editions. Total of 615pp. 9 x 12. (Available in U.S. only) 23134-8, 23135-6 Pa., Two-vol. set $15.50

KEYBOARD MUSIC, J. S. Bach. Bach-Gesellschaft edition. For harpsichord, piano, other keyboard instruments. English Suites, French Suites, Six Partitas, Goldberg Variations, Two-Part Inventions, Three-Part Sinfonias. 312pp. 8⅛ x 11. (Available in U.S. only) 22360-4 Pa. $6.95

FOUR SYMPHONIES IN FULL SCORE, Franz Schubert. Schubert's four most popular symphonies: No. 4 in C Minor ("Tragic"); No. 5 in B-flat Major; No. 8 in B Minor ("Unfinished"); No. 9 in C Major ("Great"). Breitkopf & Hartel edition. Study score. 261pp. 9⅜ x 12¼. 23681-1 Pa. $6.50

THE AUTHENTIC GILBERT & SULLIVAN SONGBOOK, W. S. Gilbert, A. S. Sullivan. Largest selection available; 92 songs, uncut, original keys, in piano rendering approved by Sullivan. Favorites and lesser-known fine numbers. Edited with plot synopses by James Spero. 3 illustrations. 399pp. 9 x 12. 23482-7 Pa. $9.95

PRINCIPLES OF ORCHESTRATION, Nikolay Rimsky-Korsakov. Great classical orchestrator provides fundamentals of tonal resonance, progression of parts, voice and orchestra, tutti effects, much else in major document. 330pp. of musical excerpts. 489pp. 6½ x 9¼. 21266-1 Pa. $7.50

TRISTAN UND ISOLDE, Richard Wagner. Full orchestral score with complete instrumentation. Do not confuse with piano reduction. Commentary by Felix Mottl, great Wagnerian conductor and scholar. Study score. 655pp. 8⅛ x 11. 22915-7 Pa. $13.95

REQUIEM IN FULL SCORE, Giuseppe Verdi. Immensely popular with choral groups and music lovers. Republication of edition published by C. F. Peters, Leipzig, n. d. German frontmaker in English translation. Glossary. Text in Latin. Study score. 204pp. 9⅜ x 12¼.
23682-X Pa. $6.00

COMPLETE CHAMBER MUSIC FOR STRINGS, Felix Mendelssohn. All of Mendelssohn's chamber music: Octet, 2 Quintets, 6 Quartets, and Four Pieces for String Quartet. (Nothing with piano is included). Complete works edition (1874-7). Study score. 283 pp. 9⅜ x 12¼.
23679-X Pa. $7.50

POPULAR SONGS OF NINETEENTH-CENTURY AMERICA, edited by Richard Jackson. 64 most important songs: "Old Oaken Bucket," "Arkansas Traveler," "Yellow Rose of Texas," etc. Authentic original sheet music, full introduction and commentaries. 290pp. 9 x 12. 23270-0 Pa. $7.95

COLLECTED PIANO WORKS, Scott Joplin. Edited by Vera Brodsky Lawrence. Practically all of Joplin's piano works—rags, two-steps, marches, waltzes, etc., 51 works in all. Extensive introduction by Rudi Blesh. Total of 345pp. 9 x 12. 23106-2 Pa. $14.95

BASIC PRINCIPLES OF CLASSICAL BALLET, Agrippina Vaganova. Great Russian theoretician, teacher explains methods for teaching classical ballet; incorporates best from French, Italian, Russian schools. 118 illustrations. 175pp. 5⅜ x 8½. 22036-2 Pa. $2.50

CHINESE CHARACTERS, L. Wieger. Rich analysis of 2300 characters according to traditional systems into primitives. Historical-semantic analysis to phonetics (Classical Mandarin) and radicals. 820pp. 6⅛ x 9¼.
21321-8 Pa. $10.00

EGYPTIAN LANGUAGE: EASY LESSONS IN EGYPTIAN HIERO-GLYPHICS, E. A. Wallis Budge. Foremost Egyptologist offers Egyptian grammar, explanation of hieroglyphics, many reading texts, dictionary of symbols. 246pp. 5 x 7½. (Available in U.S. only)
21394-3 Clothbd. $7.50

AN ETYMOLOGICAL DICTIONARY OF MODERN ENGLISH, Ernest Weekley. Richest, fullest work, by foremost British lexicographer. Detailed word histories. Inexhaustible. Do not confuse this with Concise Etymological Dictionary, which is abridged. Total of 856pp. 6½ x 9¼.
21873-2, 21874-0 Pa., Two-vol. set $12.00

A MAYA GRAMMAR, Alfred M. Tozzer. Practical, useful English-language grammar by the Harvard anthropologist who was one of the three greatest American scholars in the area of Maya culture. Phonetics, grammatical processes, syntax, more. 301pp. 5⅜ x 8½.   23465-7 Pa. $4.00

THE JOURNAL OF HENRY D. THOREAU, edited by Bradford Torrey, F. H. Allen. Complete reprinting of 14 volumes, 1837-61, over two million words; the sourcebooks for *Walden*, etc. Definitive. All original sketches, plus 75 photographs. Introduction by Walter Harding. Total of 1804pp. 8½ x 12¼.   20312-3, 20313-1 Clothbd., Two-vol. set $70.00

CLASSIC GHOST STORIES, Charles Dickens and others. 18 wonderful stories you've wanted to reread: "The Monkey's Paw," "The House and the Brain," "The Upper Berth," "The Signalman," "Dracula's Guest," "The Tapestried Chamber," etc. Dickens, Scott, Mary Shelley, Stoker, etc. 330pp. 5⅜ x 8½.   20735-8 Pa. **$4.50**

SEVEN SCIENCE FICTION NOVELS, H. G. Wells. Full novels. *First Men in the Moon, Island of Dr. Moreau, War of the Worlds, Food of the Gods, Invisible Man, Time Machine, In the Days of the Comet.* A basic science-fiction library. 1015pp. 5⅜ x 8½. (Available in U.S. only)
20264-X Clothbd. $8.95

ARMADALE, Wilkie Collins. Third great mystery novel by the author of *The Woman in White* and *The Moonstone*. Ingeniously plotted narrative shows an exceptional command of character, incident and mood. Original magazine version with 40 illustrations. 597pp. 5⅜ x 8½.
23429-0 Pa. $6.00

MASTERS OF MYSTERY, H. Douglas Thomson. The first book in English (1931) devoted to history and aesthetics of detective story. Poe, Doyle, LeFanu, Dickens, many others, up to 1930. New introduction and notes by E. F. Bleiler. 288pp. 5⅜ x 8½. (Available in U.S. only)
23606-4 Pa. $4.00

FLATLAND, E. A. Abbott. Science-fiction classic explores life of 2-D being in 3-D world. Read also as introduction to thought about hyperspace. Introduction by Banesh Hoffmann. 16 illustrations. 103pp. 5⅜ x 8½.
20001-9 Pa. $2.00

THREE SUPERNATURAL NOVELS OF THE VICTORIAN PERIOD, edited, with an introduction, by E. F. Bleiler. Reprinted complete and unabridged, three great classics of the supernatural: *The Haunted Hotel* by Wilkie Collins, *The Haunted House at Latchford* by Mrs. J. H. Riddell, and *The Lost Stradivarious* by J. Meade Falkner. 325pp. 5⅜ x 8½.
22571-2 Pa. $4.00

AYESHA: THE RETURN OF "SHE," H. Rider Haggard. Virtuoso sequel featuring the great mythic creation, Ayesha, in an adventure that is fully as good as the first book, *She*. Original magazine version, with 47 original illustrations by Maurice Greiffenhagen. 189pp. 6½ x 9¼.
23649-8 Pa. $3.50

UNCLE SILAS, J. Sheridan LeFanu. Victorian Gothic mystery novel, considered by many best of period, even better than Collins or Dickens. Wonderful psychological terror. Introduction by Frederick Shroyer. 436pp. 5⅜ x 8½. 21715-9 Pa. $6.00

JURGEN, James Branch Cabell. The great erotic fantasy of the 1920's that delighted thousands, shocked thousands more. Full final text, Lane edition with 13 plates by Frank Pape. 346pp. 5⅜ x 8½. 23507-6 Pa. $4.50

THE CLAVERINGS, Anthony Trollope. Major novel, chronicling aspects of British Victorian society, personalities. Reprint of Cornhill serialization, 16 plates by M. Edwards; first reprint of full text. Introduction by Norman Donaldson. 412pp. 5⅜ x 8½. 23464-9 Pa. $5.00

KEPT IN THE DARK, Anthony Trollope. Unusual short novel about Victorian morality and abnormal psychology by the great English author. Probably the first American publication. Frontispiece by Sir John Millais. 92pp. 6½ x 9¼. 23609-9 Pa. $2.50

RALPH THE HEIR, Anthony Trollope. Forgotten tale of illegitimacy, inheritance. Master novel of Trollope's later years. Victorian country estates, clubs, Parliament, fox hunting, world of fully realized characters. Reprint of 1871 edition. 12 illustrations by F. A. Faser. 434pp. of text. 5⅜ x 8½. 23642-0 Pa. $5.00

YEKL and THE IMPORTED BRIDEGROOM AND OTHER STORIES OF THE NEW YORK GHETTO, Abraham Cahan. Film *Hester Street* based on *Yekl* (1896). Novel, other stories among first about Jewish immigrants of N.Y.'s East Side. Highly praised by W. D. Howells—Cahan "a new star of realism." New introduction by Bernard G. Richards. 240pp. 5⅜ x 8½. 22427-9 Pa. $3.50

THE HIGH PLACE, James Branch Cabell. Great fantasy writer's enchanting comedy of disenchantment set in 18th-century France. Considered by some critics to be even better than his famous *Jurgen*. 10 illustrations and numerous vignettes by noted fantasy artist Frank C. Pape. 320pp. 5⅜ x 8½. 23670-6 Pa. $4.00

ALICE'S ADVENTURES UNDER GROUND, Lewis Carroll. Facsimile of ms. Carroll gave Alice Liddell in 1864. Different in many ways from final Alice. Handlettered, illustrated by Carroll. Introduction by Martin Gardner. 128pp. 5⅜ x 8½. 21482-6 Pa. $2.50

FAVORITE ANDREW LANG FAIRY TALE BOOKS IN MANY COLORS, Andrew Lang. The four Lang favorites in a boxed set—the complete *Red, Green, Yellow* and *Blue* Fairy Books. 164 stories; 439 illustrations by Lancelot Speed, Henry Ford and G. P. Jacomb Hood. Total of about 1500pp. 5⅜ x 8½. 23407-X Boxed set, Pa. $15.95

HOUSEHOLD STORIES BY THE BROTHERS GRIMM. All the great Grimm stories: "Rumpelstiltskin," "Snow White," "Hansel and Gretel," etc., with 114 illustrations by Walter Crane. 269pp. 5⅜ x 8½.
21080-4 Pa. $3.50

SLEEPING BEAUTY, illustrated by Arthur Rackham. Perhaps the fullest, most delightful version ever, told by C. S. Evans. Rackham's best work. 49 illustrations. 110pp. 7⅞ x 10¾.
22756-1 Pa. $2.50

AMERICAN FAIRY TALES, L. Frank Baum. Young cowboy lassoes Father Time; dummy in Mr. Floman's department store window comes to life; and 10 other fairy tales. 41 illustrations by N. P. Hall, Harry Kennedy, Ike Morgan, and Ralph Gardner. 209pp. 5⅜ x 8½.
23643-9 Pa. $3.00

THE WONDERFUL WIZARD OF OZ, L. Frank Baum. Facsimile in full color of America's finest children's classic. Introduction by Martin Gardner. 143 illustrations by W. W. Denslow. 267pp. 5⅜ x 8½.
20691-2 Pa. $3.50

THE TALE OF PETER RABBIT, Beatrix Potter. The inimitable Peter's terrifying adventure in Mr. McGregor's garden, with all 27 wonderful, full-color Potter illustrations. 55pp. 4¼ x 5½. (Available in U.S. only)
22827-4 Pa. $1.25

THE STORY OF KING ARTHUR AND HIS KNIGHTS, Howard Pyle. Finest children's version of life of King Arthur. 48 illustrations by Pyle. 131pp. 6⅛ x 9¼.
21445-1 Pa. $4.95

CARUSO'S CARICATURES, Enrico Caruso. Great tenor's remarkable caricatures of self, fellow musicians, composers, others. Toscanini, Puccini, Farrar, etc. Impish, cutting, insightful. 473 illustrations. Preface by M. Sisca. 217pp. 8⅜ x 11¼.
23528-9 Pa. $6.95

PERSONAL NARRATIVE OF A PILGRIMAGE TO ALMADINAH AND MECCAH, Richard Burton. Great travel classic by remarkably colorful personality. Burton, disguised as a Moroccan, visited sacred shrines of Islam, narrowly escaping death. Wonderful observations of Islamic life, customs, personalities. 47 illustrations. Total of 959pp. 5⅜ x 8½.
21217-3, 21218-1 Pa., Two-vol. set $12.00

INCIDENTS OF TRAVEL IN YUCATAN, John L. Stephens. Classic (1843) exploration of jungles of Yucatan, looking for evidences of Maya civilization. Travel adventures, Mexican and Indian culture, etc. Total of 669pp. 5⅜ x 8½.
20926-1, 20927-X Pa., Two-vol. set $7.90

AMERICAN LITERARY AUTOGRAPHS FROM WASHINGTON IRVING TO HENRY JAMES, Herbert Cahoon, et al. Letters, poems, manuscripts of Hawthorne, Thoreau, Twain, Alcott, Whitman, 67 other prominent American authors. Reproductions, full transcripts and commentary. Plus checklist of all American Literary Autographs in The Pierpont Morgan Library. Printed on exceptionally high-quality paper. 136 illustrations. 212pp. 9⅛ x 12¼.
23548-3 Pa. $12.50

AN AUTOBIOGRAPHY, Margaret Sanger. Exciting personal account of hard-fought battle for woman's right to birth control, against prejudice, church, law. Foremost feminist document. 504pp. 5⅜ x 8½.
20470-7 Pa. $5.50

MY BONDAGE AND MY FREEDOM, Frederick Douglass. Born as a slave, Douglass became outspoken force in antislavery movement. The best of Douglass's autobiographies. Graphic description of slave life. Introduction by P. Foner. 464pp. 5⅜ x 8½.
22457-0 Pa. $5.50

LIVING MY LIFE, Emma Goldman. Candid, no holds barred account by foremost American anarchist: her own life, anarchist movement, famous contemporaries, ideas and their impact. Struggles and confrontations in America, plus deportation to U.S.S.R. Shocking inside account of persecution of anarchists under Lenin. 13 plates. Total of 944pp. 5⅜ x 8½.
22543-7, 22544-5 Pa., Two-vol. set $12.00

LETTERS AND NOTES ON THE MANNERS, CUSTOMS AND CONDITIONS OF THE NORTH AMERICAN INDIANS, George Catlin. Classic account of life among Plains Indians: ceremonies, hunt, warfare, etc. Dover edition reproduces for first time all original paintings. 312 plates. 572pp. of text. 6⅛ x 9¼.
22118-0, 22119-9 Pa.. Two-vol. set $12.00

THE MAYA AND THEIR NEIGHBORS, edited by Clarence L. Hay, others. Synoptic view of Maya civilization in broadest sense, together with Northern, Southern neighbors. Integrates much background, valuable detail not elsewhere. Prepared by greatest scholars: Kroeber, Morley, Thompson, Spinden, Vaillant, many others. Sometimes called Tozzer Memorial Volume. 60 illustrations, linguistic map. 634pp. 5⅜ x 8½.
23510-6 Pa. $10.00

HANDBOOK OF THE INDIANS OF CALIFORNIA, A. L. Kroeber. Foremost American anthropologist offers complete ethnographic study of each group. Monumental classic. 459 illustrations, maps. 995pp. 5⅜ x 8½.
23368-5 Pa. $13.00

SHAKTI AND SHAKTA, Arthur Avalon. First book to give clear, cohesive analysis of Shakta doctrine, Shakta ritual and Kundalini Shakti (yoga). Important work by one of world's foremost students of Shaktic and Tantric thought. 732pp. 5⅜ x 8½. (Available in U.S. only)
23645-5 Pa. $7.95

AN INTRODUCTION TO THE STUDY OF THE MAYA HIEROGLYPHS, Syvanus Griswold Morley. Classic study by one of the truly great figures in hieroglyph research. Still the best introduction for the student for reading Maya hieroglyphs. New introduction by J. Eric S. Thompson. 117 illustrations. 284pp. 5⅜ x 8½.
23108-9 Pa. $4.00

A STUDY OF MAYA ART, Herbert J. Spinden. Landmark classic interprets Maya symbolism, estimates styles, covers ceramics, architecture, murals, stone carvings as artforms. Still a basic book in area. New introduction by J. Eric Thompson. Over 750 illustrations. 341pp. 8⅜ x 11¼.
21235-1 Pa. $6.95

GEOMETRY, RELATIVITY AND THE FOURTH DIMENSION, Rudolf Rucker. Exposition of fourth dimension, means of visualization, concepts of relativity as Flatland characters continue adventures. Popular, easily followed yet accurate, profound. 141 illustrations. 133pp. 5⅜ x 8½.
23400-2 Pa. $2.75

THE ORIGIN OF LIFE, A. I. Oparin. Modern classic in biochemistry, the first rigorous examination of possible evolution of life from nitrocarbon compounds. Non-technical, easily followed. Total of 295pp. 5⅜ x 8½.
60213-3 Pa. $4.00

PLANETS, STARS AND GALAXIES, A. E. Fanning. Comprehensive introductory survey: the sun, solar system, stars, galaxies, universe, cosmology; quasars, radio stars, etc. 24pp. of photographs. 189pp. 5⅜ x 8½. (Available in U.S. only)
21680-2 Pa. $3.75

THE THIRTEEN BOOKS OF EUCLID'S ELEMENTS, translated with introduction and commentary by Sir Thomas L. Heath. Definitive edition. Textual and linguistic notes, mathematical analysis, 2500 years of critical commentary. Do not confuse with abridged school editions. Total of 1414pp. 5⅜ x 8½.   60088-2, 60089-0, 60090-4 Pa., Three-vol. set $18.50

Prices subject to change without notice.

Available at your book dealer or write for free catalogue to Dept. GI, Dover Publications, Inc., 180 Varick St., N.Y., N.Y. 10014. Dover publishes more than 175 books each year on science, elementary and advanced mathematics, biology, music, art, literary history, social sciences and other areas.

On average:

what is the time required from
the point at which the ~~start~~
reaction is initiated and the physical
case of the nuclear weapon rupture